Scott Foresman - Addison Wesley

# MATH

## Practice Masters

### Grade 2

Scott Foresman - Addison Wesley

Editorial Offices: Menlo Park, California • Glenview, Illinois
Sales Offices: Reading, Massachusetts • Atlanta, Georgia • Glenview, Illinois
Carrollton, Texas • Menlo Park, California

http://www.sf.aw.com

## Overview

***Practice Masters*** provide additional exercises for students who have not mastered key skills and concepts covered in the Student Edition. A Practice master is provided for each core lesson of the Student Edition. In addition, a Practice master is also provided for each Mixed Practice and Cumulative Review lesson.

Lesson masters provide exercises similar to those in the Practice and Explore lessons of the Student Edition.

Mixed Practice masters review skills and concepts covered in the Student Edition section and include application problems that review previous material.

Cumulative Review masters cover important skills and concepts from the current chapter and from previous chapters.

ISBN 0-201-50129-5



Printed in the United States of America

1 2 3 4 5 6 7 8 9 10 – BW – 02 01 00 99 98

## Contents

### Chapter 4: Using Addition and Subtraction



### Chapter 5: Place Value and Patterns to 100



### Chapter 6: Money



### Chapter 7: Time



### Chapter 8: Two-Digit Addition



### Chapter 9: Two-Digit Subtraction

### *Chapter 10: Numbers to 1,000*



### *Chapter 11: Measurement*



### *Chapter 12: Geometry and Fractions*



### *Chapter 13: Multiplication and Division Concepts*

Name ______________________________

Practice 1-1

# Explore Counting and Comparing

How many children in your class are wearing sneakers?

How many are wearing shoes?

Use ⬭ ⬭ to show how many.

| Wearing Shoes | Wearing Sneakers |
|---|---|
| | |

1. How many children are wearing sneakers? ______

2. How many children are wearing shoes? ______

3. Which group has more? ____________________

4. Which group has fewer? ____________________

## Journal

5. Tell how you know which group has more.



**Notes for Home** Your child counted and compared numbers using *more*, *fewer*, and *equal*.
*Home Activity:* Ask your child to use *more*, *fewer*, and *equal* to describe groups of things on the dinner table, such as cups, saucers, plates, forks, knives, and spoons.

Name ______________________________

# More or Fewer

Practice 1-2

Jose

Victor

Marlena

Frank

Teresita

Pam

1. How many letters are in each name? Put the names in order from the fewest to the most number of letters.

| Names | Number of Letters |
|---|---|
| P a m | 3 |
| | |
| | |
| | |
| | |
| | |

## Problem Solving

Solve.

2. Marlena has 9 pens.
   Pam has 3 pens.
   How many more pens does Marlena have than Pam?

   ______ more pens

3. Frank has 7 books.
   Jose has 5 books.
   How many fewer books does Jose have than Frank?

   ______ fewer books



**Notes for Home** Your child compared sets. *Home Activity:* Arrange 3 sets of pens so that each set has a different number of pens. Ask your child to use *most* and *fewest* to compare the number of pens in each set.

Name ______________________________

Practice
1-3

# Skip Counting

1. How many mittens?
Count by 2s. Write the numbers.

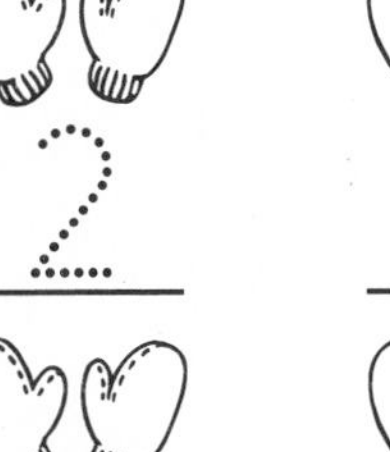

2   4   ____   ____   ____   ____

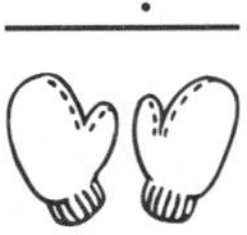

____   ____   ____   ____   ____ mittens

2. How many petals are on the flowers?
Count by 5s. Write the numbers.

____   ____   ____   ____   ____ petals

Count by 2s, 5s, or 10s. Write the numbers.

3. 6, 8, ____, ____, ____

4. 15, 20, ____, ____, ____

5. 20, 30, ____, ____, ____

6. 30, 32, ____, ____, ____

## Problem Solving Estimation

How many fingers are there in your class?
Estimate the number of fingers.
Then count the fingers. Count by 10s.

7. Estimate: ____ fingers

8. Count: ____ fingers



**Notes for Home** Your child counted by 2s, 5s, and 10s. *Home Activity:* Ask your child to count 50 items, such as beans or macaroni, by 2s, 5s, and 10s.

Name ______________________________

# Problem Solving: Look for a Pattern

Practice 1-4

Continue the patterns. Color the numbers.

1.

| 1 | 2 | 3 | 4 | 5 | 6 | 7 | 8 | 9 | 10 |
|---|---|---|---|---|---|---|---|---|---|
| 11 | 12 | 13 | 14 | 15 | 16 | 17 | 18 | 19 | 20 |
| 21 | 22 | 23 | 24 | 25 | 26 | 27 | 28 | 29 | 30 |
| 31 | 32 | 33 | 34 | 35 | 36 | 37 | 38 | 39 | 40 |
| 41 | 42 | 43 | 44 | 45 | 46 | 47 | 48 | 49 | 50 |

2.

| 1 | 2 | 3 | 4 | 5 | 6 | 7 | 8 | 9 | 10 |
|---|---|---|---|---|---|---|---|---|---|
| 11 | 12 | 13 | 14 | 15 | 16 | 17 | 18 | 19 | 20 |
| 21 | 22 | 23 | 24 | 25 | 26 | 27 | 28 | 29 | 30 |
| 31 | 32 | 33 | 34 | 35 | 36 | 37 | 38 | 39 | 40 |
| 41 | 42 | 43 | 44 | 45 | 46 | 47 | 48 | 49 | 50 |

## Visual Thinking

3. Make your own pattern. Color to show how it begins.
   Ask a friend to finish the pattern.

| 11 | 12 | 13 | 14 | 15 | 16 | 17 | 18 | 19 | 20 |
|---|---|---|---|---|---|---|---|---|---|
| 21 | 22 | 23 | 24 | 25 | 26 | 27 | 28 | 29 | 30 |
| 31 | 32 | 33 | 34 | 35 | 36 | 37 | 38 | 39 | 40 |
| 41 | 42 | 43 | 44 | 45 | 46 | 47 | 48 | 49 | 50 |
| 51 | 52 | 53 | 54 | 55 | 56 | 57 | 58 | 59 | 60 |



**Notes for Home** Your child continued number patterns. *Home Activity:* Ask your child to describe the pattern in each chart on this page. (Exercise 1: counting by 3s; Exercise 2: counting by 6s)

Name ____________________



# Mixed Practice: Lessons 1–4

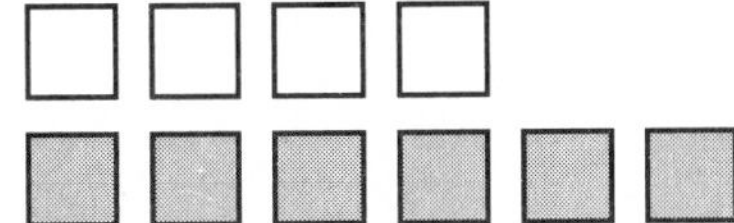

1. Circle the color that has more cubes.

   white gray

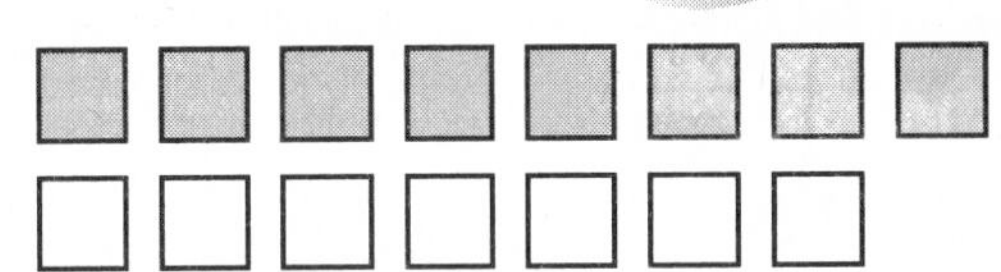

2. Circle the color that has fewer cubes.

   white gray

Use the graph to answer the questions.

| Stars | Moons |
|---|---|
| ☆☆☆ ☆☆☆ ☆☆☆ ☆☆ | ☾☾☾ ☾☾☾ ☾☾ |

3. Are there more stars or moons?

   ____________

4. How many more? ______ more

Count by 2s or 5s. Write the numbers.

5. 15, 20, 25, ______, ______, ______, ______, ______, ______

6. 6, 8, 10, ______, ______, ______, ______, ______, ______

## Problem Solving

7. Continue the pattern. Color the numbers.

| 1 | 2 | 3 | 4 | 5 | 6 | 7 | 8 | 9 | 10 |
|---|---|---|---|---|---|---|---|---|---|
| 11 | 12 | 13 | 14 | 15 | 16 | 17 | 18 | 19 | 20 |
| 21 | 22 | 23 | 24 | 25 | 26 | 27 | 28 | 29 | 30 |

## Journal

8. Draw a picture of 2 groups. Circle the group that has fewer.



**Notes for Home** Your child practiced comparing numbers and completing counting patterns. *Home Activity:* Ask your child to create a number pattern for you to continue. Then have him or her check your answers.

Name ______________________________

**Practice**
Chapter 1
**A**

# Cumulative Review

Count how many. Write the numbers.

1. 

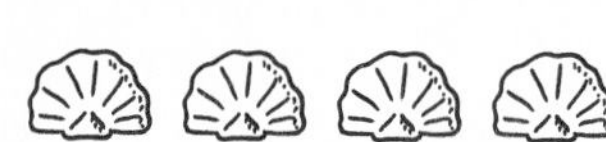

_____

2. 

_____

3. Which group has more, the whales or the shells?

__________

4. How many more?

_____ more

5. Which name has more letters?

_____________

| L | E | R | O | Y | | | |
|---|---|---|---|---|---|---|---|
| J | U | S | T | I | N | E | |

6. How many more? _____ more

## Test Prep

Fill in the ○ for the correct answer.

7. What number comes next?

46, 47, 48, 49, _____

| 45 | 59 | 50 | 60 |
|---|---|---|---|
| ○ | ○ | ○ | ○ |

8. What number comes next?

53, 54, 55, 56, _____

| 57 | 59 | 60 | 66 |
|---|---|---|---|
| ○ | ○ | ○ | ○ |



**Notes for Home** Your child reviewed number groups to 9, comparing numbers, and counting patterns.
*Home Activity:* Ask your child to say the next 5 numbers in Exercise 8. (58, 59, 60, 61, 62)

 Use with page 14.

Name ______________________________

Practice 1-5

# Graphs

Use the graphs to answer the questions.

| Which Vegetable Do You Like Better? | |
|---|---|
| Peas | |
| Carrots | |

1. How many children like peas?

   ______ children

2. How many more children like carrots than peas?

   ______ more

3. Which sandwiches do an equal number of children like best? Circle the foods.

   Ham   Turkey   Cheese

4. Which sandwich was picked the greatest number of times?

   ____________

5. **Write your own** question about one of the graphs.

   ______________________________________________

## Problem Solving Estimation

6. Do you think more children in your class like peanut butter and jelly sandwiches or tuna fish sandwiches? Circle your estimate.

   peanut butter and jelly     tuna fish

   You can make a graph to check your estimate.



**Notes for Home** Your child answered questions about graphs. *Home Activity:* Ask your child to make a graph like the one in Exercise 3 that shows family members' votes for favorite sandwiches.

Name ______________________________

Practice 1-6

# Pictographs

Use the graph. Give each answer.

1. How many children like orange juice best?

   _____ children

2. Which fruit juice is the favorite of most of the children?

   __________

| Favorite Fruit Juice | |
|---|---|
| Orange | ☺ ☺ ☺ ☺ ☺ |
| Apple | ☺ ☺ ☺ ☺ ☺ ☺ ☺ |
| Grape | ☺ ☺ ☺ |

Each ☺ means 1 child.

## Mixed Practice

Count by 2s to find each answer.

3. How many children like apple bread best?

   2 ___ 4 ___ _____ _____ _____

4. How many children like apricot bread best?

   2 ___ 4 ___ _____ _____ _____ _____ _____

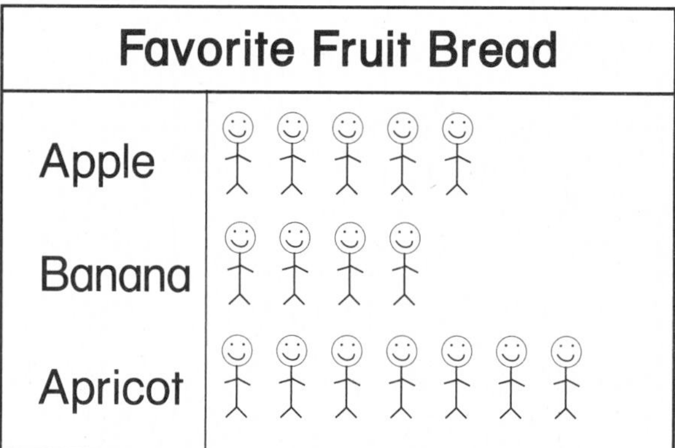


Each (stick figure) means 2 children.

## Mental Math

5. How many more children picked apple juice

   than grape juice in the graph above? _____



**Notes for Home** Your child answered questions about pictographs. *Home Activity:* Ask your child to think of a question that compares two items in one of the graphs. (Possible question: How many more children like banana bread than apple bread? (3))

Name ______________________

Practice
I-7

# Experiment and Tally

Karen tossed a 2-colored counter. Then she tallied her results. Count how many red, how many blue, and how many in all.

| Red | Blue |
|---|---|
| \|\|\| | 卌 卌 \|\| |

1. How many red? 3
2. How many blue? ______
3. How many in all? ______

| Red | Blue |
|---|---|
| 卌 \|\| | 卌 \|\|\| |

4. How many red? ______
5. How many blue? ______
6. How many in all? ______

Show the tallies for each chart.

| Red | Yellow |
|---|---|
| | |

7. Show 9 red.
8. Show 11 yellow
9. How many in all? ______

| Red | Yellow |
|---|---|
| | |

10. Show 11 red.
11. Show 18 yellow.
12. How many in all? ______

## Problem Solving Critical Thinking

13. If you toss a number cube 20 times, could it land on six 20 times? Why or why not?



**Notes for Home** Your child read and made tally charts. *Home Activity:* Ask your child to tell you which tally chart shows the most yellow tosses and the fewest yellow tosses. (Most: lower right chart with 18 tosses. Fewest: lower left chart with 11 tosses.)

Name ______________________________

Practice 1-8

# Bar Graphs

1. Do you live on a street, avenue or road? Ask 10 classmates. How many letters are there in each street name? Make tally marks.

| Number of Letters in Our Street Names | | | | | | | |
|---|---|---|---|---|---|---|---|
| 1 | 2 | 3 | 4 | 5 | 6 | 7 | 8 |
| | | | | | | | |
| 9 | 10 | 11 | 12 | 13 | 14 | 15 | 16 |
| | | | | | | | |

2. Make a bar graph. Color 1 space for each tally mark.

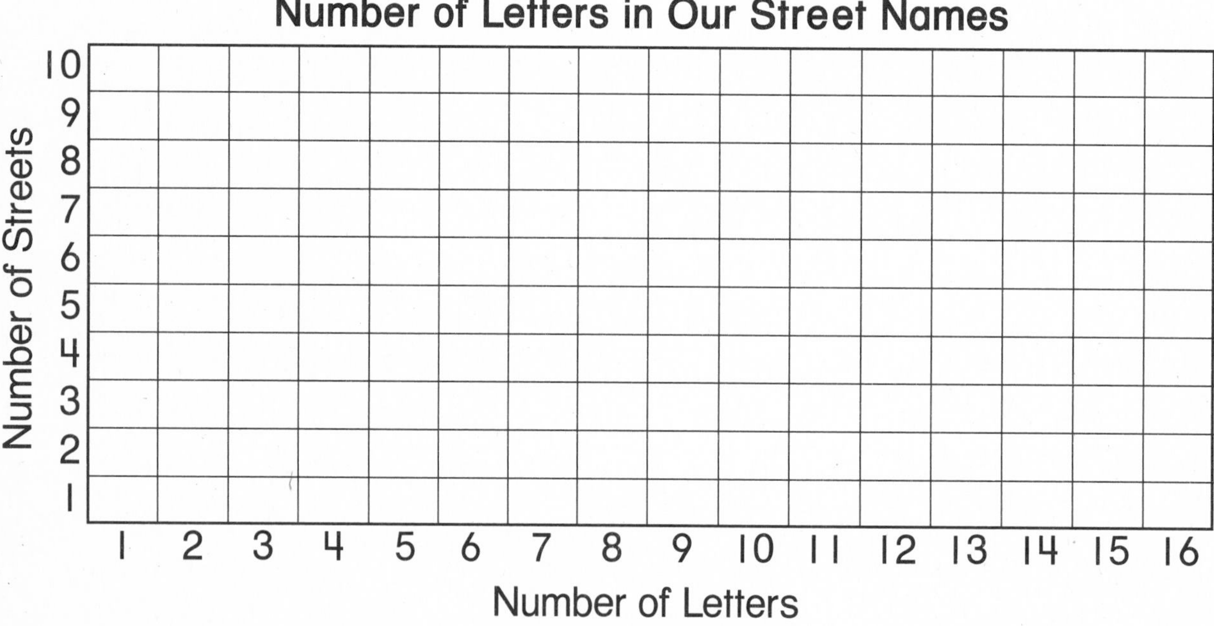


## Problem Solving Critical Thinking

3. Suppose 8 children have 9 letters in their street names. Explain how you would show this on a bar graph.

**Notes for Home** Your child has gathered and shown data using tally marks and a bar graph. *Home Activity:* Ask your child to add the street names of family members including cousins, uncles, aunts, and grandparents.

Name ______________________

Practice 1-9

# Problem Solving: Collect and Use Data

1. Show data for 8 classmates using a diagram.

Do you like roller coasters, water slides, or both?

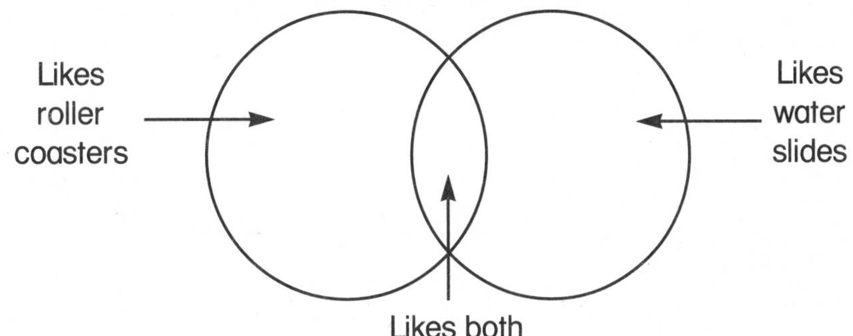


Use your diagram to answer the questions.

2. How many children like both roller coasters and water slides? ______

3. How many children like roller coasters?

______

4. How many children like roller coasters but not water slides?

______

5. How many children like water slides?

______

6. How many children like water slides but not roller coasters?

______

## Tell a Math Story

7. Tell a short story about 7 friends. Ask a friend to draw a diagram for your story.



**Notes for Home** Your child collected, organized, and used data to solve problems. *Home Activity:* Work with your child to create a diagram like the one on this page that shows how many family members like bananas, grapes, or both.

Name ______________________________

**Practice**
Chapter 1
**B**

# Mixed Practice: Lessons 5–9

Use the graph to answer the questions.

1. How many children like strawberry best? _____

2. Do more children like chocolate or vanilla?

   ________________

| Favorite Milk Flavor | |
|---|---|
| Plain | |
| Vanilla | |
| Chocolate | |
| Strawberry | |

Each carton means 1 child.

Use the graph to answer the questions.

3. Which soup was picked most often?

   ________________

4. Which soup was picked least often?

   ________________

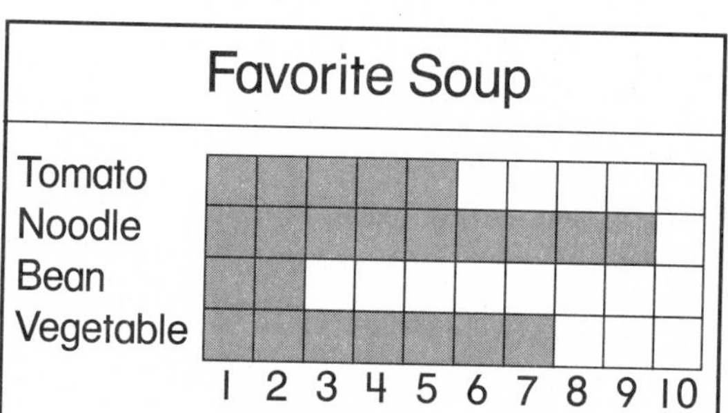


## Problem Solving

Look at the diagram. Answer the questions.

5. How many children like apples but not pears? _____

6. How many children like both apples and pears? _____

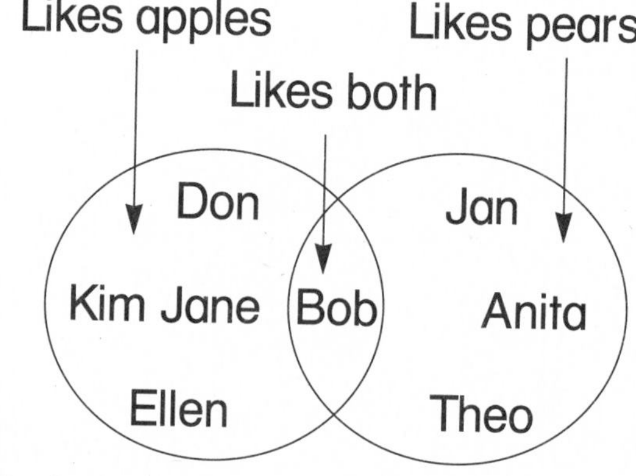


## Journal

7. Write a question about the diagram. Ask a friend to answer your question.



**Notes for Home** Your child practiced using graphs to compare information. *Home Activity:* Have your child add his or her vote to the graph about a favorite soup. Ask: *Does this change the answers to Exercises 3 and 4?* (No, 1 vote for any soup would not change the answers.)

Name ____________________________________

# Cumulative Review

Circle the number that is greater.

1. 7 5

2. 10 16

Circle the number that is less.

3. 14 11

4. 8 6

## Problem Solving

Solve.

5. There are 7 frogs.
   There are 5 toads.
   Which group has more?

   ______________

6. There are 6 wasps.
   There are 9 hornets.
   Which group has fewer?

   ______________

## Test Prep

Fill in the ○ for the correct answer.

7. Count by 2s.
   Mark the number
   that comes next.

   2, 4, 6, 8, _____

   9 ○ 10 ○ 11 ○ 12 ○

8. Count by 5s.
   Mark the number
   that comes next.

   10, 15, 20, 25, _____

   26 ○ 28 ○ 30 ○ 35 ○



**Notes for Home** Your child reviewed comparing numbers and skip counting. *Home Activity:* Ask your child to assemble 2 groups of objects at home that are equal in number, and then create a third group with fewer objects.

Name ______________________

Practice 2-1

# Explore Addition Stories

8 spoons.

Lea brings 2 more spoons.

How many spoons in all?

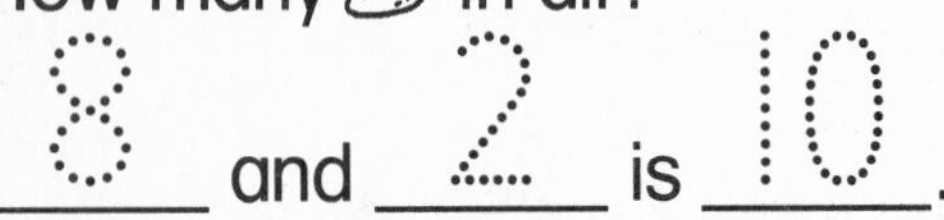

8 and 2 is 10.

Solve each problem. You can use counters.

1. 7 on a plate.

   3 more are added.

   How many in all?

   ______ and ______ is ______.

2. 5 on Tim's plate.

   4 on Kim's plate.

   How many in all?

   ______ and ______ is ______.

3. 6 on the table.

   2 more are added.

   How many in all?

   ______ and ______ is ______.

4. 3 on the table.

   5 are added.

   How many in all?

   ______ and ______ is ______.

**Talk About It** Tell a classmate a number story about this picture.

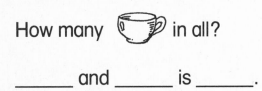

**Notes for Home** Your child solved addition stories. *Home Activity:* Ask your child to tell you an addition story about 3 honey bees flying around and 4 honey bees on flowers.

Name ______________________________

# Join Groups to Add

Practice 2-2

You can use and a .

Write the number sentence. Solve.

1. 5 are in a hive.

   4 more join them.

   How many are there now?

    5 and 4 is 9 

2. 4 sit in the sun.

   3 join them.

   How many in all?

   _____ and _____ is _____ 

3. 3 are playing.

   5 more  also play.

   How many in all?

   _____ and _____ is _____

4. 7 on the flowers.

   2 more come.

   How many are on the flowers now?

   _____ and _____ is _____ 

## Problem Solving Critical Thinking

5. Solve. You can use .

   There are 9  in all. 

   How many  are hiding under the blanket?

   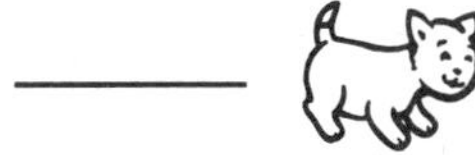



**Notes for Home** Your child wrote number sentences for addition stories. *Home Activity:* Ask you child to tell you an addition story and then explain how he or she would find the answer.

Name ______________________________

# Count On and Add Zero

**Practice 2-3**

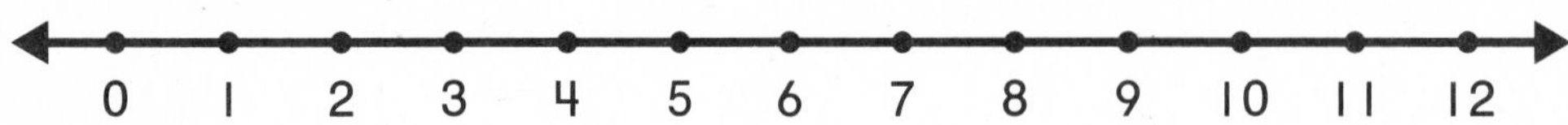


Use the number line. Write the sum.

1. $3 + 1 = $ 4 $\qquad 5 + 3 = $ ____
2. $8 + 0 = $ ____ $\qquad 9 + 2 = $ ____
3. $6 + 3 = $ ____ $\qquad 2 + 1 = $ ____
4. $1 + 2 = $ ____ $\qquad 2 + 0 = $ ____
5. $7 + 4 = $ ____ $\qquad 4 + 2 = $ ____

Add.

6.

| 8 | 1 | 6 | 5 | 3 | 9 |
|---|---|---|---|---|---|
| + 1 | + 2 | + 3 | + 0 | + 3 | + 2 |

7.

| 7 | 4 | 2 | 1 | 8 | 3 |
|---|---|---|---|---|---|
| + 3 | + 0 | + 1 | + 0 | + 3 | + 2 |

## Problem Solving Critical Thinking

8. Start with 6. Add a number so that the sum is 6. What number did you add? ______

**Notes for Home** Your child added 0, 1, 2, or 3 to numbers. *Home Activity:* Show your child from 1 to 9 buttons or beans. Have your child use them to show you how many is 0, 1, 2, and 3 more.

Name ______________________________

Practice 2-4

# Turnaround Facts

Write the number sentence for each train.

1\.

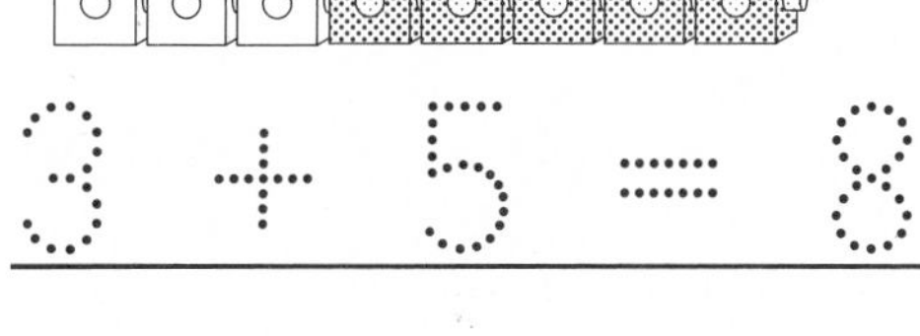

3 + 5 = 8

5 + 3 = 8

2\.

______________________

______________________

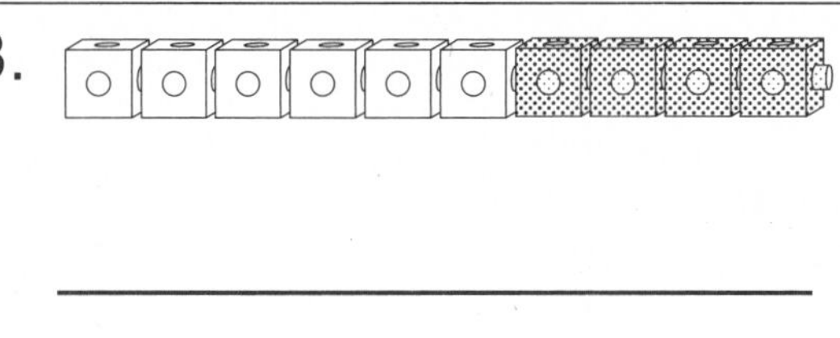

3\.

______________________

______________________

4\.

______________________

______________________

Write the turnaround fact for each number sentence.

5\. 4 + 7 = 11

______________________

6\. 6 + 5 = 11

______________________

## Problem Solving

Write the number sentence. Solve.

7\. 4  fly in the cave.

3 join them.

How many  in all?

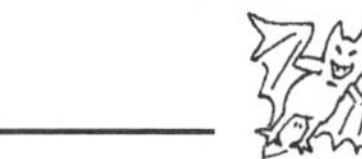

8\. 3  are in a tree.

4 are in another tree.

Now how many  are in trees?

______



**Notes for Home** Your child used turnaround facts to find sums to 12. *Home Activity:* Ask your child to tell you a set of turnaround facts with a sum of 8. (Possible answer: 5 + 3 = 8 and 3 + 5 = 8)

Name ______________________________

# Ways to Make Numbers

Use [cubes]. Show different ways to make 9.
Write the number sentences.

1.

| Ways to Make 9 | |
|---|---|
| 0 + 9 = 9 | ___ + ___ = ___ |
| ___ + ___ = ___ | ___ + ___ = ___ |
| ___ + ___ = ___ | ___ + ___ = ___ |
| ___ + ___ = ___ | ___ + ___ = ___ |
| ___ + ___ = ___ | ___ + ___ = ___ |

## Problem Solving Patterns

2. How many ways are there to make 7? ______

3. How many ways are there to make 8? ______

4. How many ways are there to make 9? ______

5. How many ways do you think there are to make 10? ______

6. How many ways do you think there are to make 11? ______

7. Why do you think so?



**Notes for Home** Your child found all the ways to make 9. *Home Activity:* Ask your child what pattern he or she can use to tell the number of ways to make 7, 6 or 5. (Possible answer: There is 1 more way than the sum; 8 ways to make 7, 7 ways to make 6, and 6 ways to make 5.)

Name ______________________________

# Problem Solving: Write a Number Sentence

Write a number sentence. Solve.

1. Dan sees 8  .

   Ann sees 3 more  .

   How many  do Dan and Ann see in all?

2. 4 are in the tree.

   4 are on the ground.

   How many in all?

   ____ + ____ = ____

3. Rita eats 5  .

   Juan eats 7  .

   How many  do they eat in all?

   ____ + ____ = ____

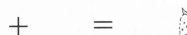

4. Theo sees 4  on a bush

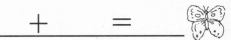

   and 2  near the bush.

   How many did he see?

   ____ + ____ = ____

## Tell a Math Story

Use the picture.
Tell a word problem to a friend.
Ask your friend to solve by writing a number sentence.

____ + ____ = ____



**Notes for Home** Your child wrote number sentences to solve story problems. *Home Activity:* Ask your child to tell you a word problem about members of your family. Have your child write the number sentence that he or she would use to solve the problem.

Name ______________________________

Practice
Chapter 2
A

## Mixed Practice: Lessons 1–6

Add.

1. $\begin{array}{r} 9 \\ +3 \\ \hline \end{array}$ $\begin{array}{r} 4 \\ +0 \\ \hline \end{array}$ $\begin{array}{r} 3 \\ +8 \\ \hline \end{array}$ $\begin{array}{r} 5 \\ +2 \\ \hline \end{array}$ $\begin{array}{r} 4 \\ +1 \\ \hline \end{array}$ $\begin{array}{r} 7 \\ +2 \\ \hline \end{array}$

These pictures show turnaround facts.
Write the number sentence for each picture.

2.

______________________________

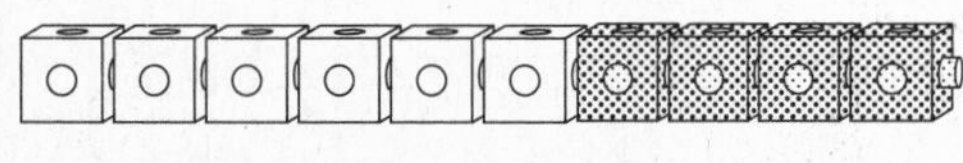

______________________________

3. 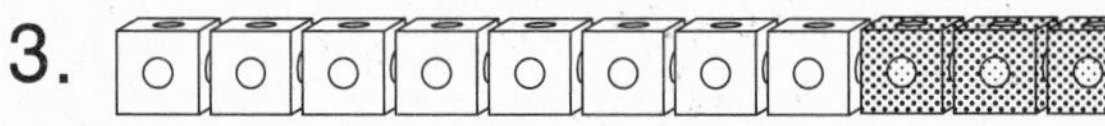

______________________________

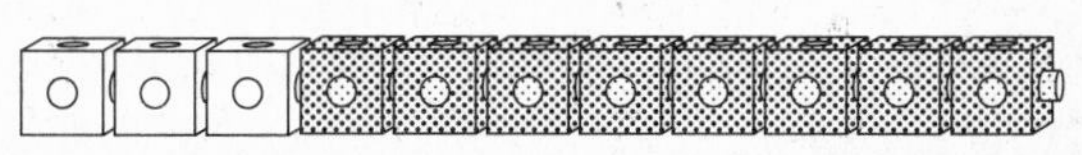

______________________________

## Problem Solving

Write a number sentence. Solve. You can use ⬭ ⬭.

4. Gloria saw 7 in the pond

She saw 2 on the shore.

How many did she see?

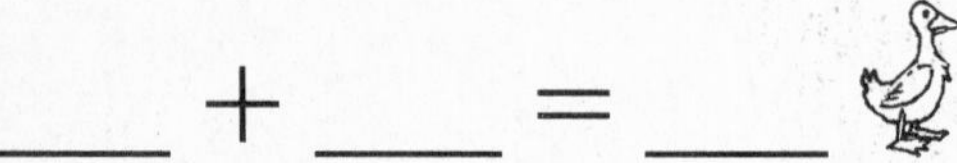

____ + ____ = ____

5. 

6 were playing ball.

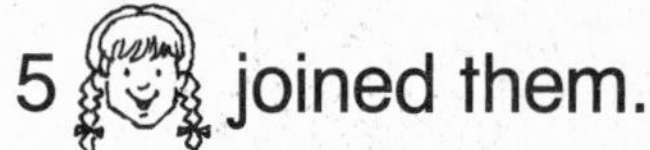

5 joined them.

How many played ball in all?

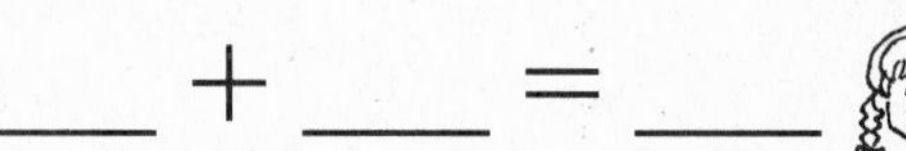

____ + ____ = ____

## Journal

6. How do you find the turnaround fact for 5 + 3 = 8? Write about it.

**Notes for Home** Your child practiced addition and problem-solving skills. *Home Activity:* Ask you child how he or she decided what number sentence to write for Exercise 4. (Possible answer: When you join groups, you add. A group of 7 and a group of 2 is 7 + 2, or 9.)

Name ______________________________

**Practice**
Chapters 1–2
A

# Cumulative Review

Count by ones. Write the numbers.

1. 43, 44, 45, ______, ______, ______, ______, ______, ______

Count back by ones. Write the numbers.

2. 18, 17, 16, ______, ______, ______, ______, ______, ______

## Problem Solving

3. Use the tally marks to make a bar graph.

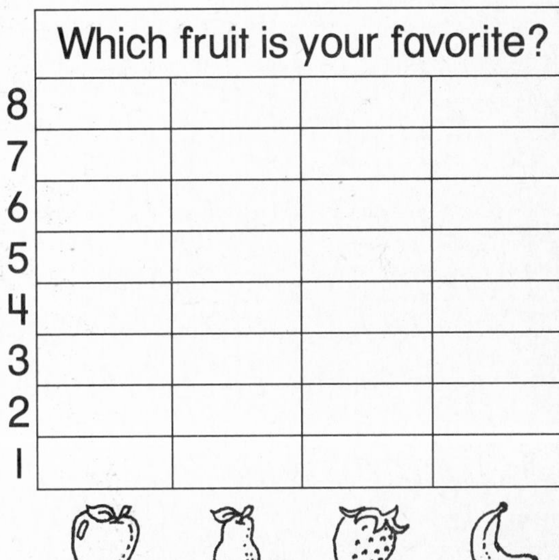


4. How many people chose ?

______ people

5. Which fruit was chosen the most often? Circle the picture.

## Test Prep

Fill in the ○ for the correct answer.

Mark the missing number in the pattern.

6. 10, 15, 20, ______, 30, 35

○ 22
○ 25
○ 27
○ 30

**Notes for Home** Your child reviewed counting, using tally marks and graphs, and finding number patterns.
*Home Activity:* Ask your child to tell which fruit was chosen least often in Exercise 3. (pear)

Name ______________________________

# Separate Groups to Subtract

Use ⬭ ◍ to subtract.

Write the number sentence.

1. 7  are in a tree.

   3 fly away.

   How many are left?

   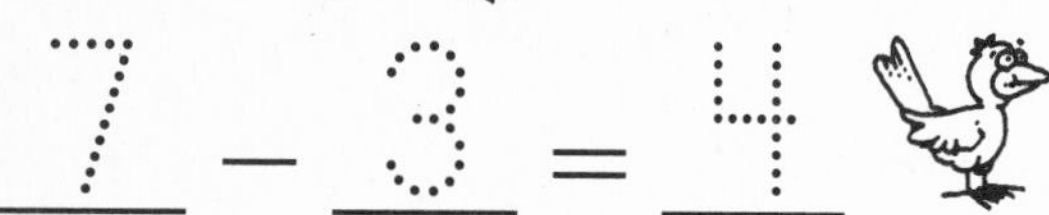
   

2. 5  are playing.

   2 run away.

   How many are left?

   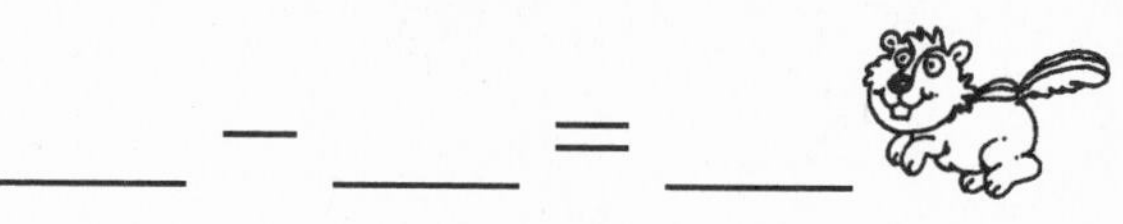
   ____ − ____ = ____

3. 8  are at the lake.

   5 fly away.

   How many are left?

   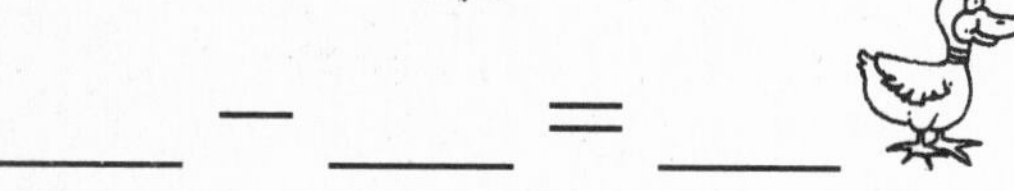
   ____ − ____ = ____

4. 4  watch the birds.

   2 walk away.

   How many are left?

   ____ − ____ = ____

## Problem Solving Visual Thinking

Draw a picture to solve.

Write the number sentence.

5. There are 6 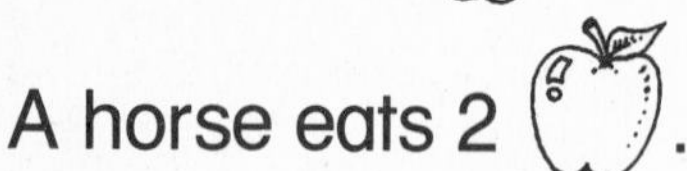 on the ground.

   A horse eats 2 .

   How many are left?

   ____ − ____ = ____

**Notes for Home** Your child used counters to subtract and wrote number sentences. *Home Activity:* Ask your child to use dry beans or macaroni to show you how to subtract 8 – 4 = (4).

Name ______________________________

# Count Back and Subtract Zero

Practice 2-8

Use the number line. Write the difference.

1. $7 - 1 = 6$    $3 - 2$    $9 - 0$    $3 - 1$    $5 - 1$    $12 - 2$

2. $3 - 0$    $11 - 2$    $6 - 1$    $2 - 2$    $1 - 0$    $9 - 1$

3. $6 - 2$    $7 - 0$    $8 - 2$    $11 - 3$    $5 - 2$    $10 - 1$

## Mixed Practice

Add or subtract.

4. $9 - 2$    $8 + 2$    $5 - 0$    $7 - 2$    $1 + 8$    $4 + 2$

## Problem Solving Critical Thinking

Start with 8. Subtract a number.

The answer is 8. What did you subtract? ______



**Notes for Home** Your child added and subtracted using a number line. *Home Activity:* Ask your child to use the number line to find 8 + 3 = 11 and 9 - 2 = 7.

Name ______________________________

# Explore How Many More

Practice 2-9

Use ⬭ ⬭ to solve.

1. There are 12 spoons.

   There are 8 knives.

   How many more spoons are there?

   4 more

2. There are 10 napkins.

   There are 8 cups.

   How many more napkins are there?

   ______ more

3. There are 9 plates.

   There are 5 bowls.

   How many more plates are there?

   ______ more

4. There are 12 spoons.

   There are 5 bowls.

   How many more spoons are there?

   ______ more

## Problem Solving Visual Thinking

5. How many more plates than bowls?

   ______ more

6. How many more plates than cups?

   ______ more



**Notes for Home** Your child used counters to compare groups. *Home Activity:* Ask your child to take 3 cups and 5 saucers and compare the two groups. (There are 2 more saucers.)

Name ______________________

Practice 2-10

# Find How Many More

Write the number sentence. Solve.

You can use 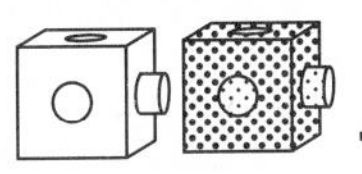 .

1. Lou eats 9 grapes.

   Sue eats 5 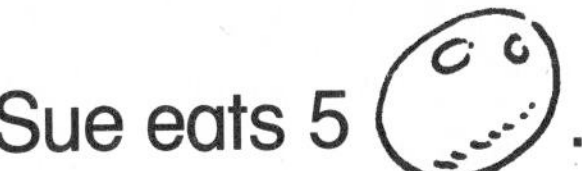 .

   How many more grapes does Lou eat than Sue?

   ____ − ____ = ____ more

2. Dan eats 8  .

   Nan eats 4  .

   How many more cherries does Dan eat than Nan?

   ____ − ____ = ____ more

3. Mario sees 12  .

   Meg sees 7  .

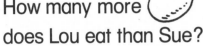

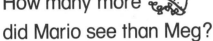

   How many more kites did Mario see than Meg?

   ____ − ____ = ____ more

4. Anna sees 10  .

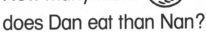

   Aldo sees 6 ladybugs.

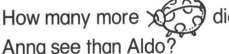

   How many more ladybugs did Anna see than Aldo?

   ____ − ____ = ____ more

## Problem Solving Visual Thinking

5. Draw less than 8 cherries on the plate.

   How many more  are there than  ?

   ____ − ____ = ____ more

**Notes for Home** Your child used subtraction to compare groups. *Home Activity:* Show your child two groups of objects, such as 5 cups and 3 saucers. Have your child write a number sentence that tells how many more are in the larger group. (Possible answer: 5 – 3 = 2; there are 2 more cups.)

Name ______________________

Practice 2-11

# Relate Addition and Subtraction

Add or subtract.

Write the number sentence. Solve.

1. Kathy has 9  .

   Anne brings 5 more  .

   How many are there in all?

   ___ + ___ = ___

2. 14 are in a box.

   Anne took 5  .

   How many  were left?

   ___ − ___ = ___

3. 5 are on a leaf.

   7 more join them.

   How many are on the leaf now?

   ___ + ___ = ___

4. There are 12 on a leaf.

   7 go away.

   How many are on the leaf now?

   ___ − ___ = ___

## Tell a Math Story

Look at the picture. Tell stories to match the number sentences.

5. $4 + 3 = 7$

6. $7 - 3 = 4$

**Notes for Home** Your child chose addition or subtraction to solve word problems. *Home Activity:* Ask your child to tell you a story for the picture at the bottom of the page.

Name ______________________________

Practice 2-12

# Problem Solving: Choose an Operation

Circle **add** or **subtract**.

Write the number sentence. Solve.

1. 6 swans are on a pond.

   3 more swans join them.

   How many swans are on the pond now?

   **add** **subtract**

   6 + 3 = 9

2. 3 dogs play in a field.

   1 dog runs away.

   How many dogs are on the field now?

   **add** **subtract**

   ______________________

3. There are 5  .

   Pat drinks 2  .

   How many glasses are there now?

   **add** **subtract**

   ______________________

4. Jo cooks 7 hot dogs.

   Vi cooks 4 more  .

   How many cooked hot dogs are there now?

   **add** **subtract**

   ______________________

## Write About It

5. Make up your own word problem.

   Have a friend write a number sentence to solve it.



**Notes for Home** Your child practiced choosing addition or subtraction to solve problems. *Home Activity:* Ask your child to make up two problems, one that can be solved by adding and one that can be solved by subtracting.

Name ________________________________

# Mixed Practice: Lessons 7–12

**Practice Chapter 2 B**

Subtract. You can use ⬭ ⬭ .

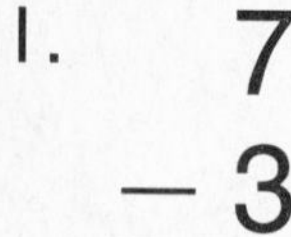

1. $\begin{array}{r} 7 \\ -3 \\ \hline \end{array}$ $\begin{array}{r} 9 \\ -2 \\ \hline \end{array}$ $\begin{array}{r} 6 \\ -4 \\ \hline \end{array}$ $\begin{array}{r} 12 \\ -5 \\ \hline \end{array}$ $\begin{array}{r} 5 \\ -0 \\ \hline \end{array}$ $\begin{array}{r} 11 \\ -3 \\ \hline \end{array}$ $\begin{array}{r} 8 \\ -8 \\ \hline \end{array}$

## Problem Solving

Subtract. Write the number sentence.

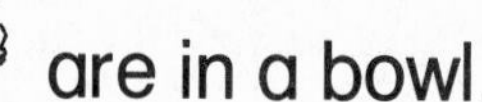
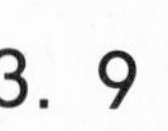

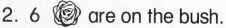

2. 6 (roses) are on the bush.

Martha cuts 5 (roses).

How many (roses) are left?

________________ (roses)

3. 9 (grapes) are in a bowl.

Birds eat 5 (grapes).

How many (grapes) are left?

________________ (grapes)

Circle **add** or **subtract**. Write a number sentence.
Solve. You can use ⬭ ⬭ .

4. 3 girls are walking.
2 more girls join them.
How many girls are walking now?

**add** **subtract**

________________ girls

5. 8 boys are on seesaws.
6 boys go home.
How many boys are on the seesaw now?

**add** **subtract**

________________ boys

## Journal

6. Write your own word problem using the numbers 6, 6, and 12.
Would you add or subtract to solve it? Write the number sentence.



**Notes for Home** Your child practiced subtraction and problem-solving skills. *Home Activity:* Ask your child to tell you a word problem that can be solved by adding.

Name ______________________________



# Cumulative Review

Write the number sentence. Solve.

1. 8 are playing.

3 run away.

How many are still playing?

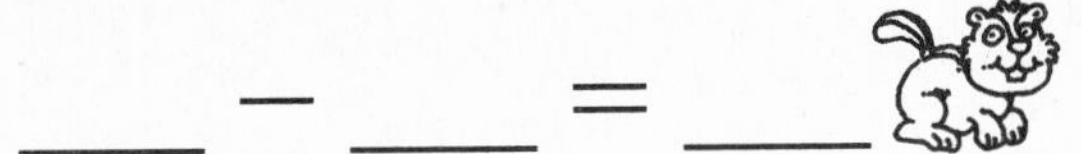

____ − ____ = ____

2. 7 are in a box.

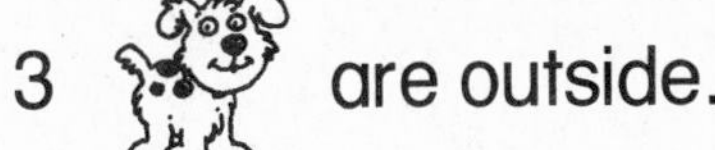

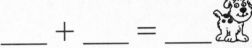

3 are outside.

How many are there in all?

____ + ____ = ____

Count back by ones. Write the numbers.

3. 36, 35, 34, ____, ____, ____, ____, ____, ____

Count by ones. Write the numbers.

4. 73, 74, 75, ____, ____, ____, ____, ____, ____

## Test Prep

Fill in the ○ for the correct answer.

5. Which train and number sentence show the turnaround fact for this train and number sentence?

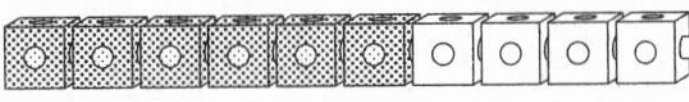

6 + 4 = 10

○ 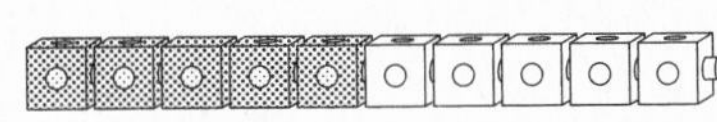

5 + 5 = 10

○ 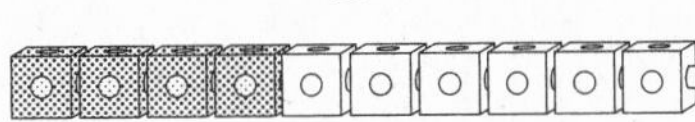

4 + 6 = 10

○ 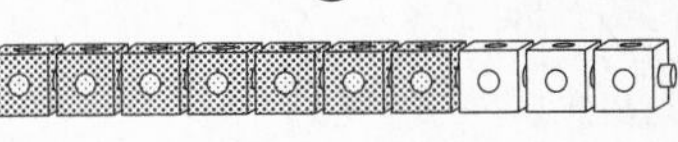

7 + 3 = 10



**Notes for Home** Your child reviewed addition and subtraction skills. *Home Activity:* Ask your child to tell what the turnaround fact for 7 + 3 = 10 would be. (3 + 7 = 10)

Name ______________________________

# Explore Doubles

Practice 3-1

$5 + 5 = 10$

Add. Write the sums. You can use [cubes].

1. $3 + 3 =$ ____  $6 + 6 =$ ____  $8 + 8 =$ ____
2. $7 + 7 =$ ____  $1 + 1 =$ ____  $4 + 4 =$ ____
3. $2 + 2 =$ ____  $9 + 9 =$ ____  $5 + 5 =$ ____
4. $7 + 7$  $6 + 6$  $5 + 5$  $4 + 4$  $3 + 3$  $2 + 2$  $1 + 1$
5. $3 + 3$  $7 + 7$  $6 + 6$  $4 + 4$  $9 + 9$  $4 + 4$  $8 + 8$

## Talk About It

Look at Exercise 4. What pattern do you see in the sums?



**Notes for Home** Your child found the sums for doubles facts (such as 4 + 4 = 8). *Home Activity:* Ask your child to give one example of a doubles fact (3 + 3 = 6) and one example of an addition sentence that is not a doubles fact (3 + 5 = 8).

Name ____________________

# Use Doubles Plus One

Add.

1. 5 + 5 = 10   5 + 6 = ____   6 + 5 = ____

2. 8 + 8 = ____   8 + 9 = ____   9 + 8 = ____

3.

| 6 | 6 | 7 |
|---|---|---|
| + 6 | + 7 | + 6 |

4.

| 7 | 7 | 8 |
|---|---|---|
| + 7 | + 8 | + 7 |

5.

| 2 | 5 | 1 | 9 | 6 | 7 | 4 |
|---|---|---|---|---|---|---|
| + 2 | + 5 | + 1 | + 9 | + 6 | + 7 | + 4 |

6.

| 5 | 2 | 6 | 5 | 8 | 2 | 4 |
|---|---|---|---|---|---|---|
| + 6 | + 1 | + 7 | + 4 | + 7 | + 3 | + 3 |

## Mixed Practice   Add.

7.

| 7 | 4 | 9 | 6 | 7 | 6 | 8 |
|---|---|---|---|---|---|---|
| + 0 | + 4 | + 5 | + 7 | + 3 | + 6 | + 9 |

## Problem Solving Critical Thinking

8. A has landed on a mirror. How many legs can you see? Explain your answer.



**Notes for Home** Your child solved addition facts with sums through 18. *Home Activity:* Ask your child how to solve 6 + 7. (6 + 6 = 12 plus 1 = 13)

Name ______________________________

Practice 3-3

# Explore Making 10

Put a picture in each empty box.
Complete the number sentence.

1. 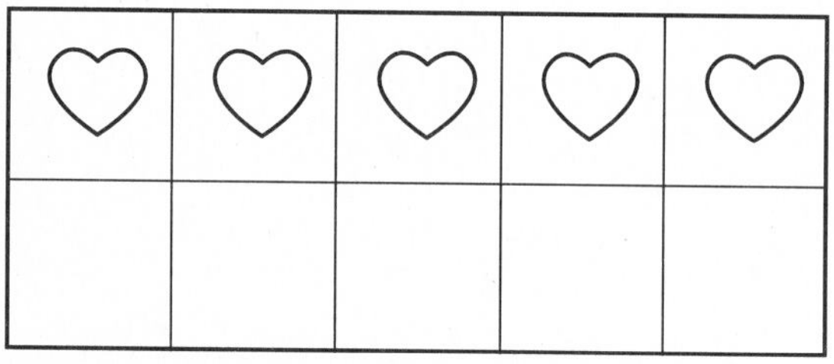 $5 + \_\_\_ = \_\_\_$

2. 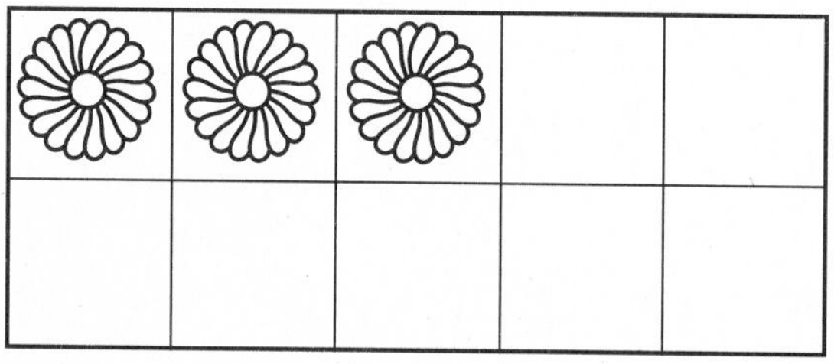 $3 + \_\_\_ = \_\_\_$

3. 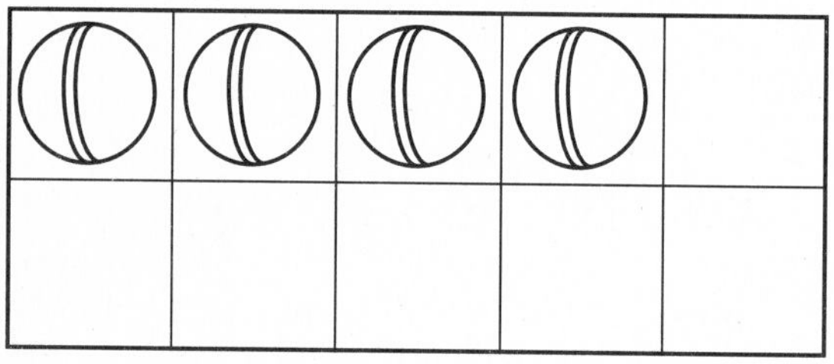 $4 + \_\_\_ = \_\_\_$

4. 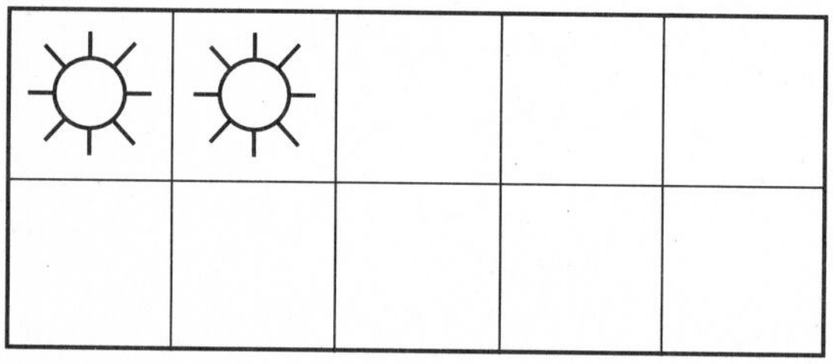 $2 + \_\_\_ = \_\_\_$

**Talk About It** What number would you add to 10 to make the sum of 10?



**Notes for Home** Your child drew pictures and wrote number sentences with the sum of 10. *Home Activity:* Ask your child to use objects to show 5 + 5 = 10 and to write the number sentence.

Name ______________________________

Practice 3-4

# Make 10 When Adding 9

Add. Write the addition sentence.

1. 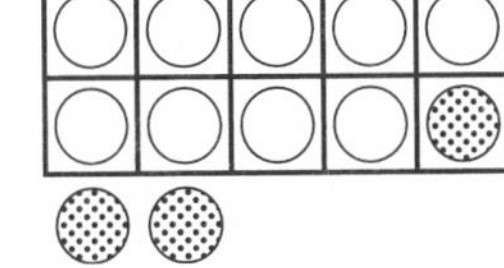

9 + 3 = 12

2. 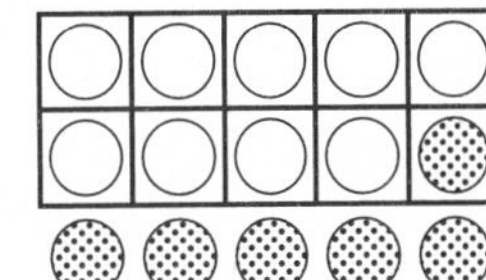

____ + ____ = ____

3. 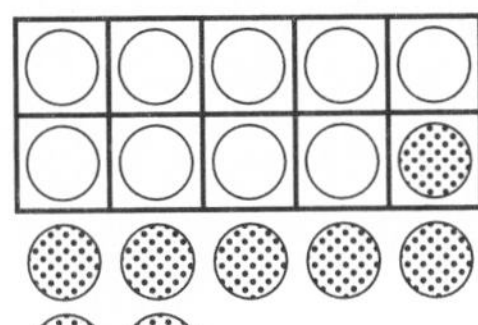

____ + ____ = ____

4. 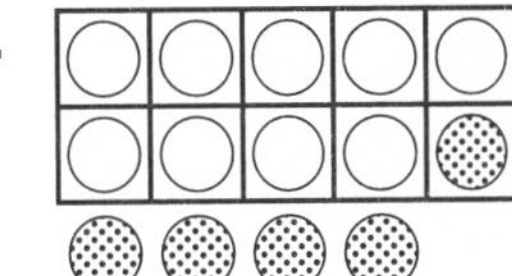

____ + ____ = ____

Add.

5.

| 9 | 9 | 9 | 9 | 9 | 9 | 9 |
|---|---|---|---|---|---|---|
| + 5 | + 8 | + 2 | + 7 | + 3 | + 6 | + 4 |

**Mixed Practice** Add.

6. 5 + 4 = ____ 7 + 7 = ____ 9 + 8 = ____

## Problem Solving Visual Thinking

Frank has 9 stamps on his card.

He gets 8 more stamps.

How many stamps does he have in all? _____ stamps

How many stamps will he carry over to a new card? _____ stamps



**Notes for Home** Your child practiced adding 9 to another number by first making a ten. *Home Activity:* Ask your child to explain how he or she solved Exercise 3.

Name ____________________

Practice 3-5

# Make 10 When Adding 6, 7, or 8

Add. Write the addition sentence.

1. 7 + 6 = 13

2. ___ + ___ = ___

3. ___ + ___ = ___

4. ___ + ___ = ___

Add.

5.

| 6 | 4 | 7 | 8 | 9 | 8 | 5 |
|---|---|---|---|---|---|---|
| + 7 | + 7 | + 5 | + 5 | + 6 | + 8 | + 6 |

## Problem Solving Critical Thinking

6. Maria tossed these numbers.

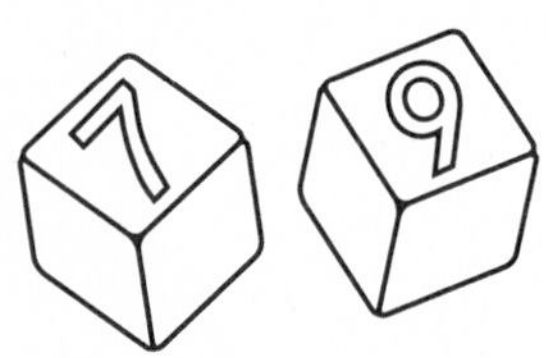


What is the sum? ______

7. Roberto tossed a sum of 13. Circle the cubes that he might have rolled.

**Notes for Home** Your child practiced adding 6, 7, or 8 to another number by first making a ten. *Home Activity:* Ask your child to explain how he or she would find 7 + 5. (7 + 3 = 10 plus 2 = 12)

Name ______________________________

# Problem Solving: Make a List

Martha has 15 special marbles.
Her father built 2 boxes for Martha to keep them.

Find all the ways Martha can put
15 marbles in 2 boxes.
You can use .
Write your numbers in the list.

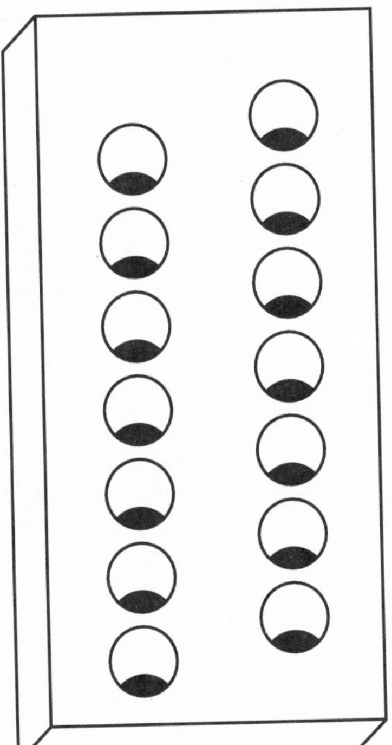
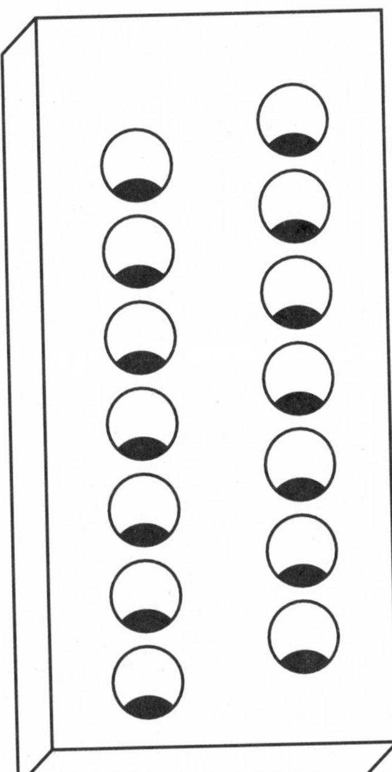

| Left Box | Right Box |
|---|---|
| 14 | 1 |
| ____ | ____ |
| ____ | ____ |
| ____ | ____ |
| ____ | ____ |
| ____ | ____ |
| ____ | ____ |
| ____ | ____ |
| ____ | ____ |
| ____ | ____ |
| ____ | ____ |
| ____ | ____ |
| ____ | ____ |
| ____ | ____ |

## Patterns

What patterns do you see in your list?



**Notes for Home** Your child practiced making a list to solve a problem. *Home Activity:* Ask your child to make a list to show all the ways that 6 bananas can be put in 2 baskets. (1 and 5, 2 and 4, 3 and 3, 4 and 2, 5 and 1)

Name ____________________

Practice
Chapter 3
A

# Mixed Practice: Lessons 1–6

Add.

1. $6 + 6 =$ ____  $5 + 5 =$ ____  $4 + 4 =$ ____

Complete the number sentences.

2. 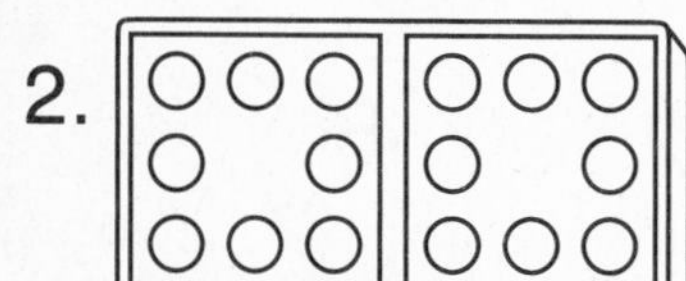

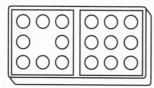

$8 + 8 =$ ___

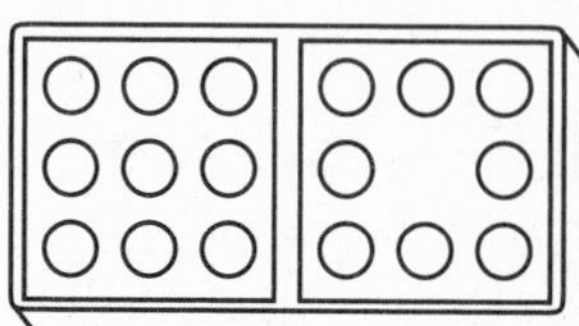

$8 +$ ___ $=$ ___

$9 +$ ___ $=$ ___

Add. Write the number sentences.

3. 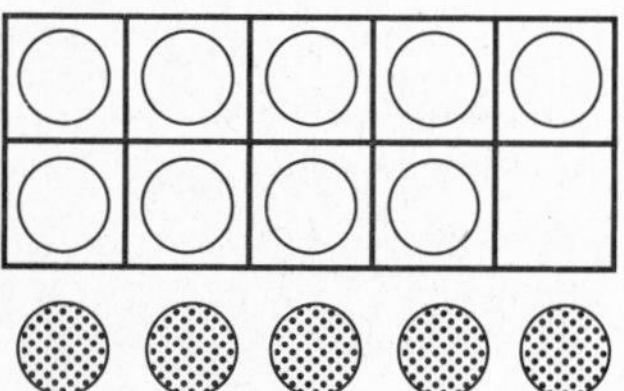

____ + ____ = ____

4. 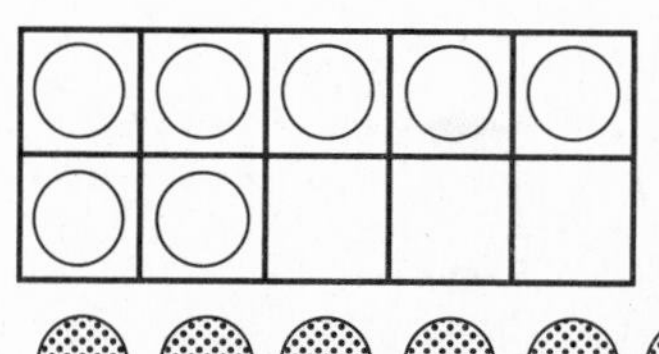

____ + ____ = ____

## Problem Solving

Write a number sentence. Solve.

5. Mark's cat had 6 kittens. His dog had 5 puppies. How many puppies and kittens are there in all?

____ + ____ = ____

6. Amir has 8 red cars and 7 blue cars. How many cars does he have in all?

____ + ____ = ____

## Journal

Draw a picture to show doubles plus one.



**Notes for Home** Your child practiced concepts, skills, and problem solving from Lessons 1 through 6.
*Home Activity:* Ask your child to use a 10-frame to show you how he or she would find the sum of 8 + 6. (14)

Name ______________________________

Practice
Chapters 1–3
A

# Cumulative Review

Continue the pattern.
Write the missing numbers.

1. 2, 4, 6, _____, _____, _____

2. 4, 8, 12, _____, _____, _____

Add.

3. $6 + 8 =$ ___  $9 + 3 =$ ___  $4 + 7 =$ ___

## Problem Solving

Solve. Write a number sentence.

4. Stephanie had 6 stickers.
Suli gave her 7 more.
How many stickers does she have in all?

_____ + _____ = _____ stickers

## Test Prep

Fill in the ○ to show the correct answer.

5. Which color do most children like best?

○ Brown ○ Yellow ○ Blue ○ Red

6. How many more children like blue than brown?

○ 5 ○ 3 ○ 4 ○ 6

| Favorite Colors | |
|---|---|
| Brown | ☺☺☺ |
| Yellow | ☺☺☺☺☺☺☺☺☺ |
| Blue | ☺☺☺☺☺☺☺ |
| Red | ☺☺☺☺☺ |



**Notes for Home** Your child reviewed number patterns, addition and subtraction facts to 12, and pictographs.
*Home Activity:* Ask your child explain how he or she determined the pattern in Exercise 2.

Name ______________________

Practice 3-7

# Use Doubles to Subtract

Add or subtract.

Match each doubles fact with a subtraction fact.

| | |
|---|---|
| 1. 8 − 4 = 4 | 8 + 8 = ____ |
| 2. 18 − 9 = ____ | 5 + 5 = ____ |
| 3. 16 − 8 = ____ | 9 + 9 = ____ |
| 4. 10 − 5 = ____ | 4 + 4 = 8 |

Subtract. Write the double that helps.

5. 12 − 6 = 6 6 + 6 = 12

6. 6 − 3 = ____ ____ + ____ = ____

7. 14 − 7 = ____ ____ + ____ = ____

## Mental Math

Felix and Dina have shell collections. Both collections have two kinds of shells which are equal in number. Write the number of shells each child has.

8. Felix has 16 shells.

____ are pink shells.

____ are white shells.

9. Dina has 14 shells.

____ are conch shells.

____ are snail shells.



**Notes for Home** Your child matched addition and subtraction facts. *Home Activity:* Ask your child what doubles fact helps to find 12 − 6. (6 + 6 = 12)

Name ______________________________

Practice 3-8

# Use Addition Facts to Subtract

Add or subtract. Color each addition fact to match the related subtraction fact. Use a different color for each set of facts.

1.

| | | | |
|---|---|---|---|
| 11 <br> − 5 | 16 <br> − 8 | 13 <br> − 9 | 9 <br> − 6 |
| 18 <br> − 9 | 12 <br> − 7 | 14 <br> − 6 | 15 <br> − 8 |

2.

| | | | |
|---|---|---|---|
| 8 <br> + 8 | 3 <br> + 6 | 9 <br> + 9 | 5 <br> + 7 |
| 4 <br> + 9 | 7 <br> + 8 | 6 <br> + 5 | 8 <br> + 6 |

## Tell a Math Story

3. Tell an addition story and a related subtraction story for the picture.

**Notes for Home** Your child used addition facts to subtract. *Home Activity:* Ask your child to explain how 4 + 8 = 12 helps to find 12 − 8 = 4.

Name ______________________________



# Relate Addition and Subtraction

Write a number sentence. Solve.

1. Stacy had 5 celery sticks on her plate. She gave 3 to her brother. How many were left?

   ______________

2. There were 2 carrot sticks on Stacy's plate. Her brother gave her 3 of his carrot sticks. How many carrot sticks does Stacy have?

   ______________

## Write About It

3. Use the numbers 8, 9, and 17.
   Write an addition story and a related subtraction story.

Write number sentences for your stories.

______________ ______________

**Notes for Home** Your child practiced writing and solving story problems with related facts. *Home Activity:* Ask your child to write related addition and subtraction facts using these numbers: 9, 4, 13. (9 + 4 = 13 or 4 + 9 = 13 and 13 – 4 = 9 or 13 - 9 = 4)

Name ______________________

Practice 3-10

# Problem Solving:
## Group Decision Making

Work with a group to make a bar graph.

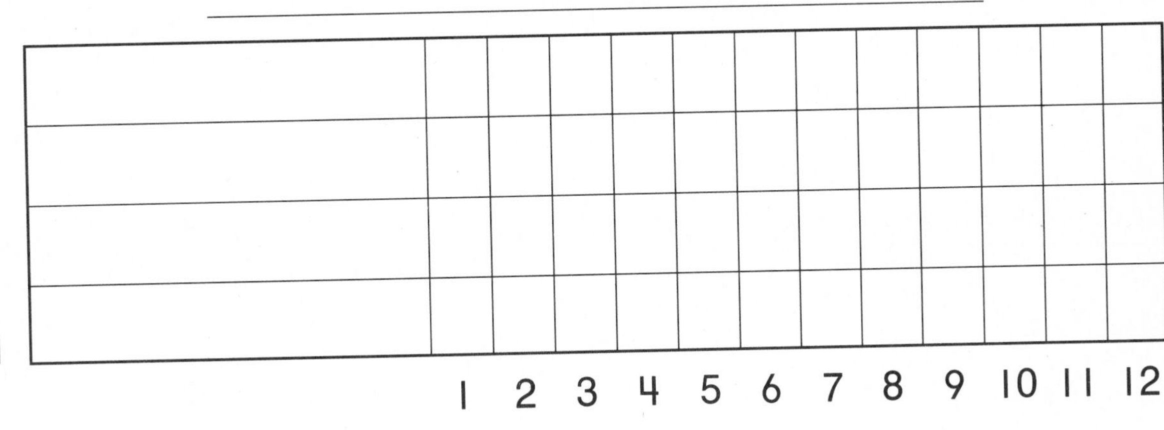


1. Write the title of your graph at the top.
2. Put a choice at the start of each row.
3. Label the side and bottom of your graph.
4. Color to show how many votes for each choice.

**Write your own.** With your group, decide on 2 questions that can be answered by your graph. Write your questions.

5. ______________________

6. ______________________

### Journal

7. What did you learn about working in a group? What will you do the same way the next time? What might you change? Why?



**Notes for Home** Your child made a bar graph. *Home Activity:* Ask your child to describe how he or she worked with a group to collect the information and to create the graph.

Name ______________________________

# Mixed Practice: Lessons 7–10

Add or subtract.

1. $\begin{array}{r} 8 \\ +8 \\ \hline \end{array}$ $\begin{array}{r} 16 \\ -8 \\ \hline \end{array}$

2. $\begin{array}{r} 9 \\ +8 \\ \hline \end{array}$ $\begin{array}{r} 17 \\ -8 \\ \hline \end{array}$

3. $\begin{array}{r} 8 \\ +6 \\ \hline \end{array}$ $\begin{array}{r} 14 \\ -6 \\ \hline \end{array}$

4. $\begin{array}{r} 18 \\ -9 \\ \hline \end{array}$ $\begin{array}{r} 8 \\ +5 \\ \hline \end{array}$ $\begin{array}{r} 6 \\ +5 \\ \hline \end{array}$ $\begin{array}{r} 15 \\ -7 \\ \hline \end{array}$ $\begin{array}{r} 9 \\ +6 \\ \hline \end{array}$ $\begin{array}{r} 11 \\ -4 \\ \hline \end{array}$ $\begin{array}{r} 12 \\ -8 \\ \hline \end{array}$

## Problem Solving

Write a number sentence. Solve.

5. Steven had 8 pennies.
He found 7 more.
How many does he have now?

______________ pennies

6. Steven had 15 pennies.
He gave 7 to his sister.
How many does he have left?

______________ pennies

Use the graph to answer the questions.

7. Which fruit got the most votes?

______________

8. How many more votes did Apples get than Grapes? ______ more votes

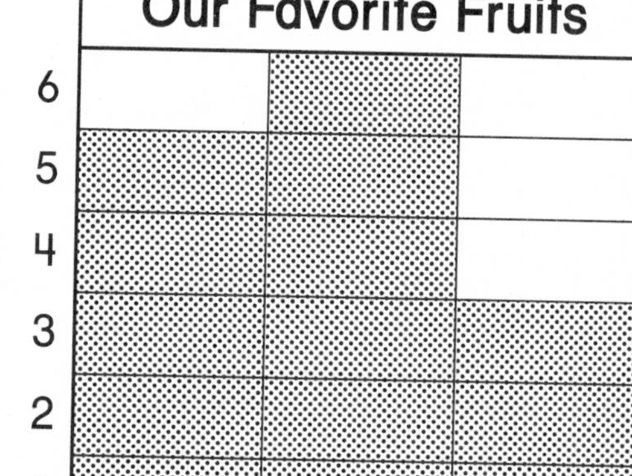


## Journal

9. Draw a picture to show these related facts:

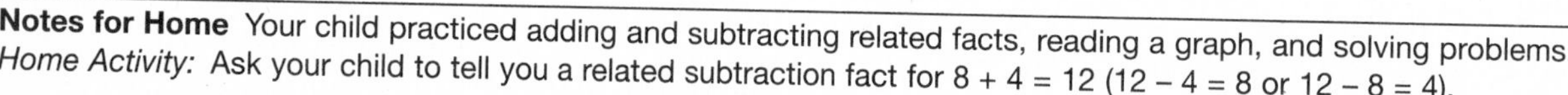

$8 + 6 = 14 \qquad 14 - 6 = 8$

**Notes for Home** Your child practiced adding and subtracting related facts, reading a graph, and solving problems. *Home Activity:* Ask your child to tell you a related subtraction fact for 8 + 4 = 12 (12 – 4 = 8 or 12 – 8 = 4).

Name ______________________________

# Cumulative Review

**Practice**
Chapters 1–3
**B**

Write the number sentence. Then write the turnaround fact.

1.

______________

______________

2.

______________

______________

## Problem Solving

Write a number sentence. Solve.

3. Markus has 6 toy trucks
   Marcy brings 6 more.
   How many do they have in all?

   ____________ toy trucks

4. Marcy brings 7 toy trucks.
   Markus still has 6.
   How many do they have now?

   ____________ toy trucks

## Test Prep

Fill in the ○ for the correct answer.
What fact matches each picture?

5.  

| 12 − 4 | 7 + 4 | 7 + 5 | 7 − 5 |
|---|---|---|---|
| ○ | ○ | ○ | ○ |

6. 

| 13 − 9 | 9 + 4 | 13 + 4 | 9 − 4 |
|---|---|---|---|
| ○ | ○ | ○ | ○ |



**Notes for Home** Your child reviewed addition and subtraction facts to 12. *Home Activity:* Ask your child to tell you the turnaround fact for 2 + 9. (9 + 2 = 11)

Name ______________________________

# Explore Fact Families

**Practice 4-1**

5 + 9 = 14

14 − 5 = 9

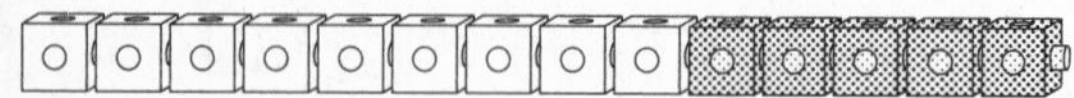

9 + 5 = 14

14 − 9 = 5

---

Complete each fact family.

Add or subtract.

1.

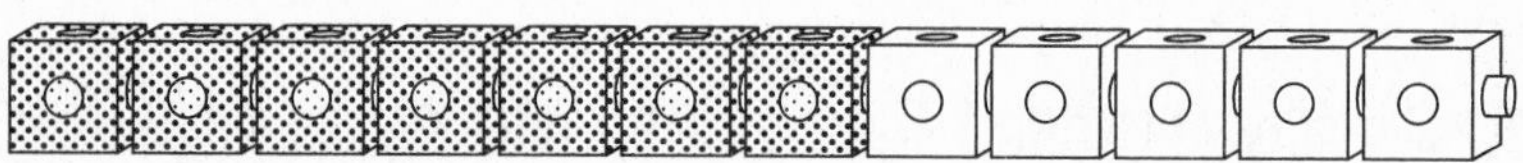

7 + 5 = ____ 12 − 7 = ____

5 + 7 = ____ 12 − 5 = ____

---

2.

8 + 5 = ____ 13 − 5 = ____

5 + 8 = ____ 13 − 8 = ____

## Talk About It

Tell the fact family for the numbers 8, 6, and 14.



---

**Notes for Home** Your child added and subtracted using fact families. *Home Activity:* Ask your child to write the fact family for the numbers 6, 6, and 12. (6 + 6 = 12; 12 - 6 = 6)

Name ______________________________

Practice 4-2

# Fact Families

Complete each fact family. Add or subtract

1. $4 + 9 =$ ____

$9 + 4 =$ ____

$13 - 9 =$ ____

$13 - 4 =$ ____

2. $7 + 9 =$ ____

$9 + 7 =$ ____

$16 - 9 =$ ____

$16 - 7 =$ ____

3. $8 + 9 =$ ____

$9 + 8 =$ ____

$17 - 9 =$ ____

$17 - 8 =$ ____

4. $9 + 6 =$ ____

$6 + 9 =$ ____

$15 - 6 =$ ____

$15 - 9 =$ ____

5. $\begin{array}{r} 8 \\ +8 \\ \hline \end{array}$ $\begin{array}{r} 16 \\ -8 \\ \hline \end{array}$

6. $\begin{array}{r} 6 \\ +6 \\ \hline \end{array}$ $\begin{array}{r} 12 \\ -6 \\ \hline \end{array}$

## Problem Solving Critical Thinking

Write two different fact families using the number 11.



**Notes for Home** Your child added and subtracted using fact families. *Home Activity:* Ask your child to explain why he or she can write only two number facts using 6 and 12. (Possible answer: A fact family with doubles has only 2 facts; others have four.)

Name ______________________________

Practice 4-3

# Use Addition to Check Subtraction

Use these numbers. Write a subtraction fact.

Write an addition fact to check.

1. 

6

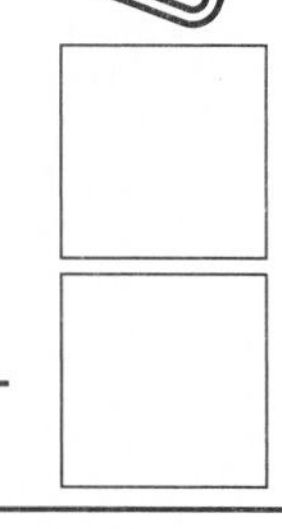

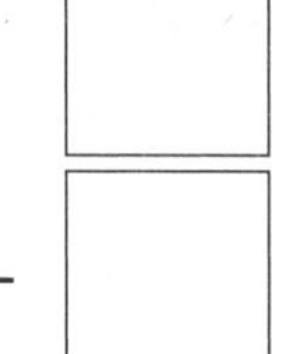

2. 

3. 15 9

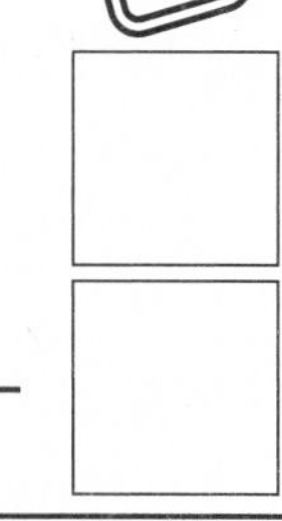

4. 13

5. 

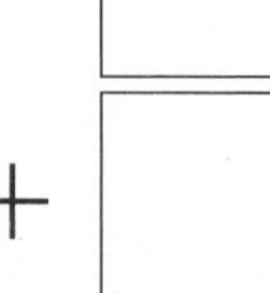


6. 

8

## Problem Solving

Complete the number sentence. 15 − 7 = ______

Write two related addition facts that you can use to check your answer.

**Notes for Home** Your child checked subtraction problems using addition. *Home Activity:* Ask your child to subtract 14 – 8 and to check the answer by adding. (14 – 8 = 6; 8 + 6 = 14)

Name ______________________

Practice 4-4

# Problem Solving: Draw a Picture

Draw a picture to solve the problem.

1. Tia made 8 muffins. She ate 1 muffin and Sara ate 2 muffins. They each ate 1 muffin later. How many muffins were left?

   ______ muffins

## Write About It

2. Write another problem. Ask a friend to draw a picture to solve it.

   ______________________

   ______________________

   ______________________

   ______________________

   ______________________



**Notes for Home** Your child drew pictures to solve problems. *Home Activity:* Have your child draw pictures to solve this word problem: There were four apples in the bowl. Jim took one to school for lunch. His mother had one. His brother ate two more. How many apples were left? (No apples were left.)

Name ______________________________

# **Mixed Practice:** Lessons 1–4

Write the number sentences to make a fact family.

1.

____ + ____ = ____  ____ − ____ = ____

____ + ____ = ____  ____ − ____ = ____

Subtract. Then write a related addition fact.

2. 14 − 9 = ____  ____ + ____ = ____

3. 13 − 5 = ____  ____ + ____ = ____

## Problem Solving

Draw a picture to solve the problem.

4. Kim blew 16 bubbles.
His brother broke 5.
3 more flew away.
How many were left?

____ bubbles

## Journal

5. Write a problem about a picnic. Draw a picture.
Write the fact family that your picture shows.



**Notes for Home** Your child practiced addition and subtraction facts and solving problems. *Home Activity:* Ask your child to write a related addition fact for 16 – 8 = 8. (8 + 8 = 16)

Name ______________________

Practice
Chapters 1–4
A

# Cumulative Review

Add.

1.

| 8 | 7 | 6 | 9 | 8 | 9 | 7 |
|---|---|---|---|---|---|---|
| + 5 | + 6 | + 9 | + 7 | + 7 | + 9 | + 5 |

## Problem Solving

Use the graph to answer the questions.

2. How many children like plain popcorn?

   ______ children

3. How many more children like plain popcorn than butter popcorn?

   ______ more children

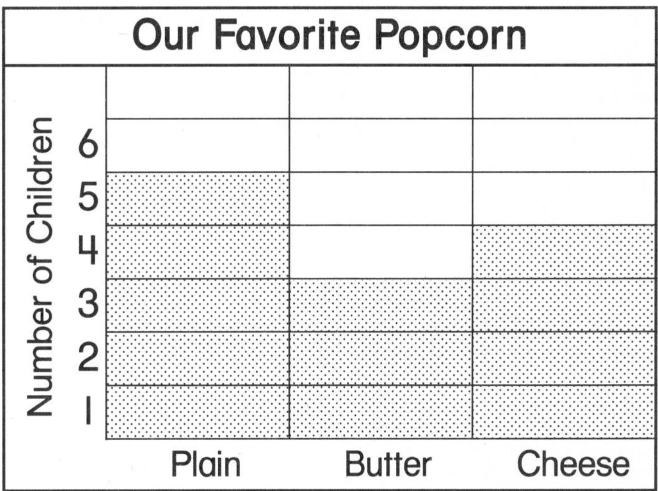


## Test Prep

Fill in the ○ for the correct answer.

Solve each problem.

4. Roy has 8 green balls and 9 red balls. How many balls does he have?

   16 ○ 5 ○ 18 ○ 17 ○

5. Mr. Brown's class has 18 books. 9 are math books. How many are science books?

   6 ○ 9 ○ 8 ○ 7 ○



**Notes for Home** Your child reviewed addition facts, reading a graph, and solving word problems.
*Home Activity:* Ask your child how many fewer children like butter popcorn than cheese popcorn on the graph? (1)

Name ______________________



# Missing Addends

Find the missing number.
Use the fact family to help you.

1.

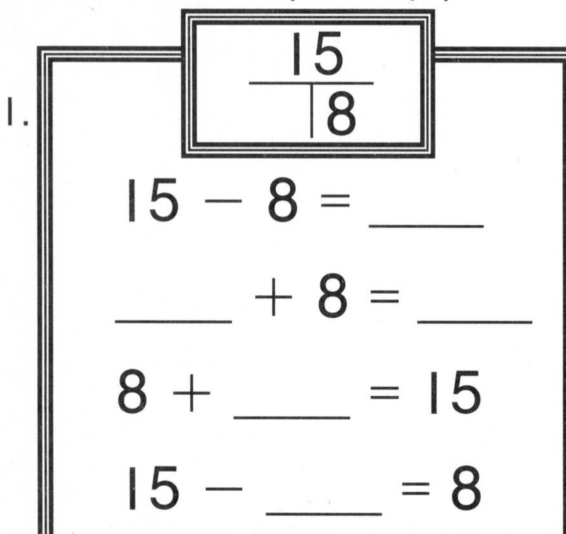

15 / 8

$15 - 8 =$ ____

____ $+ 8 =$ ____

$8 +$ ____ $= 15$

$15 -$ ____ $= 8$

2.

17 / 9

____ $+ 9 = 17$

$17 - 9 =$ ____

$9 +$ ____ $= 17$

$17 -$ ____ $= 9$

3. There were 13 children in line for lemonade. There were 8 children in the first line. How many were in the second line?

   ____ children

4. Ben had 5 kiddie car rides the first day. He rode 9 times the second day. How many rides did he have in all?

   ____ rides

## Problem Solving Patterns

5. Find the missing numbers. Find the pattern.
   Write the next fact.

| 7 | 7 | 7 | 7 | ☐ |
|---|---|---|---|---|
| + ☐ | + ☐ | + ☐ | + ☐ | + ☐ |
| 8 | 10 | 12 | 14 | ☐ |



**Notes for Home** Your child used fact families to find missing numbers. *Home Activity:* Ask your child to solve 9 + __ = 15. (6)

Name ______________________________

Practice 4-6

# Three Addends

Add across.

5 + 4 + 6 = 15

Add down.

$$\begin{array}{r} 4 \\ 7 \\ +\ 2 \\ \hline 13 \end{array}$$

1.

| | | | |
|---|---|---|---|
| 2 | 1 | 5 | |
| 4 | 7 | 0 | |
| 6 | 3 | 5 | |
| | | | |

2.

| | | | |
|---|---|---|---|
| 4 | 4 | 5 | |
| 7 | 2 | 7 | |
| 5 | 4 | 3 | |
| | | | |

## Problem Solving

3. A team needs 10 points to win a prize. Find each team's total score. Circle the names of the winning teams.

| Team | First Race | Second Race | Third Race | Total Score |
|---|---|---|---|---|
| Cats | 8 | 0 | 1 | ______ points |
| Stars | 6 | 2 | 4 | ______ points |
| Foxes | 7 | 4 | 3 | ______ points |
| Bears | 1 | 5 | 5 | ______ points |



**Notes for Home** Your child added three numbers. *Home Activity:* Ask your child which team in the Problem Solving chart won the most points. (Foxes)

Name ______________________________

# Use Addition and Subtraction Rules

Practice 4-7

Follow the rule. Add or subtract.

1.

| Add 7 | |
|---|---|
| 7 | |
| 6 | |
| 9 | |

2.

| Subtract 4 | |
|---|---|
| 12 | |
| 17 | |
| 13 | |

3.

| Subtract 6 | |
|---|---|
| 14 | |
| 11 | |
| 15 | |

Add the numbers in the first column.

Then follow the rule.

4.

| | Add 4 |
|---|---|
| 5 + 6 | |
| 3 + 7 | |
| 2 + 6 | |

5.

| | Add 6 |
|---|---|
| 4 + 5 | |
| 6 + 5 | |
| 3 + 1 | |

## Problem Solving

Write your own rule for each chart.

Then follow the rule. Add or subtract.

6.

| Add _____ | |
|---|---|
| 5 | |
| 7 | |
| 8 | |

7.

| Subtract _____ | |
|---|---|
| 18 | |
| 11 | |
| 13 | |

8.

| Subtract _____ | |
|---|---|
| 14 | |
| 12 | |
| 15 | |



**Notes for Home** Your child added and subtracted. *Home Activity:* Ask your child to choose three numbers less than 10 and add 3 to each of them.

Name ______________________________

Practice 4-8

# What's My Rule?

Find the rule. Then write the missing number.

1.

| | |
|---|---|
| 10 | 7 |
| 5 | 2 |
| 7 | 4 |
| 4 | |

2.

| | |
|---|---|
| 2 + 5 | 12 |
| 3 + 5 | 13 |
| 4 + 6 | 15 |
| 7 + 5 | |

**Write you own** tables.
Fill in the numbers.
Ask a friend to find the rule.

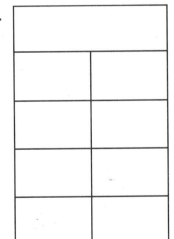

3.

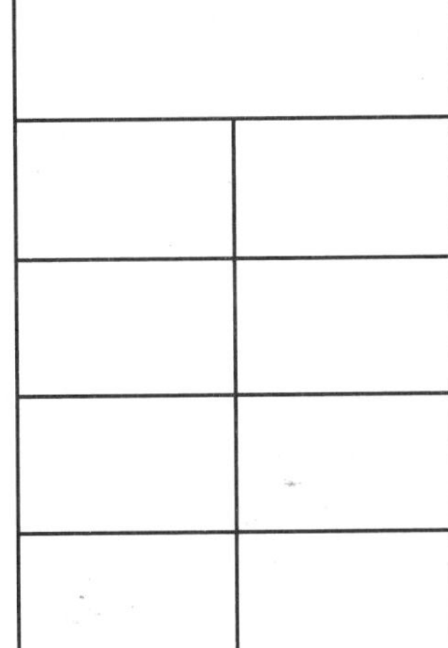

4.

| | |
|---|---|
| | |
| | |
| | |
| | |

## Problem Solving

5. Shane made 6 key chains. Luis make 3 key chains. Rona made 5 key chains. They each sold 1 key chain at the class fair. How many key chains does each have now?

Shane: ______ key chains

Luis: ______ key chains

Rona: ______ key chains



**Notes for Home** Your child found the rule (such as add 3 or subtract 5) for addition and subtraction tables. *Home Activity:* Ask your child to explain his or her reasoning for solving the Problem Solving exercises.

Name ______________________________

# Problem Solving:
## Multiple-Step Problems

Use ⬭ ⬭.

Write each number sentence. Solve.

1. At the beach, Sam found 12 seashells. He lost 7. $12 - 7 = 5$ seashells

   Later, he found 6 more shells. How many does he have now? ______ seashells

2. Jamal bought 15 stickers. He used 7. ______ stickers

   He used 5 more. How many stickers does Jamal have now? ______ stickers

3. On the beach, Ali found 10 pennies. He spent 5. ______ pennies

   He spent 5 more. How many pennies does he have now? ______ pennies

## Tell a Math Story

4. Tell a story problem about balloons. Include addition and subtraction in your story. Ask a friend to solve your problem.



**Notes for Home** Your child practiced solving word problems. *Home Activity:* Ask your child to tell you the word problem he or she made up for *Tell a Math Story*.

Name ____________________

Practice Chapter 4 B

# Mixed Practice: Lessons 5–9

Find the missing number in the facts family.

1. 8 + ____ = 15

____ + 8 = 15

15 − 8 = ____

15 − ____ = 8

Add.

2.

| 8 | 6 | 7 |
|---|---|---|
| 1 | 3 | 3 |
| + 2 | + 6 | + 5 |

Follow the rule.
Write the missing numbers.

3.

| Add 7 | |
|---|---|
| 5 | |
| 4 | |

Find the rule.
Write the rule.

4.

| | |
|---|---|
| 17 | 9 |
| 14 | 6 |

## Problem Solving

Write each number sentence. Solve.

5. Bob bought 9 plums.
He gave 2 to Sally. ____ plums

He bought 3 more plums.
How many plums does Bob have now? ____ plums

## Journal

6. Write all the ways you can solve 6 + 4 + 5.

**Notes for Home** Children practiced finding missing numbers, adding three numbers, and solving problems.
*Home Activity:* Ask your child to tell you how to find the missing numbers in Exercise 5.

Name ______________________________

# Cumulative Review

Practice
Chapters 1-4
B

Add.

Write the number sentence.

1. 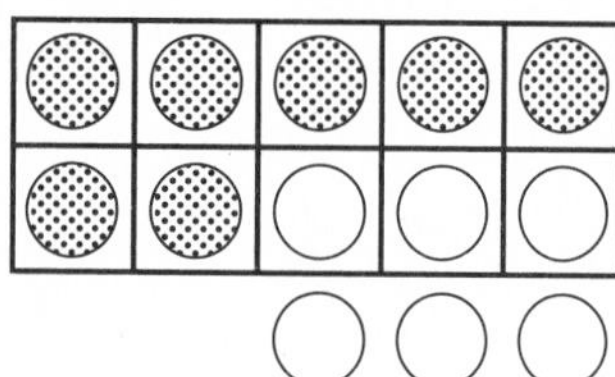

____ + ____ = ____

2. 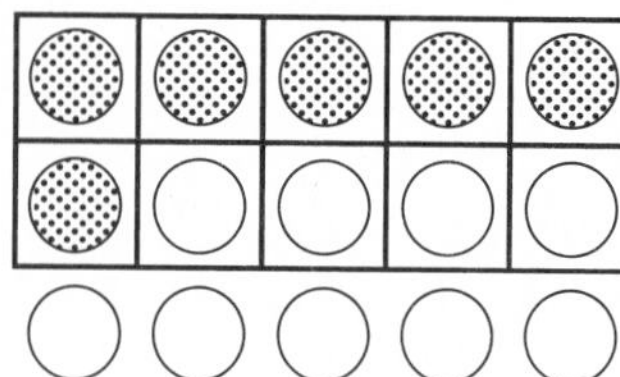

____ + ____ = ____

## Problem Solving

Use the graph to answer the questions.

3. How many children had pony rides on Friday?

   ____ children

4. On which day did the most children take pony rides?

   ______________

| Number of Children on Pony Rides | |
|---|---|
| Friday | |
| Saturday | |
| Sunday | |

Each (figure) stands for 10 children.

## Test Prep

Fill in the ○ for the correct answer.

5. Which fact is shown in the picture.

3 + 5 ○ 4 + 4 ○ 5 + 4 ○ 5 + 5 ○

6. Add 7 more.
   How many in all?

   13 ○
   14 ○
   15 ○



**Notes for Home** Your child reviewed numbers, used graphs to solve problems, and practiced addition facts.
*Home Activity:* Ask your child to use the graph on this page to find how many children had pony rides on Sunday.

Name ____________________

Practice 5-1

# Explore Estimation

| tens | ones |
|---|---|
| 1 ten | 5 ones |

Estimate. Try to take 10 .

Use your tens/ones mat. Make tens and ones.

Write how many tens and ones.

| | Try to take this many. | Write how many. |
|---|---|---|
| 1. | 30 | ______ tens ______ ones |
| 2. | 40 | ______ tens ______ ones |
| 3. | 50 | ______ tens ______ ones |
| 4. | 60 | ______ tens ______ ones |
| 5. | 70 | ______ tens ______ ones |
| 6. | 80 | ______ tens ______ ones |
| 7. | 90 | ______ tens ______ ones |

**Talk About It** Which time did you get the closest to your estimate? How close did you get? Tell a classmate.



**Notes for Home** Your child used grouping by tens to estimate and count. *Home Activity:* Put some macaroni or dried beans in 3 piles. Ask your child to divided each pile into groups of tens and ones, and to count how many there are in each pile.

Name ______________________

# Record Numbers

**Practice 5-2**

Write how many tens and ones. Write the number.

1. 7 tens 5 ones

75

2. ______ tens ______ ones

______

Write the number.

| | | |
|---|---|---|
| 3. | 1 ten 4 ones | 14 |
| 4. | 6 tens 3 ones | ______ |
| 5. | 2 tens 5 ones | ______ |
| 6. | 8 tens 0 ones | ______ |
| 7. | 5 tens 0 ones | ______ |
| 8. | 0 tens 7 ones | ______ |
| 9. | 9 tens 6 ones | ______ |
| 10. | 6 tens 9 ones | ______ |

## Problem Solving Critical Thinking

11. Look at the numbers you wrote for Exercises 9 and 10. How are the numbers alike? How are they different?



**Notes for Home** Your child wrote numbers as tens and ones and as 2-digit numbers. *Home Activity:* Tell your child a number such as 4 tens and 6 ones and ask him or her to tell you the 2-digit number. (46.)

Name ______________________________

Practice 5-3

# Number Words

Write the number.

1. thirty-seven 37
2. fifty-six ______
3. eighty ______
4. seventy-one ______
5. Use the clues to write each word. Fill in the puzzle.

| Across | Down |
|---|---|
| 1. 28 | 2. 2 |
| 7. 1 | 3. 17 |
| 8. 5 | 4. 80 |
| 9. 20 | 5. 90 |
| 10. 10 | 6. 30 |
| 11. 70 | 8. 40 |
| 13. 60 | 11. 6 |
| 14. 4 | 12. 2 |

## Problem Solving Critical Thinking

6. Pick a number that is greater than 10 and less than 100. What are some ways to show the number?

______________________________

**Notes for Home** Your child practiced writing number words. *Home Activity:* Have your child think of a number between 40 and 60 and write the numeral and word for it. (Possible answer: 52, fifty-two)

Name ______________________________

# Tell About 100

Practice 5-4

These show 100.

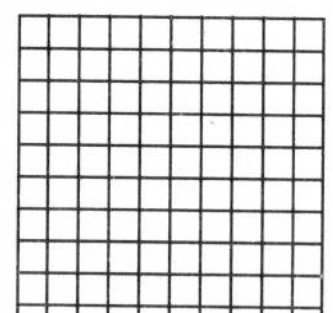

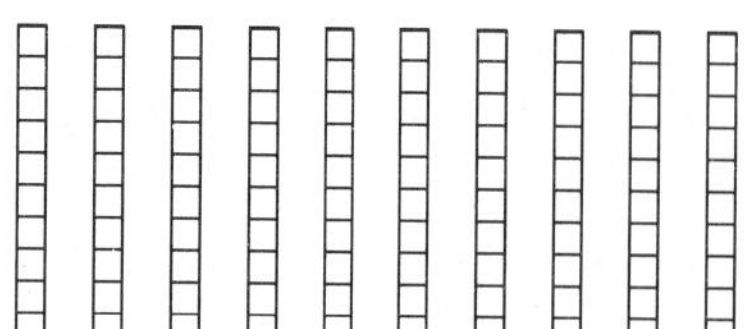

1. Color 70 red.
   Color 30 blue.
   Write how many.

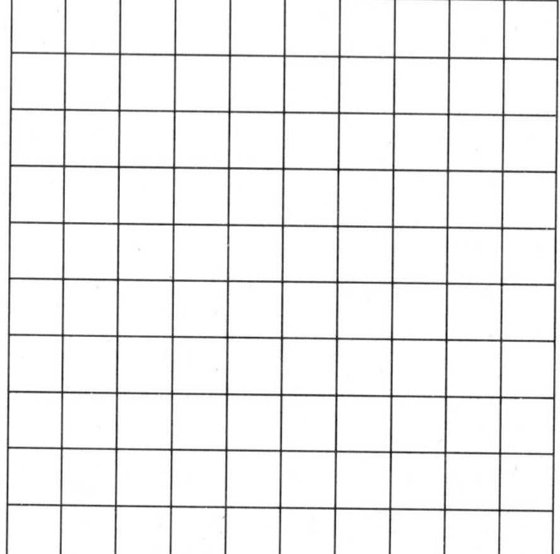

70 and 30 is 100.

## Write your own.

2. Color some tens yellow.
   Color the rest of the tens green.
   Write how many.

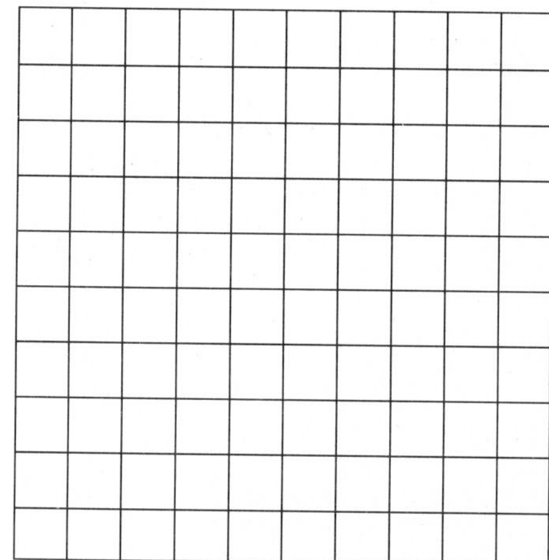

_____ and _____ is 100.

## Problem Solving Critical Thinking

3. How could you use 4 colors to show 100?

**Notes for Home** Your child used a grid to show combinations of numbers that make 100. *Home Activity:* Tell your child 3 different numbers less than 100. Ask your child to tell you the numbers, that when added to each, would make 100.

Name ______________________________

Practice 5-5

# Problem Solving: Use Data from a Graph

| Coin Collections | |
|---|---|
| Abe | ○○○○○○ |
| Beth | ○○○○ |
| Carlos | ○○ |
| Dory | ○○○○○○○ |

Each ○ means 2 coins.

Use the graph to solve.

1. How many coins did Abe collect?
   12 coins

2. How many coins did Carlos collect?
   _____ coins

3. How many coins did Beth and Dory collect in all?
   _____ coins

4. How many more coins did Dory collect than Abe?
   _____ more

## Visual Thinking

5. Carlos adds 14 more coins to his collection. What would you add to the graph? Explain.



**Notes for Home** Your child used a graph to answer questions. *Home Activity:* Ask your child to show you how to use the graph to count the coins in Dory's collection. (Possible answer: Each picture stands for 2. Count by 2s: 2, 4, 6, 8, 10, 12, 14.)

Name ______________________________



# Mixed Practice: Lessons 1–5

Write how many tens and ones.
Write the number.

1.

| tens | ones |
| --- | --- |
| (6 tens) | (3 ones) |

______ tens ______ ones

______

Write the number.

2. twenty-seven

______

3. seventy-three

______

4. sixty-nine

5. forty-two

## Problem Solving

Use the graph to answer the questions.

6. How many more books does Larry have than Leon?

______ more

7. How many books do Leon and Lacy have together?

______ books

| Book Collections | |
| --- | --- |
| Larry | (4 books) |
| Leon | (3 books) |
| Lacy | (8 books) |

Each  means 5 books

## Journal

8. Pick an even and an odd number between 10 and 100.
Draw pictures of tens and ones to show your numbers.



**Notes for Home** Your child counted by tens and ones, wrote numbers, and read graphs. *Home Activity:* Write the words for 3 numbers below 100. Ask your child to read the words aloud and to write the numbers. (Sample: twenty-two: 22; fifteen: 15; ninety-seven: 97)

 Use with page 167.

Name ______________________________

Practice
Chapters 1–5
A

# Cumulative Review

Add or subtract.

1. $\begin{array}{r} 7 \\ +5 \\ \hline \end{array}$ $\begin{array}{r} 15 \\ -6 \\ \hline \end{array}$ $\begin{array}{r} 5 \\ +8 \\ \hline \end{array}$ $\begin{array}{r} 10 \\ -4 \\ \hline \end{array}$ $\begin{array}{r} 14 \\ -6 \\ \hline \end{array}$ $\begin{array}{r} 4 \\ -1 \\ \hline \end{array}$ $\begin{array}{r} 13 \\ -6 \\ \hline \end{array}$

2. $\begin{array}{r} 6 \\ +7 \\ \hline \end{array}$ $\begin{array}{r} 15 \\ -8 \\ \hline \end{array}$ $\begin{array}{r} 9 \\ +9 \\ \hline \end{array}$ $\begin{array}{r} 11 \\ -3 \\ \hline \end{array}$ $\begin{array}{r} 8 \\ +0 \\ \hline \end{array}$ $\begin{array}{r} 5 \\ +6 \\ \hline \end{array}$ $\begin{array}{r} 10 \\ -2 \\ \hline \end{array}$

## Problem Solving

Solve.

3. Tia has 6 seashells.
Then she finds 4 more.
How many seashells does
Tia have now?

_____ seashells

4. Tom has 9 seashells.
He gives 3 to Tia.
How many seashells does
Tom have now?

_____ seashells

## Test Prep

Fill in the ○ for the correct answer.

5. $7 + 2 + 6 =$ _____

○ 10 ○ 9 ○ 15 ○ 8

6. $4 + 3 + 7 =$ _____

○ 16 ○ 7 ○ 10 ○ 14



**Notes for Home** Your child reviewed addition and subtraction facts and problem solving. *Home Activity:* Ask your child how many tens and ones are in the number 85. (8 tens and 5 ones)

Name ______________________________

# Hundred Chart and Skip Counting Patterns

**Practice 5-6**

| 1 | 2 | 3 | 4 | 5 | 6 | 7 | 8 | 9 | 10 |
|---|---|---|---|---|---|---|---|---|---|
| 11 | 12 | 13 | 14 | 15 | 16 | 17 | 18 | 19 | 20 |
| 21 | 22 | 23 | 24 | 25 | 26 | 27 | 28 | 29 | 30 |
| 31 | 32 | 33 | 34 | 35 | 36 | 37 | 38 | 39 | 40 |
| 41 | 42 | 43 | 44 | 45 | 46 | 47 | 48 | 49 | 50 |
| 51 | 52 | 53 | 54 | 55 | 56 | 57 | 58 | 59 | 60 |
| 61 | 62 | 63 | 64 | 65 | 66 | 67 | 68 | 69 | 70 |
| 71 | 72 | 73 | 74 | 75 | 76 | 77 | 78 | 79 | 80 |
| 81 | 82 | 83 | 84 | 85 | 86 | 87 | 88 | 89 | 90 |
| 91 | 92 | 93 | 94 | 95 | 96 | 97 | 98 | 99 | 100 |

1. Count by 4s on the chart. Shade each number.
2. Count by 7s on the chart. Circle each number.
3. Which numbers were both shaded and circled?

   ______________________

4. What patterns do you see in the chart when you count by 4s?

   ______________________________________________

   ______________________________________________

5. What patterns do you see when you count by 7s?

   ______________________________________________

   ______________________________________________

## Mental Math

6. Ellen has 4 robot models. Each model has 5 arms. How many arms are there?

   ______ arms

**Notes for Home** Your child counted by 4s and by 7s to 100. *Home Activity*: Ask your child to count by 2s and then by 5s on the chart.

Name ____________________

Practice 5-7

# Before, After, Between

Use the number line. Answer each question.

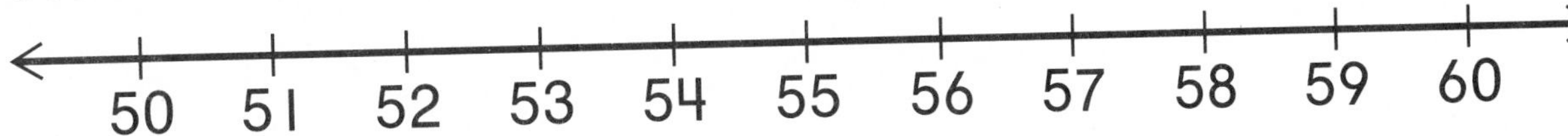


1. Draw a box around the number that is one before 57.

2. Put a line under the number that comes after 52.

3. Circle the number that is between 54 and 56.

4. Put an X on all the numbers that are between 56 and 60.

Answer each question.

5. What number is one before 73? ______

6. What number is one after 27? ______

7. What number is between 93 and 95? ______

8. What number is one before 90? ______

## Problem Solving Critical Thinking

9. Solve the riddle.
   I am between 37 and 41.
   I have 4 tens.

   What number am I? ______

   Make up your own riddles for a classmate to solve.



**Notes for Home** Your child answered questions about numbers. *Home Activity:* Pick a number from the number line on this page. Ask your child to describe it using before, between, and after. (Possible answer: 53 is before 54, 53 is between 52 and 54, and 53 is after 52.)

Name ______________________

Practice 5-8

# Find the Nearest Ten

## Write your own.

Pick a number on the number line. Put a dot above that number.
Write your answer.

1. 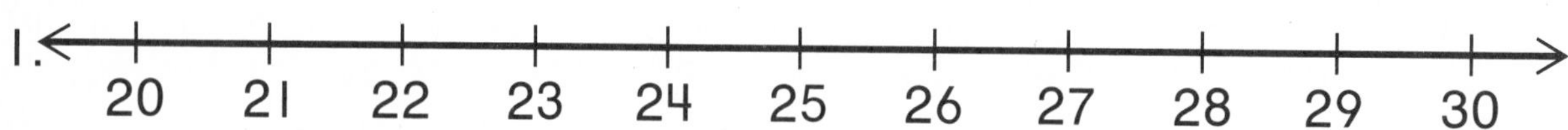


Is your number closer to 20 or 30? _____

2. 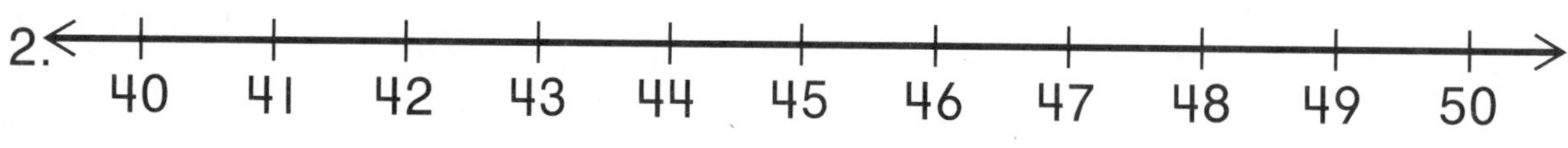


Is your number closer to 40 or 50? _____

3. 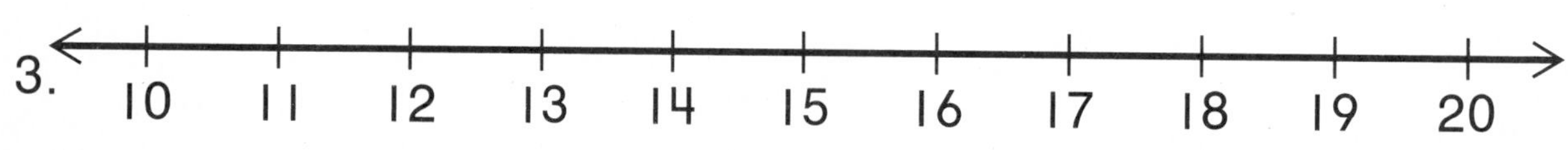


Is your number closer to 10 or 20? _____

For each number, write the nearest ten.

4. 57 60 5. 32 _____

6. 71 _____ 7. 24 _____

8. 46 _____ 9. 18 _____

10. 93 _____ 11. 79 _____

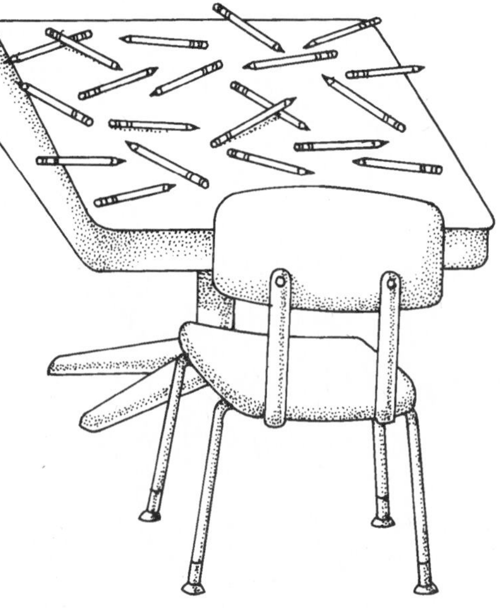

## Problem Solving Estimation

12. About how many pencils in all?
Circle you estimate.

About 20 About 50

**Notes for Home** Your child found the nearest ten. (For example, 40 is the nearest ten for 36.)
*Home Activity:* Tell your child a number less than 100. Ask him or her to tell you the nearest ten for that number.

Name ____________________

Practice 5-9

# Compare Numbers

Circle the number that is least.

| | | | | | | |
|---|---|---|---|---|---|---|
| 1. | 38 | 52 | 19 | 2. 27 | 96 | 43 |
| 3. | 61 | 47 | 72 | 4. 81 | 18 | 55 |

Circle the number that is greatest.

| | | | | | | |
|---|---|---|---|---|---|---|
| 5. | 76 | 68 | 81 | 6. 91 | 96 | 99 |
| 7. | 45 | 61 | 38 | 8. 51 | 29 | 35 |

Write the numbers in order from least to greatest.

| | | | | | | |
|---|---|---|---|---|---|---|
| 9. | 46 | 18 | 37 | 18 | 37 | 46 |
| 10. | 89 | 56 | 72 | ____ | ____ | ____ |
| 11. | 19 | 65 | 38 | ____ | ____ | ____ |
| 12. | 93 | 48 | 89 | ____ | ____ | ____ |

## Problem Solving

Three friends sold calendars for their club.
Josh sold 76 calendars.
Jane sold 58 calendars.
June sold the least number of calendars.
How many calendars could June have sold?

______ calendars



**Notes for Home** Your child compared numbers using *least* and *greatest* and put numbers in order. *Home Activity:* Tell your child 3 numbers less than 100. Ask him or her to put them in order from least to greatest and from greatest to least.

Name ______________________________

# Ordinal Numbers

Practice 5-10

1. Color the 1st car blue.
2. Color the 10th car brown.
3. Color the second car red.
4. Color the 7th car orange.
5. Color the 4th car yellow.
6. Color the eighth car purple.

Answer each question.

7. How many cars are behind the 8th car? _____
8. How many cars are behind the 4th car? _____
9. How many cars are in front of the 6th car? _____
10. How many cars are in front of the 10th car? _____

## Problem Solving

11. Solve.

    6 children are in front of you.
    7 children are behind you.
    What number are you? _____

**Notes for Home** Your child used ordinal numbers from 1st through 20th. *Home Activity:* Ask your child to use ordinal numbers to describe the order of something in your home.

 Use with pages 179–180.

Name ______________________

Practice 5-11

# Odd and Even Numbers

Write how many in all. Then write **even** or **odd**.

1\. 27 ______

2\. ______ ______

Write **even** or **odd**.

3\. 36 even

4\. 47 ______

5\. 53 ______

6\. 78 ______

**Write your own.** Write two odd numbers. Then write two even numbers.

7\. Odd numbers: ______ ______

8\. Even numbers: ______ ______

## Problem Solving Patterns Algebra Readiness

9\. Is the number 4,625 odd or even? How do you know?

______________________________



**Notes for Home** Your child worked with odd and even numbers. *Home Activity:* Ask your child: *I am thinking of an odd number between 56 and 59. What number is it?* (57)

Name ______________________________

Practice 5-12

# Problem Solving:
## Group Decision Making

1. Work with your group. Collect some items.
   As a group, sort your items the way you like best.
   Decide as a group how to show your sorted items.
   Draw how you sorted them.

## Journal

2. Why did you choose this way to sort your items?

**Notes for Home** Your child made decisions with a group about how to sort items. *Home Activity:* With your child, list 10 items that you see around you. Discuss with your child ways you could sort the items.

Name ______________________________

Practice
Chapter 5
B

# Mixed Practice: Lessons 6–12

Count by 3s. Write the numbers.

1. 3, 6, 9, 12, _____, _____, _____, _____

Write the missing numbers.

2. ←—|—|—|—|—|—|—|—|—|—→

45 46 _____ _____ 49 _____ _____ 52 _____

For each number, write the nearest ten.

3. 47 _____ 4. 82 _____ 5. 64 _____

Write these numbers in order from least to greatest.

6. 76 39 82 _____ _____ _____

## Problem Solving

Use the picture to answer the questions.

7. What is the shirt number of the third soccer player? _____

8. What is the shirt number of the fifth soccer player? _____

## Journal

9. Are these numbers even or odd? 14 8 26 4
How do you know? ______________________________

**Notes for Home** Your child practiced number skills from this chapter. *Home Activity:* Ask your child to think of 2 odd numbers less than 100 and tell you how he or she knows they are odd.

Name ______________________________

Practice
Chapters 1–5
B

# Cumulative Review

Add or subtract.

1.

| 9 | 16 | 15 | 8 | 11 | 9 | 12 |
|---|---|---|---|---|---|---|
| + 7 | − 8 | − 7 | + 6 | − 4 | + 9 | + 6 |

## Problem Solving

Write the number sentences. Solve.

2. Marsha has 17 books.
Rob has 8 books
How many more books does
Marsha have than Rob?

_____________ more books

3. Eric has 13 marbles.
Kate has 7 marbles.
How many more marbles does
Eric have than Kate?

_____________ more marbles

## Test Prep

Fill in the ○ for the correct answer.

4. Debbie has 11 stickers.
She gives 7 stickers to Joan.
How many stickers does
she have now?

○ 11 − 0 = 11
○ 11 + 7 = 18
○ 11 − 7 = 4
○ 7 + 7 = 14

5. Rachel has 7 hair ribbons.
Janet gives her 8 more.
How many hair ribbons does
Rachel have now?

○ 7 + 7 = 14
○ 8 − 7 = 1
○ 8 + 8 = 16
○ 8 + 7 = 15



**Notes for Home** Your child reviewed addition and subtraction facts and problem solving. *Home Activity:* Ask you child to tell you a subtraction fact with a difference of 7. (Possible answers: 12 − 5 = 7; 10 − 3 = 7)

Name ______________________________

Practice 6-1

# Explore Counting Dimes, Nickels, and Pennies

Count by 10s. Count on by 5s. Count on by ones.

57¢ in all

---

Use the coins. Count the money. Write the total amount.

1.

2.

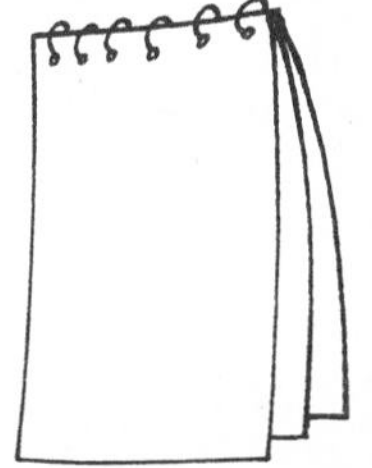

Use these coins. Draw the coins. Write the total amount.

3. 2 dimes, 1 nickel, and 3 pennies

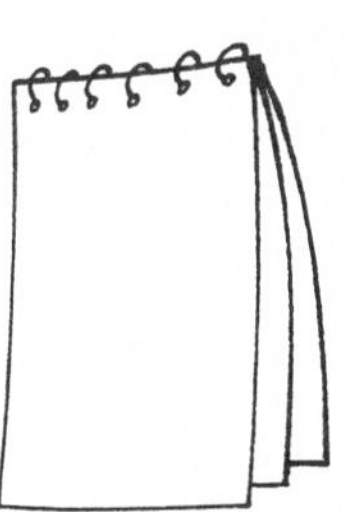

4. 1 dime, 3 nickels, 5 pennies

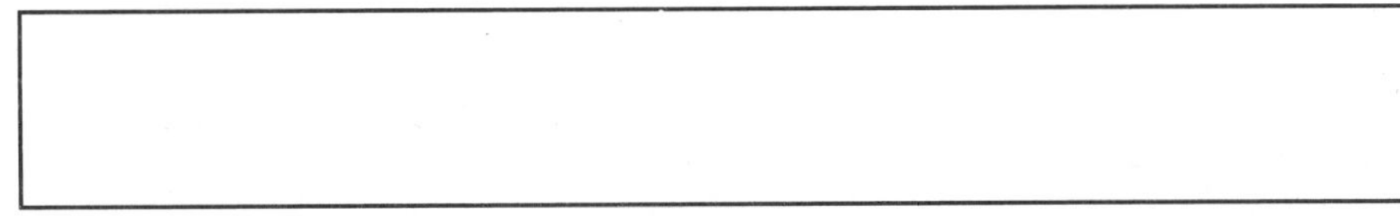

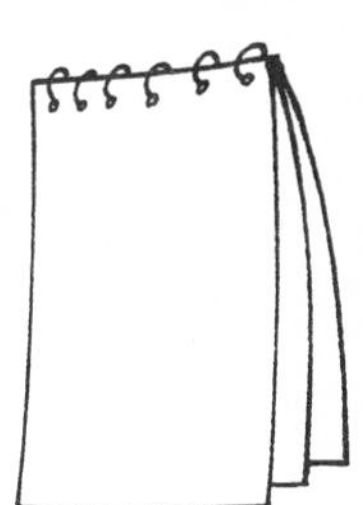

**Talk About It** Is it easier for you to count coins from greatest value to least, or least to greatest value? Why?

---

**Notes for Home** Your child counted groups of dimes, nickels, and pennies. *Home Activity:* Ask your child to draw dimes, nickels, and pennies to show 52¢.

Name ________________________________

# Quarters

**Practice 6-2**

Use coins. Count the money. Write the total amount.

1. 

98¢

2. 

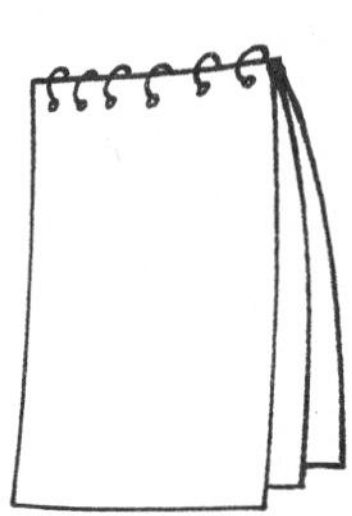

---

Use these coins. Draw the coins. Write how much in all.

3. I quarter, 4 dimes, I nickel, and 3 pennies

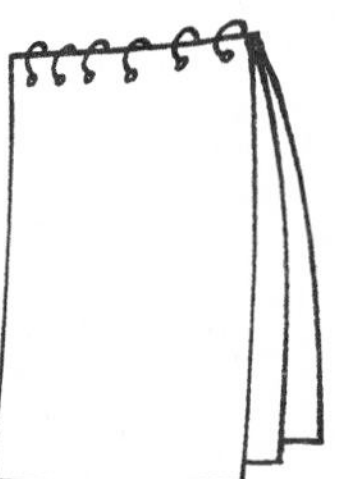

4. You pick 5 coins.

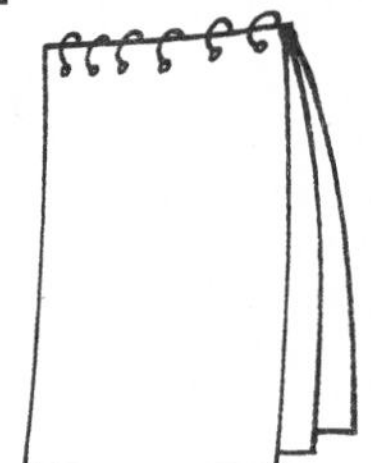

## Problem Solving Visual Thinking

5. Would you like to have the stack of nickels or the stack of dimes to spend? Explain.

---

**Notes for Home** Your child counted groups of coins that included quarters. *Home Activity:* Tell your child an amount less than a dollar. Have him or her show you this amount using any combinations of quarters, dimes, nickels, and pennies.

Name ______________________________



# Half Dollars

Fill in the table to show some ways to make 50¢.

Write how many of each coin is used. Use coins to help.

| Half dollar | Quarters | Dimes | Nickels | Value of coins |
|---|---|---|---|---|
| 1 | 0 | 0 | 0 | 50¢ |
| 0 | | 0 | 0 | |
| 0 | | 3 | | 50¢ |
| 0 | 1 | 0 | | 50¢ |
| 0 | 0 | | 0 | |
| 0 | 0 | 0 | | |
| 0 | | | 8 | 50¢ |

## Problem Solving

How much could one of these cost?

Choose a price between 50¢ and 79¢.

Draw coins. Write the price.

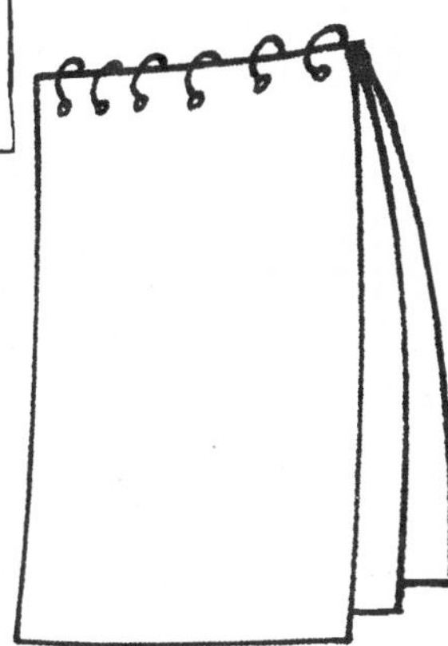



**Notes for Home** Your child used coins to show 50¢. *Home Activity:* Ask your child which coins have the greatest value: 10 dimes, 2 quarters, or 1 fifty-cent piece. (They all have the same value.)

Name ___________________________

# Problem Solving: Make a List

Practice 6-4

1. Yoko needs 40¢ to buy juice from a vending machine. Use coins. Find all the ways to make 40¢ using quarters, dimes, and nickels.

| | | | |
|---|---|---|---|
| Use 1 quarter. | | | |
| Use 1 quarter again. | | | |
| | | | |
| | | | |
| | | | |
| | | | |
| | | | |

## Critical Thinking

Taro has these coins in his hand.
He has 50¢ in all.
What coins could he have in his pocket?

Show 2 ways. Draw the coins.

2.

3.

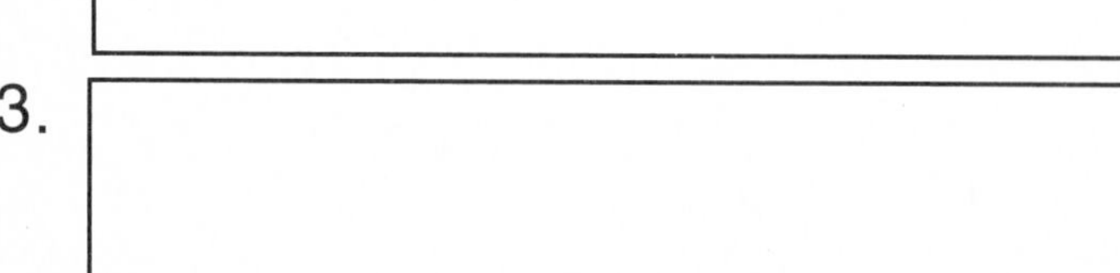

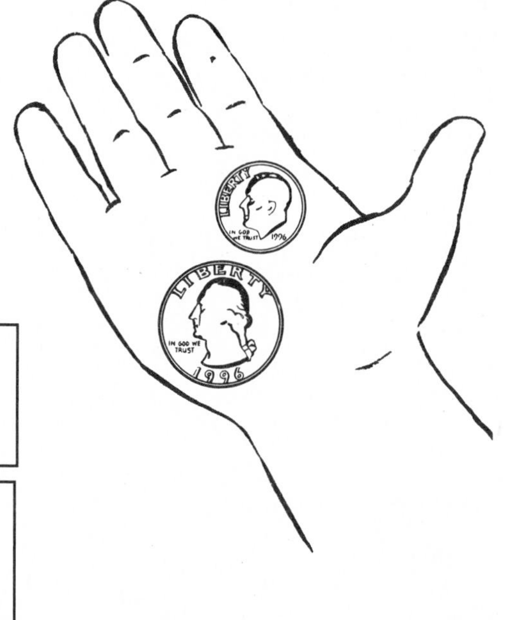



**Notes for Home** Your child found ways to make 40¢ and put the information into an organized list. *Home Activity:* Use quarters, dimes, and nickels. Ask your child to show you all the ways to make 50¢. (There are 10 different ways. Possible answers: 2 quarters; 1 quarter and 2 dimes and 1 nickel; 5 dimes; 10 nickels.)

Name ______________________________



# Mixed Practice: Lessons 1–4

Use coins. Count the money. Write the total amount.

1\.  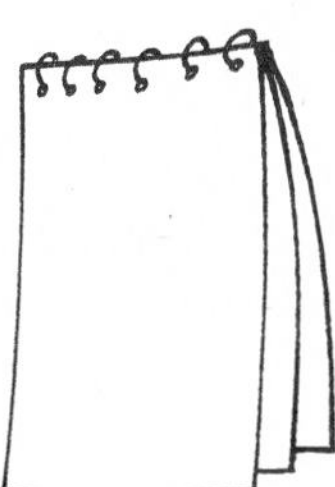

Use these coins. Draw the coins. Write the total amount.

2\. 1 half dollar, 1 quarter, 1 dime, 2 nickels, 2 pennies

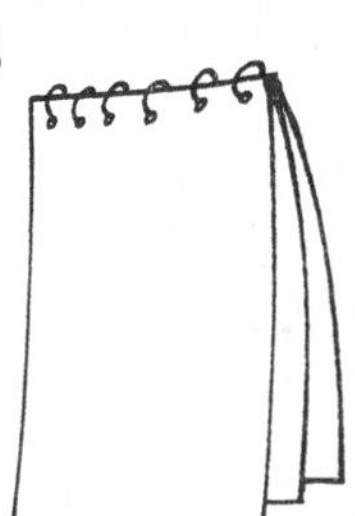

## Problem Solving

3\. Randi needs 30¢ for a vending machine. Use coins. Find all the ways to make 30¢ using quarters, dimes, and nickels. Make a list.

|  |  |  |
|---|---|---|
| | | |
| | | |
| | | |
| | | |
| | | |

## Journal

Choose an amount between 27¢ and 63¢. Write the amount.
Use coins. Show the amount in 2 different ways. Draw the coins.

**Notes for Home** Your child practiced making a list and counting half dollars, quarters, dimes, nickels, and pennies.
*Home Activity:* Have your child use coins to show you different ways to make 40¢.

Name ______________________________

**Practice**
Chapters 1–6
**A**

# Cumulative Review

Count by ones, 5s, or 10s.
Write the numbers.

1. 55, 60, 65, ____, ____, ____

2. 40, 50, 60, ____, ____, ____

3. 14, 15, 16, ____, ____, ____

4. 0, 5, 10, ____, ____, ____

## Problem Solving

Use the graph to answer the questions.

| School Calendars Sold | |
|---|---|
| Gloria | XXXXX |
| Markus | XXXXXXX |
| Tony | XXX |
| Debbie | XXXXXX |

Each X stands for 5 calendars.

5. How many calendars did Debbie sell?

_____ Calendars

6. How many more calendars did Markus sell than Tony?

_____ more calendars

## Test Prep

Fill in the ○ for the correct answer.

7. Mark the word that names this number.

67

○ sixteen
○ twenty-seven
○ sixty-seven
○ sixty

8. Mark the number for this word.

forty

| 50 | 14 | 4 | 40 |
|---|---|---|---|
| ○ | ○ | ○ | ○ |



**Notes for Home** Your child reviewed skip counting, pictographs, and number words. *Home Activity:* Ask your child to read the graph and tell you who sold the most calendars (Markus) and who sold the next greatest number. (Debbie).

Name ______________________________

# Coin Combinations

Practice 6-5

Use the fewest coins to show each amount.

Draw the coins.

1. 

2. 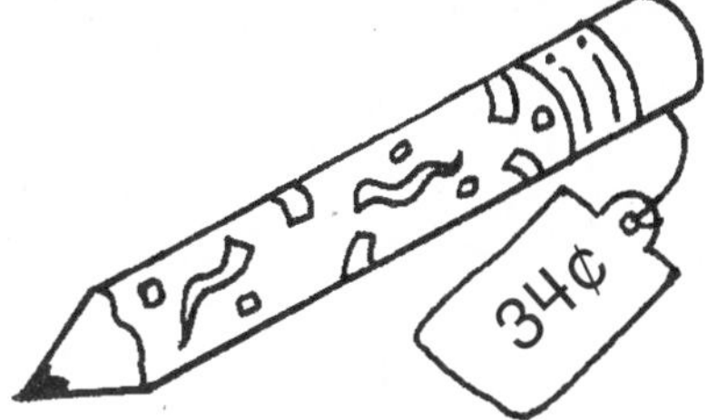


3. 

4. 

## Problem Solving

5. Draw the same amount of money using the least number of coins.

**Notes for Home** Your child practiced showing amounts of money using the fewest coins. *Home Activity:* Ask your child to think of an amount between 25¢ and 99¢, and to show the amount using the fewest number of coins.

Name ______________________________

# Dollar Bill

Practice 6-6

Use some , , , and .

Fill in the table to show some ways to make $1.00.
Write how many of each coin is used. Use coins to help.

| Half dollar | Quarters | Dimes | Nickels | Value of coins |
|---|---|---|---|---|
| 2 | 0 | 0 | 0 | $1.00 |
| 0 | | 0 | 0 | $1.00 |
| 0 | 0 | | 0 | |
| 0 | 0 | 0 | | $1.00 |
| 1 | | 0 | 0 | |
| 1 | 0 | | 0 | |
| 0 | 3 | | | $1.00 |
| 0 | | 3 | | $1.00 |
| 0 | | | 5 | $1.00 |

## Journal

Pretend that you have $1.00 to spend.
What are some things you could buy that cost exactly $1.00?

**Notes for Home** Your child made different coin combinations for $1.00. *Home Activity:* Ask your child how many of each coin it takes to make $1.00: pennies (100), nickels (20), dimes (10), quarters (4), and half-dollars (2).

Name ______________________________

# Problem Solving: Act It Out

Practice 6-7

Take turns buying and selling. Use dimes to pay for items.
Use pennies to make change.

| | Cost | Amount Paid | Change |
|---|---|---|---|
| 1. | 35¢ | 4 dimes | 5¢ |
| 2. | | | |
| 3. | | | |
| 4. | | | |
| 5. | | | |

## Problem Solving Critical Thinking

6. Use the picture. Name 2 items you could buy with 8 dimes. How much would you have left over?

______________________________



**Notes for Home** Your child used coins to make change. *Home Activity:* Ask your child to point to the highest-priced item and the lowest-priced item, and tell how many dimes it would take to buy each. (95¢: 10 dimes; 18¢: 2 dimes)

Name ______________________________



# Mixed Practice: Lessons 5–7

Use the fewest coins to show the amount.
Draw the coins.

1.

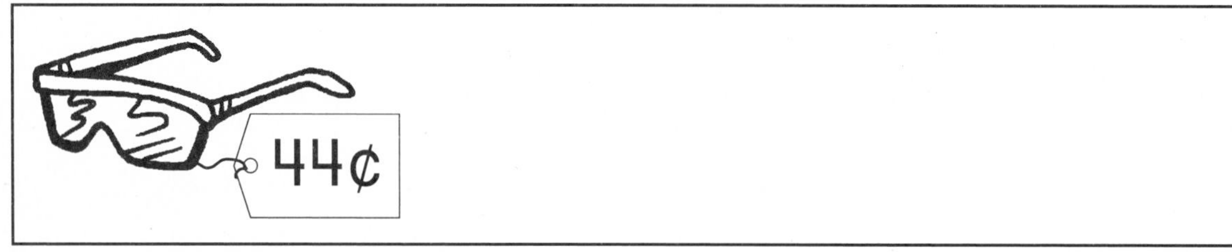


Use some , , , and .

Show 2 ways to make $1.00. Draw the coins.

2.

3.

## Problem Solving

Solve.

4. Leon has 5 dimes. He buys a model truck for 48¢.How much change should she get back?

______

## Journal

5. What coins could you use to pay for something that costs 63¢? What change would you get back?

**Notes for Home** Your child practiced choosing coins to show amounts of money and making change to solve problems. *Home Activity:* Ask your child to draw 2 other ways to show the amount in Exercise 1.

Name ___________________________________

Practice
Chapters 1–6
B

# Cumulative Review

For each number, write the nearest ten.

1. Is 56 closer to 50 or 60?

   56 is closer to ______.

2. Is 84 closer to 80 or 90?

   84 is closer to ______.

Write the numbers in order from least to greatest.

3. 83   29   45   ______ ______ ______

## Problem Solving

Solve the riddles.

4. I am between 27 and 37.
   I have 5 ones.
   What number am I? ______

5. I am less than 41.
   I have 4 tens.
   What number am I? ______

## Test Prep

Fill in the ○ for the correct answer.

6. Which sentence tells about the picture?

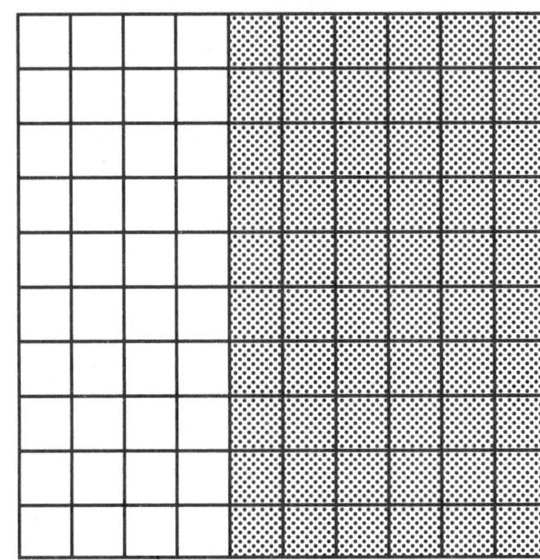

○ 40 and 60 is 100.

○ 35 and 65 is 100.

○ 30 and 70 is 100.

○ 15 and 85 is 100.



**Notes for Home** Your child reviewed ordering numbers, finding the nearest ten for a number, and solving problems. *Home Activity:* Ask your child to put 48, 27, 51, and 39 in order from least to greatest. (27, 39, 48, 51)

Name ______________________________

# Explore One Minute

**Practice 7-1**

How many times can you do each activity in one minute? Estimate. Then do the activity. Write how many.

1. Write a five-letter word.

   Estimate: ______ times

   How many? ______ times

2. Draw a star.

   Estimate: ______ times

   How many? ______ times

3. Do jumping jacks.

   Estimate: ______ times

   How many? ______ times

4. Bounce a ball.

   Estimate: ______ times

   How many? ______ times

**Talk About It** Where your estimates accurate? Do you think you could make better estimates now? Why or why not? Compare your answers with a classmate.



**Notes for Home** Your child estimated how many times he or she could do an activity in one minute. Then he or she timed the activity to check. *Home Activity:* Ask your child to name two other activities that take one minute.

Name ______________________________

Practice 7-2

# Estimate Time

Draw an activity you can do in each amount of time.

1. More than one minute

2. Less than one minute

3. About one minute



## Tell a Math Story

4. You have one minute to tell someone about school.
What would you say?

**Notes for Home** Your child drew a picture of an activity that would take less than, more than, and about one minute. *Home Activity*: Ask your child to name one more activity for each amount of time.

Name ______________________________

# Time to the Hour

Practice 7-3

Draw the clock hands to show each time.

1. 
5:00

2. 
12:00

3. 
4:00

**Write your own.** Choose your own time.
Draw the clock hands. Write the time.

4. 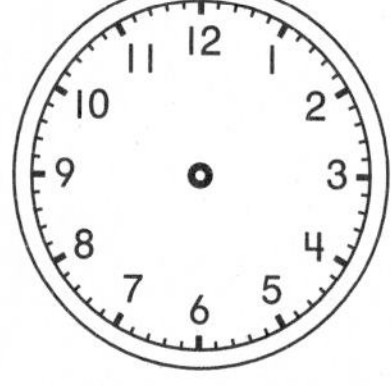
_____ :00

5. 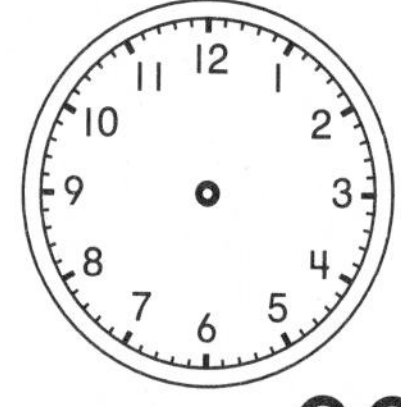
_____ :00

6. 
_____ :00

## Problem Solving Visual Thinking

Look at the picture. What time do you think it is?
Circle the time. How do you know?

7. 
8:00 3:00

8. 
3:00 12:00

**Notes for Home** Your child showed time to the hour. *Home Activity:* Ask your child to tell where the hour hand and minute hand would be at 4:00. (The minute hand would be at 12, the hour hand at 4.)

Name ______________________

Practice 7-4

# Elapsed Time

Use your clock. Draw the clock hands.
Write the ending times.

1. Start

9:00

2 hours later

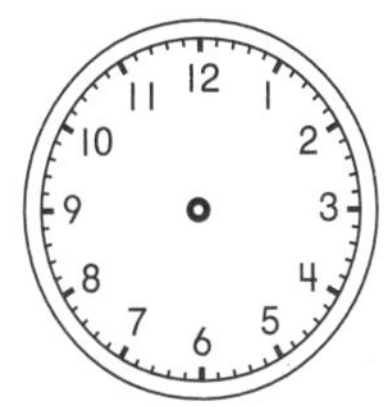

Stop

11:00

2. Start

5:00

3 hours later

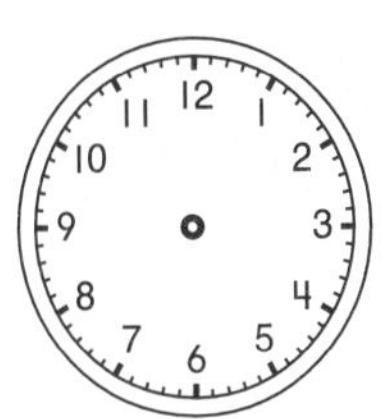

Stop

___:___

---

Use your clock. When will each activity end?
Write the ending time.

3. Melvin went to a friend's house at 3:00. He left after 1 hour. What time did Melvin leave?

___:___.

4. Dena came home from school at 3:00. Her mother came home 2 hours later. They made dinner for 1 hour. What time was it then?

___:___.

## Problem Solving Critical Thinking

Solve.

5. Tony stopped playing the flute at 7:00. He had played for 1 hour.

What time did he start playing? ___:___



**Notes for Home** Your child solved problems involving the passing of time. *Home Activity:* Ask your child to tell you how many hours have gone by between 6:00 and 9:00 in the evening. (3 hours)

Name ______________________________

**Practice 7-5**

# Problem Solving:
## Use Data from a Table

| School Play Rehearsals | | |
|---|---|---|
| **Day** | **Start** | **End** |
| Monday | 2:00 | 4:00 |
| Tuesday | 3:00 | 5:00 |
| Wednesday | 2:00 | 5:00 |
| Thursday | 2:00 | 6:00 |
| Friday | 3:00 | 6:00 |

Use the table. Solve the problems.
Write each answer.

1. This Monday, classes end 1 hour before rehearsal begins. What time do classes end?

   1:00

3. How long is rehearsal on Wednesday?

   ______ hours

2. On what day is rehearsal the longest? How long is it?

   ______________ hours

4. Which days have rehearsals that last 2 hours?

   ______________________

   Which days have rehearsals that last 3 hours?

   ______________________

### Journal

5. Copy this table into your journal. Add another column at the right that tells how long rehearsal was each day.

**Notes for Home** Your child used a table to solve problems. *Home Activity:* Ask your child to tell you how many hours children rehearsed in all. (2 + 2 + 3 + 4 + 3 = 14 hours in all)

Name ______________________________

# Mixed Practice: Lessons 1–5

1. Estimate how many times you can count to 20 in one minute. Then do the activity. Write how many.

Estimate: ______ times

How many? ______ times

Write the time.

2. 

___:___

3. 

___:___

Read both clocks.
How many hours have gone by?

4.  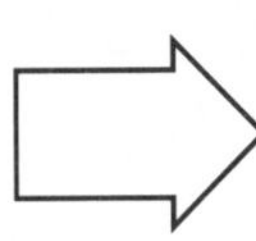 

______ hours

## Problem Solving

Use the table.
Answer the question.

| Party Times | Start | End |
|---|---|---|
| Make crafts | 1:00 | 2:00 |
| Play "Treasure Hunt" | 2:00 | 3:00 |
| Eat a snack | 3:00 | 4:00 |

5. How long is the party?

______ hours

## Journal

6. Draw two clocks.
Show 8 o'clock on one.
Show 4 hours later on the other.

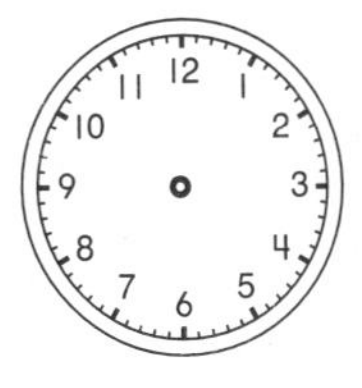

4 hours later

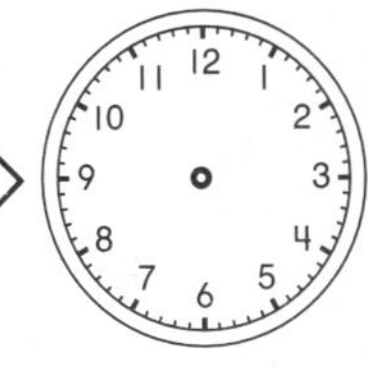



**Notes for Home** Your child practiced showing and telling time. *Home Activity:* Draw 3 clocks, each with a different time. Ask your child to tell you what time each clock would show 3 hours later.

Name ______________________

Practice
Chapters 1–7
A

# Cumulative Review

Count by 2s. Write the numbers.

1. ____, 14, ____, ____, ____, 22, ____, ____, ____, 30

Count by 5s. Write the numbers.

2. ____, 10, ____, ____, ____, 30, ____, ____

Add or subtract.

3.

| 8 | 8 | 3 | 7 | 5 | 8 | 7 |
|---|---|---|---|---|---|---|
| + 5 | + 8 | + 7 | + 8 | + 4 | + 9 | + 6 |

4.

| 13 | 14 | 15 | 12 | 13 | 17 | 12 |
|---|---|---|---|---|---|---|
| − 8 | − 6 | − 7 | − 9 | − 7 | − 8 | − 7 |

## Test Prep

Fill in the ○ for the correct answer.

Count the money. How much in all?

| 89¢ | 94¢ | 96¢ | 66¢ |
|---|---|---|---|
| ○ | ○ | ○ | ○ |



**Notes for Home** Your child reviewed counting by 5s and 10s, addition and subtraction facts, and counting groups of coins. *Home Activity:* Ask your child to count by 10s to 100.

Name ______________________

Practice 7-6

# Tell Time to Five Minutes

Write the time for each clock.

1. 

10:10

2. 

___:___

3. 

___:___

Draw the minute hand to show the time.

4. 

4:05

5. 

8:50

6. 

11:55

## Problem Solving

Solve. Write the time.

7. The muffins went into the oven at 10 minutes before 4. At what time did they go in the oven?

3:___

8. Jon started his homework at 25 minutes before 8. At what time did he begin his homework?

___:___



**Notes for Home** Your child told time to 5 minute intervals. *Home Activity:* Ask your child to tell where the minute hand would point at 2:40. (8)

Name ______________________

Practice 7-7

# Tell Time to the Half Hour

Write the time shown on each clock.

1. 

______

2. 

______

3. 

______

4. 

______

5. 

______

6. 

______

7. **Write your own** time.
Use a half hour.
Draw a picture showing
what you do at that time.

____ : ____

half past ____

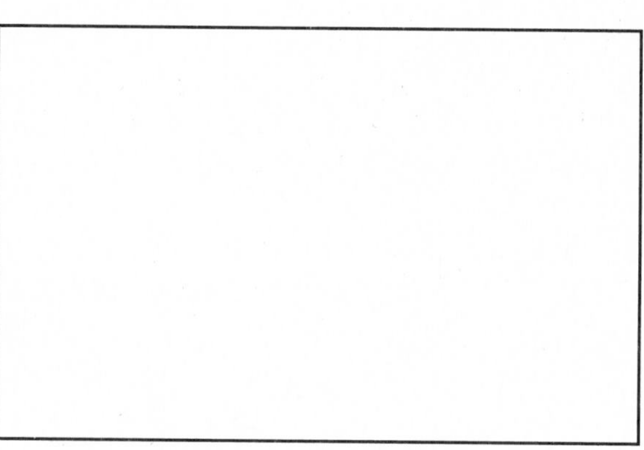

## Problem Solving Patterns

8. Write the times to continue the pattern.

7:00, 7:30, 8:00, ___:___, ___:___, ___:___

**Notes for Home** Your child told time to the half hour. *Home Activity:* Ask your child where the minute hand and the hour hand point at 10:30. (The minute hand points at the 6, the hour hand points between the 10 and 11.)

Name ______________________

Practice 7-8

# Tell Time to the Quarter Hour

Write the time for each clock.

1.

12:15

15 minutes after 12

2.

____ : ____

______ minutes after ______

______ minutes before ______

3.

____ : ____

half past ______

4.

____ : ____

______ minutes after ______

______ minutes before ______

## Problem Solving Visual Thinking

5. Some watches do not show all the numbers. Write the time shown on this watch.

____ : ____

**Notes for Home** Your child learned how to tell time in 15 minute intervals. *Home Activity:* Ask your child to tell you the time for each 15-minute interval from 7:00 to 8:00. (7:00, 7:15, 7:30, 7:45, 8:00)

Name ____________________________________

# Problem Solving:
## Make a Table

**Practice 7-9**

1. The calendar shows all the months and days in a year.
   Circle the first and last day of school.
   Circle a month in which a friend or relative has a birthday.

| January | | | | | | |
|---|---|---|---|---|---|---|
| S | M | T | W | T | F | S |
| | | | 1 | 2 | 3 | 4 |
| 5 | 6 | 7 | 8 | 9 | 10 | 11 |
| 12 | 13 | 14 | 15 | 16 | 17 | 18 |
| 19 | 20 | 21 | 22 | 23 | 24 | 25 |
| 26 | 27 | 28 | 29 | 30 | 31 | |

| February | | | | | | |
|---|---|---|---|---|---|---|
| S | M | T | W | T | F | S |
| | | | | | | 1 |
| 2 | 3 | 4 | 5 | 6 | 7 | 8 |
| 9 | 10 | 11 | 12 | 13 | 14 | 15 |
| 16 | 17 | 18 | 19 | 20 | 21 | 22 |
| 23 | 24 | 25 | 26 | 27 | 28 | |

| March | | | | | | |
|---|---|---|---|---|---|---|
| S | M | T | W | T | F | S |
| | | | | | | 1 |
| 2 | 3 | 4 | 5 | 6 | 7 | 8 |
| 9 | 10 | 11 | 12 | 13 | 14 | 15 |
| 16 | 17 | 18 | 19 | 20 | 21 | 22 |
| 23/30 | 24/31 | 25 | 26 | 27 | 28 | 29 |

| April | | | | | | |
|---|---|---|---|---|---|---|
| S | M | T | W | T | F | S |
| | | 1 | 2 | 3 | 4 | 5 |
| 6 | 7 | 8 | 9 | 10 | 11 | 12 |
| 13 | 14 | 15 | 16 | 17 | 18 | 19 |
| 20 | 21 | 22 | 23 | 24 | 25 | 26 |
| 27 | 28 | 29 | 30 | | | |

| May | | | | | | |
|---|---|---|---|---|---|---|
| S | M | T | W | T | F | S |
| | | | | 1 | 2 | 3 |
| 4 | 5 | 6 | 7 | 8 | 9 | 10 |
| 11 | 12 | 13 | 14 | 15 | 16 | 17 |
| 18 | 19 | 20 | 21 | 22 | 23 | 24 |
| 25 | 26 | 27 | 28 | 29 | 30 | 31 |

| June | | | | | | |
|---|---|---|---|---|---|---|
| S | M | T | W | T | F | S |
| 1 | 2 | 3 | 4 | 5 | 6 | 7 |
| 8 | 9 | 10 | 11 | 12 | 13 | 14 |
| 15 | 16 | 17 | 18 | 19 | 20 | 21 |
| 22 | 23 | 24 | 25 | 26 | 27 | 28 |
| 29 | 30 | | | | | |

| July | | | | | | |
|---|---|---|---|---|---|---|
| S | M | T | W | T | F | S |
| | | 1 | 2 | 3 | 4 | 5 |
| 6 | 7 | 8 | 9 | 10 | 11 | 12 |
| 13 | 14 | 15 | 16 | 17 | 18 | 19 |
| 20 | 21 | 22 | 23 | 24 | 25 | 26 |
| 27 | 28 | 29 | 30 | 31 | | |

| August | | | | | | |
|---|---|---|---|---|---|---|
| S | M | T | W | T | F | S |
| | | | | | 1 | 2 |
| 3 | 4 | 5 | 6 | 7 | 8 | 9 |
| 10 | 11 | 12 | 13 | 14 | 15 | 16 |
| 17 | 18 | 19 | 20 | 21 | 22 | 23 |
| 24/31 | 25 | 26 | 27 | 28 | 29 | 30 |

| September | | | | | | |
|---|---|---|---|---|---|---|
| S | M | T | W | T | F | S |
| | 1 | 2 | 3 | 4 | 5 | 6 |
| 7 | 8 | 9 | 10 | 11 | 12 | 13 |
| 14 | 15 | 16 | 17 | 18 | 19 | 20 |
| 21 | 22 | 23 | 24 | 25 | 26 | 27 |
| 28 | 29 | 30 | | | | |

| October | | | | | | |
|---|---|---|---|---|---|---|
| S | M | T | W | T | F | S |
| | | | 1 | 2 | 3 | 4 |
| 5 | 6 | 7 | 8 | 9 | 10 | 11 |
| 12 | 13 | 14 | 15 | 16 | 17 | 18 |
| 19 | 20 | 21 | 22 | 23 | 24 | 25 |
| 26 | 27 | 28 | 29 | 30 | 31 | |

| November | | | | | | |
|---|---|---|---|---|---|---|
| S | M | T | W | T | F | S |
| | | | | | | 1 |
| 2 | 3 | 4 | 5 | 6 | 7 | 8 |
| 9 | 10 | 11 | 12 | 13 | 14 | 15 |
| 16 | 17 | 18 | 19 | 20 | 21 | 22 |
| 23/30 | 24 | 25 | 26 | 27 | 28 | 29 |

| December | | | | | | |
|---|---|---|---|---|---|---|
| S | M | T | W | T | F | S |
| | 1 | 2 | 3 | 4 | 5 | 6 |
| 7 | 8 | 9 | 10 | 11 | 12 | 13 |
| 14 | 15 | 16 | 17 | 18 | 19 | 20 |
| 21 | 22 | 23 | 24 | 25 | 26 | 27 |
| 28 | 29 | 30 | 31 | | | |

2. Make a table using the calendar.
   Use tallies to show how many months have 3 or 4 full weeks.

| **Months with 3 full weeks** | **Months with 4 full weeks** |
|---|---|
| | |

## Journal

3. Look at this year's calendar. Make a table using tallies to show how many months have the last day on a weekend and how many have the last day on a weekday.

**Notes for Home** Your child made a table to solve problems. *Home Activity:* Ask your child to show you his or her journal entries and to explain the entries.

Name ______________________

Practice
Chapter 7
B

# Mixed Practice: Lessons 6–9

Write the time for each clock.

1. 

___ : ___

____ minutes after____

2. 

___ : ___

half past _____

3. 

___ : ___

____ minutes after____

____ minutes before ____

Write the time for each clock.

4. 

___ : ___

5. 

___ : ___

## Problem Solving

Use the calendar to answer the questions.

| March | | | | | | |
|---|---|---|---|---|---|---|
| S | M | T | W | T | F | S |
| | | | | | | 1 |
| 2 | 3 | 4 | 5 | 6 | 7 | 8 |
| 9 | 10 | 11 | 12 | 13 | 14 | 15 |
| 16 | 17 | 18 | 19 | 20 | 21 | 22 |
| 23/30 | 24/31 | 25 | 26 | 27 | 28 | 29 |

6. How many Saturdays are in this month? ______

7. On what day of the week is the last day of the month? ___________

## Journal

8. Draw two clocks. Show 6:15 on one clock.
Show 6:45 on the other clock.
Tell how much time has passed. What time will it be in 15 minutes?



**Notes for Home** Your child told time and used a calendar. *Home Activity*: Ask your child to tell you the time right now. What time will it be in 5 minutes? 15 minutes? 30 minutes? 1 hour?

Name ______________________

Practice
Chapters 1–7
B

# Cumulative Review

Use the graph. Answer the questions.

**How I Spend My Time on a School Day**

| Activity | 1 | 2 | 3 | 4 | 5 | 6 | 7 | 8 | 9 | 10 |
|---|---|---|---|---|---|---|---|---|---|---|
| School | ▒ | ▒ | ▒ | ▒ | ▒ | ▒ | ▒ | | | |
| Homework | ▒ | ▒ | | | | | | | | |
| Playing | ▒ | ▒ | ▒ (half) | | | | | | | |
| Eating | ▒ | ▒ | ▒ (half) | | | | | | | |
| Sleeping | ▒ | ▒ | ▒ | ▒ | ▒ | ▒ | ▒ | ▒ | | |
| Hours | 1 | 2 | 3 | 4 | 5 | 6 | 7 | 8 | 9 | 10 |

1. Which activity did this child spend the most time doing?

______________________

2. What did the child spend about the same time doing?

______________________

Add or subtract.

3. $\begin{array}{r} 7 \\ +9 \\ \hline \end{array}$ $\begin{array}{r} 17 \\ -8 \\ \hline \end{array}$ $\begin{array}{r} 12 \\ -7 \\ \hline \end{array}$ $\begin{array}{r} 14 \\ -6 \\ \hline \end{array}$ $\begin{array}{r} 7 \\ +5 \\ \hline \end{array}$ $\begin{array}{r} 13 \\ -7 \\ \hline \end{array}$ $\begin{array}{r} 6 \\ +8 \\ \hline \end{array}$

## Test Prep

Fill in the ○ for the correct answer.

4. What number completes the table?

**Ways to Show 35¢**

| Nickels | Dimes |
|---|---|
| 7 | 0 |
| ? | 1 |
| 3 | 2 |
| 1 | 3 |

4 ○ 6 ○ 8 ○ 5 ○

**Notes for Home** Your child reviewed using a graph, addition and subtraction facts, and making an organized list.
*Home Activity:* Ask your child how many hours they spend each day doing the activities in the graph.

Name ______________________________

Practice 8-1

# Explore Adding Tens

How many in all?

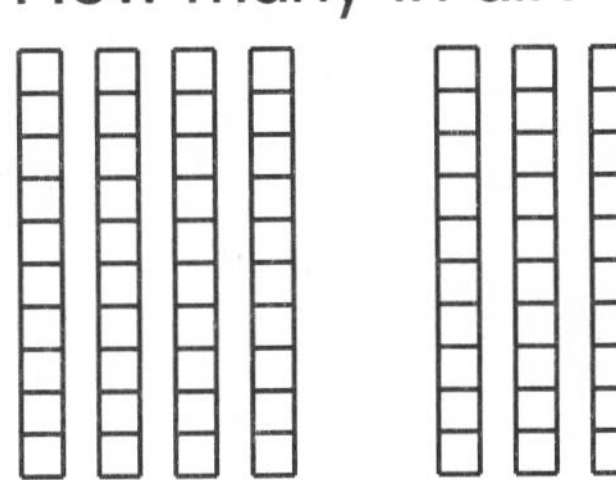

4 tens + 3 tens = 7 tens

40 + 30 = 70

Use  to find how many in all.

1. 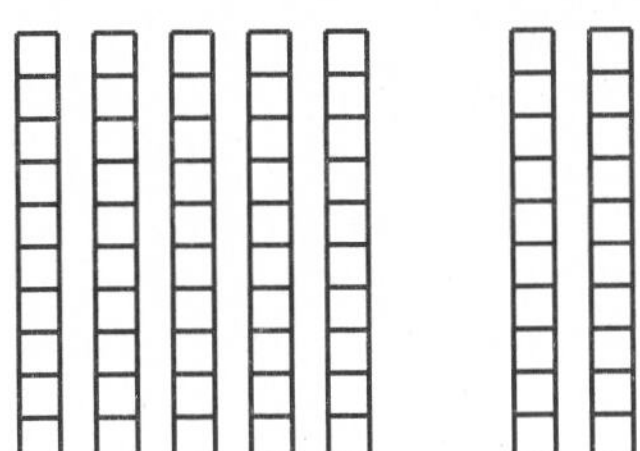

____ tens + ____ tens = ____ tens

____ + ____ = ____

2. 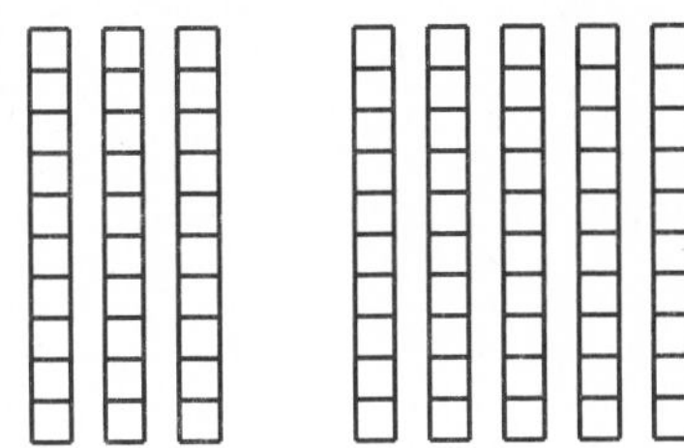

____ tens + ____ tens = ____ tens

____ + ____ = ____

**Write your own** problems about adding tens.

3. Draw the ▭ you use.

____ tens + ____ tens = ____ tens

____ + ____ = ____

4. Draw the ▭ you use.

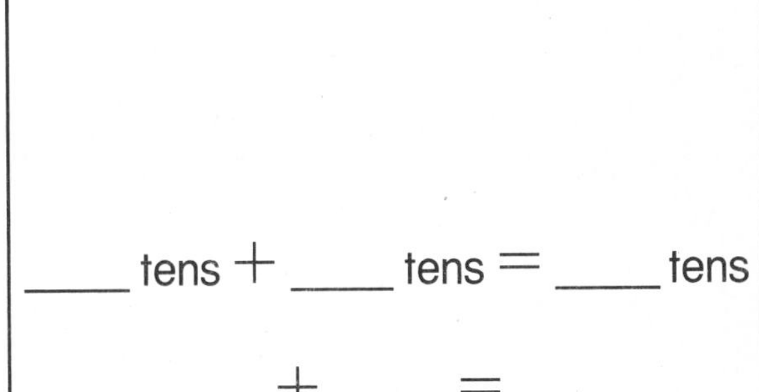

____ tens + ____ tens = ____ tens

____ + ____ = ____

**Talk About It** Tell a classmate how 4 + 2 and 40 + 20 are alike and how they are different.



**Notes for Home** Your child explored adding tens. *Home Activity:* Ask your child to tell you the sum of 3 and 3. (6) Then ask him or her to tell you the sum of 30 and 30. (60)

Name ____________________

# Add Tens with a Hundred Chart

Practice 8-2

Add. You can use the hundreds chart.

1. 34 + 10 = ____  25 + 40 = ____

2. 68 + 20 = ____  86 + 10 = ____

3. 50 + 30 = ____  73 + 10 = ____

| 1 | 2 | 3 | 4 | 5 | 6 | 7 | 8 | 9 | 10 |
|---|---|---|---|---|---|---|---|---|---|
| 11 | 12 | 13 | 14 | 15 | 16 | 17 | 18 | 19 | 20 |
| 21 | 22 | 23 | 24 | 25 | 26 | 27 | 28 | 29 | 30 |
| 31 | 32 | 33 | 34 | 35 | 36 | 37 | 38 | 39 | 40 |
| 41 | 42 | 43 | 44 | 45 | 46 | 47 | 48 | 49 | 50 |
| 51 | 52 | 53 | 54 | 55 | 56 | 57 | 58 | 59 | 60 |
| 61 | 62 | 63 | 64 | 65 | 66 | 67 | 68 | 69 | 70 |
| 71 | 72 | 73 | 74 | 75 | 76 | 77 | 78 | 79 | 80 |
| 81 | 82 | 83 | 84 | 85 | 86 | 87 | 88 | 89 | 90 |
| 91 | 92 | 93 | 94 | 95 | 96 | 97 | 98 | 99 | 100 |

## Problem Solving Patterns

4. Add. What patterns do you see?

40 + 30 = ____

41 + 30 = ____

42 + 30 = ____

43 + 30 = ____

44 + 30 = ____

**Write your own** number sentences to make a pattern.

____ + ____ = ____

____ + ____ = ____

____ + ____ = ____

____ + ____ = ____

____ + ____ = ____



**Notes for Home** Your child practiced adding tens. *Home Activity:* Ask your child to show you a pattern that starts with the number sentence 20 + 20 = ___. (Possible answers : 21 + 20 = 41, 22 + 20 = 42, 23 + 20 = 43, and so on.)

 Use with pages 271–272.

Name ______________________

Practice 8-3

# Add Using Mental Math

Use mental math to add.

1. 14 + 30 = 44     56 + 20 = ____
2. 37 + 40 = ____     29 + 50 = ____
3. 63 + 20 = ____     82 + 10 = ____
4. 55 + 30 = ____     72 + 20 = ____
5. 75 + 10 = ____     41 + 30 = ____

## Problem Solving Patterns

Add. Use mental math. Then write the number sentences to continue the patterns.

6. 22 + 20 = ____
   22 + 30 = ____
   22 + 40 = ____
   ____ + ____ = ____
   ____ + ____ = ____

7. 48 + 10 = ____
   48 + 20 = ____
   48 + 30 = ____
   ____ + ____ = ____
   ____ + ____ = ____

8. Describe the patterns you see.

______________________________________________

______________________________________________



**Notes for Home** Your child practiced using mental math to add. *Home Activity:* Ask your child to tell you how old he or she will be 10 years from now, 20 years from now, and 30 years from now.

Name ______________________

Practice 8-4

# Estimate Two-Digit Sums

Find the nearest ten. Estimate the sum.

1. Think:

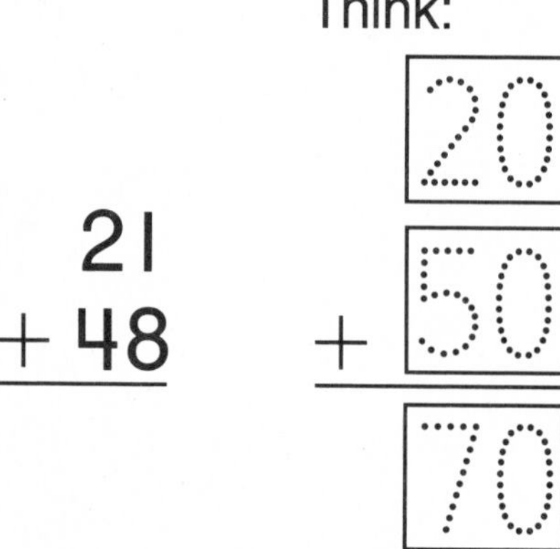


21 + 48 is about 70.

2. Think:

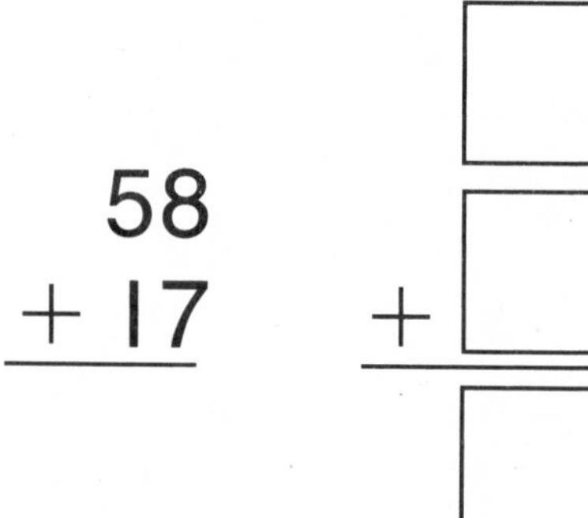

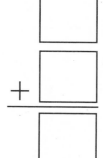

58 + 17 is about _____.

3. Think:

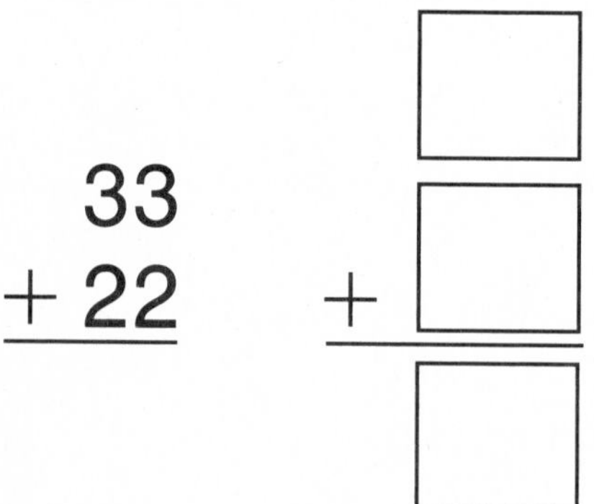


33 + 22 is about _____.

4. Think:

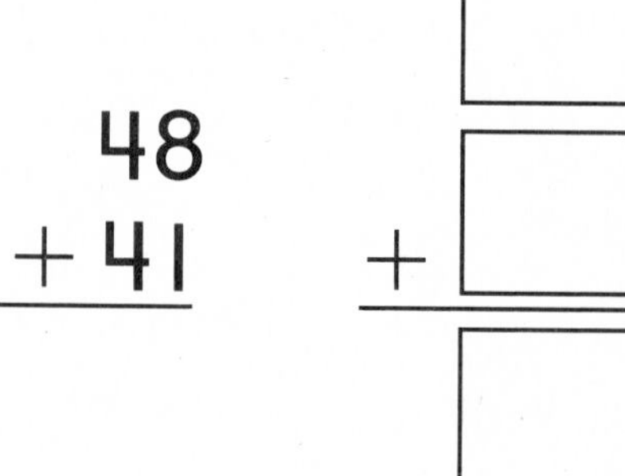


48 + 41 is about _____.

## Problem Solving Estimation

5. This graph shows how many children chose sandwiches for lunch yesterday. About how many children chose sandwiches for lunch? _____
About how many chose turkey sandwiches? _____

**Sandwiches Eaten**

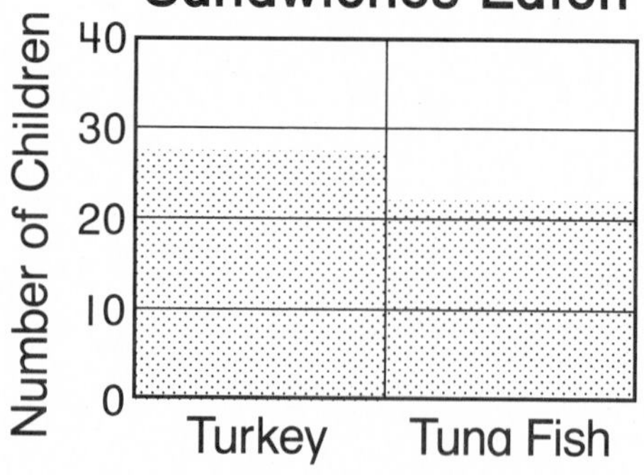

Number of Children: 0, 10, 20, 30, 40

Turkey | Tuna Fish



**Notes for Home** Your child used nearest tens to estimated sums. *Home Activity:* Ask your child to tell you how to estimate the sum of 32 and 18. (32 is about 30 and 18 is about 20. 30 plus 20 is 50.)

Name ______________________________

Practice 8-5

# Problem Solving: Make Predictions

1. Predict. Which fruit do you think your classmates like best?

______________________________

2. Why do you think so?

______________________________

______________________________

3. Ask your classmates. Record the results.

| Fruit | Tally | Total |
|---|---|---|
| | | |
| | | |
| | | |
| | | |
| | | |
| | | |

4. Was your prediction close? ______________

## Critical Thinking

5. What do you think you can do to make better predictions?

**Notes for Home** Your child made a prediction and then found information to test the prediction. *Home Activity:* Have your child make a prediction and then test it. Predict how many people or how many birds will you see in the next 15 minutes.

Name ____________________________

**Practice 8-6**

# Explore Addition With or Without Regrouping

15 children ride bikes to school. 8 children walk.
How many children in all?

| Tens | Ones |
| --- | --- |
| | |

Start with 15.

| Tens | Ones |
| --- | --- |
| | |

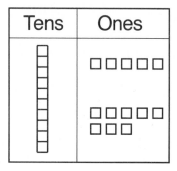

Add 8.

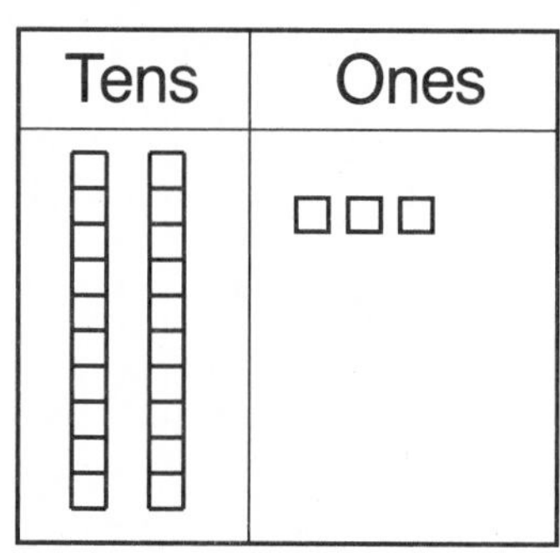


Regroup 10 ones as 1 ten.

Write how many in all. __2__ tens __3__ ones __23__ in all

Use [tens | ones chart], [ten rod], and [one cube].

1. Show 26. Add 9.
   How many in all?
   ______ tens ______ ones
   ______ in all

2. Show 48. Add 5.
   How many in all?
   ______ tens ______ ones
   ______ in all

3. Show 12. Add 5.
   How many in all?
   ______ ten ______ ones
   ______ in all

4. Show 37. Add 8.
   How many in all?
   ______ tens ______ ones
   ______ in all

**Talk About It** Explain to a classmate when it is important to regroup.



**Notes for Home** Your child explored regrouping in addition. *Home Activity:* Have your child use dry beans or macaroni to show how to regroup when adding 16 and 7. (6 + 7 = 1 ten and 3 ones; 16 + 7 = 23)

Name ______________________________

Practice 8-7

# Add With or Without Regrouping

Use [tens | ones mat], [tens rod], and [ones cube].

| | Show this many. | Add this many. | Do you need to regroup? | Solve. |
|---|---|---|---|---|
| 1. | 27 | 5 | yes | 27 + 5 = ____ |
| 2. | 45 | 3 | | 45 + 3 = ____ |
| 3. | 58 | 8 | | 58 + 8 = ____ |
| 4. | 34 | 7 | | 34 + 7 = ____ |
| 5. | 75 | 4 | | 75 + 4 = ____ |
| 6. | 13 | 9 | | 13 + 9 = ____ |
| 7. | 66 | 6 | | 66 + 6 = ____ |

## Problem Solving Critical Thinking

8. Which one-digit numbers can you add to 15 without needing to regroup? How do you know?

_______________________________________________

_______________________________________________

**Notes for Home** Your child decided when to regroup to add numbers and then found the sums. *Home Activity:* Ask your child to show you two addition problems, one where you must regroup and one where you do not have to regroup. (Possible answer: you must regroup for 15 + 6; you do not regroup for 15 + 4.)

Name ______________________________

# Record Addition

Practice 8-8

Add. Then circle the exercise if you regrouped.

Use tens | ones, (ten rod), and (one cube)

1.

| tens | ones |
|---|---|
| ☐ | |
| 4 | 3 |
| + | 7 |
| 5 | 0 |

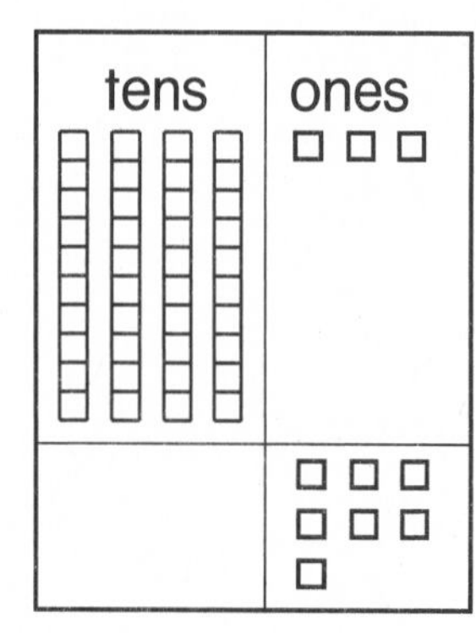

2.

| tens | ones |
|---|---|
| ☐ | |
| 3 | 7 |
| + | 1 |
| | |

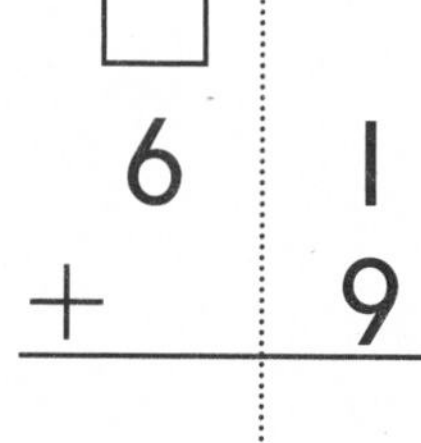

3.

| tens | ones |
|---|---|
| ☐ | |
| 5 | 3 |
| + | 8 |

| tens | ones |
|---|---|
| ☐ | |
| 7 | 2 |
| + | 4 |

| tens | ones |
|---|---|
| ☐ | |
| 6 | 1 |
| + | 9 |

| tens | ones |
|---|---|
| ☐ | |
| 4 | 5 |
| + | 7 |

4.

| tens | ones |
|---|---|
| ☐ | |
| 3 | 9 |
| + | 6 |

| tens | ones |
|---|---|
| ☐ | |
| 8 | 6 |
| + | 3 |

| tens | ones |
|---|---|
| ☐ | |
| 2 | 5 |
| + | 8 |

| tens | ones |
|---|---|
| ☐ | |
| 1 | 8 |
| + | 4 |

## Problem Solving Critical Thinking

5. Lenny dropped grape jam on his math paper.
Now Lenny cannot read some of the numbers.
What could the missing numbers be?
How do you know?

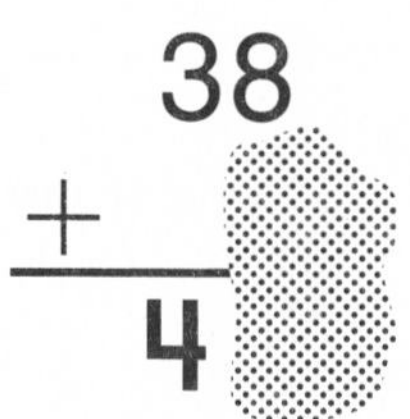




**Notes for Home** Your child added tens and ones where regrouping was sometime required. *Home Activity:* Ask your child to write addition problems where regrouping is and is not required, and explain his or her reasoning.

Name ______________________

Practice
Chapter 8
A

# Mixed Practice: Lessons 1–8

Estimate the sum.

1\.

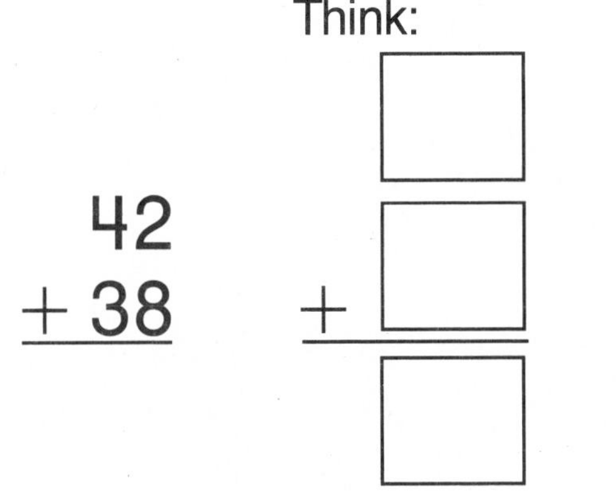


42 + 38 is about _____.

Add. Use mental math.

2\. 38 + 20 = ____

42 + 50 = ____

19 + 30 = ____

## Problem Solving

3\. Complete the chart. Fill in the totals.

| Color of Shirts | Tally | Totals |
|---|---|---|
| yellow | ~~////~~ / | |
| red | ~~////~~ //// | |
| white | /// | |

4\. Ms. April's class made a chart to show the color of shirts worn by the students. What color shirt would you predict to see most often in Mr. May's class? ______________

## Journal

6\. Make a chart to show the color of shirts worn by the students in your class. What color shirt do you see most often?



**Notes for Home** Your child practiced adding tens, using mental math, estimating sums, and solving problems. *Home Activity:* Have your child look at Exercise 2 and tell you which of the problems has the greater sum and why.

Name ______________________________

# Cumulative Review

**Practice**
Chapters 1–8
**A**

Add or subtract.

1. $\begin{array}{r} 5 \\ +\,5 \\ \hline \end{array}$ $\begin{array}{r} 10 \\ -\,5 \\ \hline \end{array}$

2. $\begin{array}{r} 4 \\ +\,4 \\ \hline \end{array}$ $\begin{array}{r} 8 \\ -\,4 \\ \hline \end{array}$

3. $\begin{array}{r} 6 \\ +\,6 \\ \hline \end{array}$ $\begin{array}{r} 12 \\ -\,6 \\ \hline \end{array}$

4. $\begin{array}{r} 7 \\ +\,7 \\ \hline \end{array}$ $\begin{array}{r} 14 \\ -\,7 \\ \hline \end{array}$

Write how many. Then write **even** or **odd**.

5. 

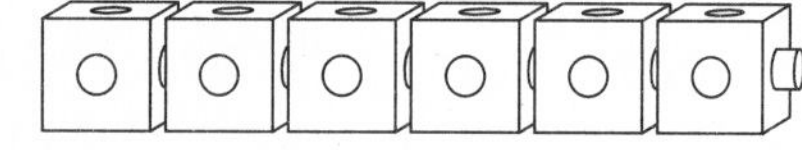

______ __________

6. 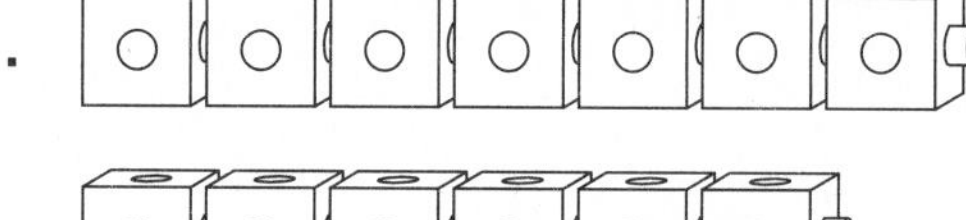

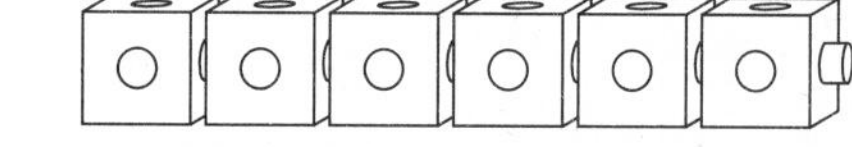

______ __________

## Test Prep

Fill in the ○ for the correct answer.

Use the picture to answer the questions.

7. Which is clown C?
   - ○ first
   - ○ second
   - ○ third
   - ○ fourth

8. Which is clown E?
   - ○ second
   - ○ third
   - ○ fifth
   - ○ sixth



**Notes for Home** Your child reviewed concepts from earlier chapters. *Home Activity:* Ask your child which clown in the picture is first and which is last. (Clown A is first and clown F is last.)

Name ______________________________

Practice 8-9

# Add Two-Digit Numbers With or Without Regrouping

Use [tens | ones mat], [tens rod], and [ones cube]. Regroup if you need to.

1.

| tens | ones | tens | ones | tens | ones | tens | ones |
|---|---|---|---|---|---|---|---|
| 1 | | ☐ | | ☐ | | ☐ | |
| 2 | 5 | 4 | 6 | 7 | 1 | 3 | 5 |
| + 1 | 7 | + 2 | 3 | + 1 | 5 | + 4 | 7 |
| 4 | 2 | | | | | | |

2.

| tens | ones | tens | ones | tens | ones | tens | ones |
|---|---|---|---|---|---|---|---|
| ☐ | | ☐ | | ☐ | | ☐ | |
| 5 | 9 | 8 | 6 | 1 | 7 | 6 | 4 |
| + 3 | 6 | + 1 | 2 | + 4 | 8 | + 2 | 6 |
| | | | | | | | |

3.

| tens | ones | tens | ones | tens | ones | tens | ones |
|---|---|---|---|---|---|---|---|
| ☐ | | ☐ | | ☐ | | ☐ | |
| 3 | 9 | 5 | 8 | 7 | 4 | 4 | 1 |
| + 2 | 6 | + 4 | 1 | + 1 | 9 | + 3 | 9 |
| | | | | | | | |

## Problem Solving Visual Thinking

4. We started with this.

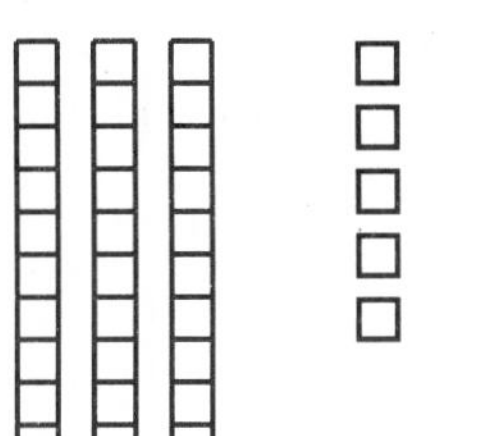

Now we have this.

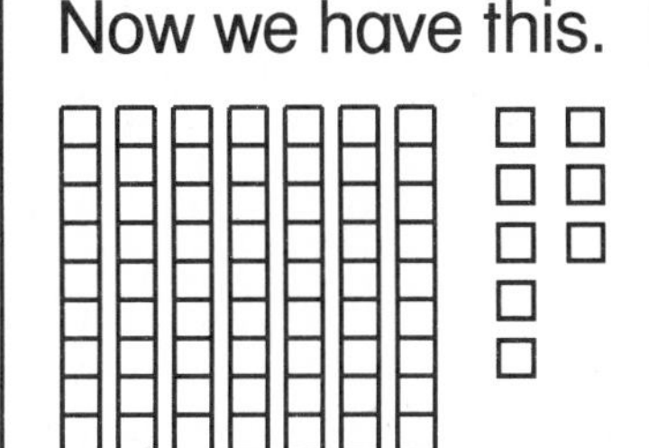

Draw what was added.



**Notes for Home** Your child added two-digit numbers with and without regrouping. *Home Activity:* Have your child use dried beans or macaroni to explain why it sometimes is necessary to regroup.

Name ______________________________

# Add Two-Digit Numbers

**Practice 8-10**

Add. Regroup if you need to.

1. $\begin{array}{r} 27 \\ +24 \\ \hline \end{array}$ $\begin{array}{r} 52 \\ +\ \ 9 \\ \hline \end{array}$ $\begin{array}{r} 34 \\ +57 \\ \hline \end{array}$ $\begin{array}{r} 19 \\ +43 \\ \hline \end{array}$ $\begin{array}{r} 44 \\ +55 \\ \hline \end{array}$

2. $\begin{array}{r} 51 \\ +29 \\ \hline \end{array}$ $\begin{array}{r} 73 \\ +16 \\ \hline \end{array}$ $\begin{array}{r} 18 \\ +36 \\ \hline \end{array}$ $\begin{array}{r} 35 \\ +55 \\ \hline \end{array}$ $\begin{array}{r} 67 \\ +11 \\ \hline \end{array}$ $\begin{array}{r} 33 \\ +38 \\ \hline \end{array}$

3. $\begin{array}{r} 14 \\ +66 \\ \hline \end{array}$ $\begin{array}{r} 68 \\ +27 \\ \hline \end{array}$ $\begin{array}{r} 26 \\ +72 \\ \hline \end{array}$ $\begin{array}{r} 57 \\ +15 \\ \hline \end{array}$ $\begin{array}{r} 35 \\ +36 \\ \hline \end{array}$ $\begin{array}{r} 40 \\ +49 \\ \hline \end{array}$

## Problem Solving

4. Kevin's apples weigh 32 pounds. Which two baskets are his?

______________________________

**Write your own** math story about the apple baskets. Ask a friend to solve it.

______________________________

______________________________

______________________________

______________________________

**Notes for Home** Your child added two-digit numbers with and without regrouping. *Home Activity:* Have your child tell you how to find the sum of 46 + 25. (Add the ones. 6 + 5 = 11. Regroup. Add the tens. 1 + 4 + 2 = 7. The sum is 71.)

Name ______________________________

Practice 8-11

# Add Money

Add.

1.

| 14¢ | 43¢ | 27¢ | 48¢ | 35¢ | 57¢ |
|---|---|---|---|---|---|
| + 18¢ | + 25¢ | + 53¢ | + 24¢ | + 44¢ | + 24¢ |
| 32¢ | | | | | |

2.

| 61¢ | 83¢ | 78¢ | 35¢ | 57¢ | 82¢ |
|---|---|---|---|---|---|
| + 29¢ | + 16¢ | + 16¢ | + 63¢ | + 31¢ | + 10¢ |

**Mixed Practice** Add.

3.

| 45¢ | 21¢ | 37 | 13 | 56¢ | 78 |
|---|---|---|---|---|---|
| + 38¢ | + 49¢ | + 26 | + 57 | + 19¢ | + 7 |

4.

| 62 | 34¢ | 18 | 25¢ | 70 | 18¢ |
|---|---|---|---|---|---|
| + 24 | + 7¢ | + 63 | + 39¢ | + 16 | + 13¢ |

## Problem Solving Critical Thinking

5. Peg has 75¢. Which two items could she buy?

____________ and ____________

**Notes for Home** Your child added amounts of money up to 99¢. *Home Activity:* Ask your child: *How much money would you have in all if you had 25¢ and 38¢?* (63¢)

Name ______________________

Practice 8-12

# Add Three Numbers

Add.

1.

| 37 | 64 | 43 | 16 | 24 | 10 |
|---|---|---|---|---|---|
| 23 | 14 | 32 | 51 | 25 | 20 |
| + 12 | + 19 | + 8 | + 13 | + 35 | + 30 |
| 72 | | | | | |

2.

| 21 | 54 | 18 | 45 | 37 | 56 |
|---|---|---|---|---|---|
| 17 | 12 | 31 | 23 | 42 | 31 |
| + 31 | + 26 | + 8 | + 11 | + 1 | + 4 |

3.

| 14 | 68 | 26 | 52 | 35 | 16 |
|---|---|---|---|---|---|
| 31 | 10 | 32 | 11 | 34 | 17 |
| + 6 | + 7 | + 24 | + 15 | + 6 | + 10 |

## Problem Solving Critical Thinking

The shelf cannot hold more than 90 pounds. How many pounds can be in the last box?

_______ pounds

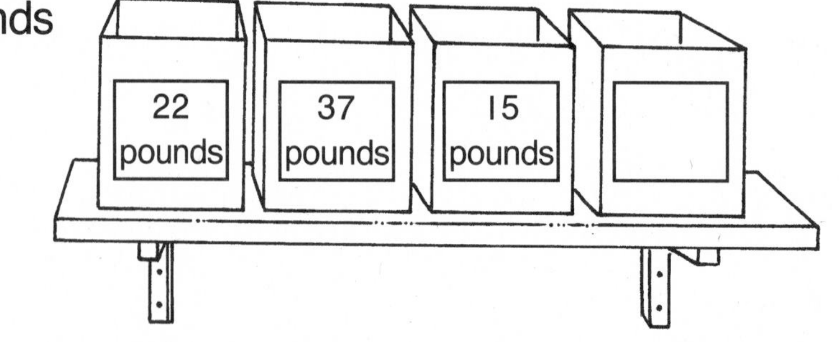




**Notes for Home** Your child has found the sum of 3 numbers. *Home Activity:* Ask your child to explain his or her reasoning for solving the Problem Solving exercise.

Name ______________________

Practice 8-13

# Problem Solving: Guess and Check

Solve. Show and check each guess.

1. Libis has 58¢.
   She wants to buy two toys.
   What can she buy?

   Libis can buy the ______________ and the ______________.

2. Which other two toys can Libis buy with 58¢?

   Libis can buy the ______________ and the ______________.

3. Armando has 50¢.
   He wants to buy two toys.
   What can he buy?

   Armando can buy the ______________ and the ______________.

## Estimation

4. Libis wants to buy 3 toys. Does she have enough money? How do you know?

   ______________________________________________

   ______________________________________________



**Notes for Home** Your child solved problems by guessing and testing. *Home Activity:* Ask your child if it is possible to buy 3 toys with 70¢. (Yes, you can buy toys B, D, and F for less than 70¢.)

Name ____________________________

Practice
Chapter 8
B

## Mixed Practice: Lessons 9–13

Add. Regroup if you need to.

1.

| | | | | | |
|---|---|---|---|---|---|
| 26 | 58 | 32 | 16 | 45 | 27 |
| + 12 | + 29 | + 48 | + 33 | + 29 | + 18 |

2.

| | | | | |
|---|---|---|---|---|
| 34¢ | 51¢ | 15¢ | 63¢ | 22¢ |
| + 49¢ | + 16¢ | + 28¢ | + 17¢ | + 51¢ |

3.

| | | | | | |
|---|---|---|---|---|---|
| 42 | 37 | 25 | 51 | 11 | 30 |
| 15 | 43 | 23 | 24 | 50 | 46 |
| + 15 | + 7 | + 22 | + 19 | + 6 | + 13 |

### Problem Solving

Solve. Show and check each guess.

4. Sue has 56¢.
She wants to buy two toys.
What can she buy?

Toy A 31¢
Toy B 29¢
Toy C 24¢
Toy D 38¢

She can buy the ________ and the ________.

### Journal

5. How does making a guess that is not the answer help you make the next guess?

**Notes for Home** Your child reviewed adding two-digit numbers with and without regrouping, adding three numbers, and using the strategy of guess and check to solve problems. *Home Activity:* Ask your child how much money he or she would need to buy the two most expensive toys shown in Exercise 4. (31¢ + 38¢ = 69¢.)

Name ______________________________

Practice
Chapters 1–8
B

# Cumulative Review

Circle the numbers you would add first.
Look for doubles and numbers that make 10. Add.

1.

| | | | | | |
|---|---|---|---|---|---|
| 4 | 8 | 5 | 1 | 4 | 3 |
| 5 | 1 | 3 | 7 | 5 | 6 |
| + 6 | + 2 | + 5 | + 9 | + 4 | + 7 |

Draw coins. Show two different ways to make 75¢.

2.

3.

Draw coins. Show two different ways to make 30¢.

4.

5.

## Test Prep

Fill in the ○ for the correct answer.
Which group of numbers is in order
from the least to the greatest?

6. ○ 27, 36, 58, 45
○ 24, 22, 18, 9
○ 48, 66, 75, 80
○ 53, 70, 68, 92

7. ○ 18, 28, 31, 16
○ 12, 22, 32, 23
○ 25, 37, 26, 38
○ 39, 40, 78, 87



**Notes for Home** Your child reviewed skills from earlier chapters. *Home Activity:* Ask your child to think of 3 numbers that have a sum less than 10. (Possible answers: 1 + 2 + 3, 2 + 5 + 2, 4 + 4 + 1, and so on.)

Name ______________________________

Practice 9-1

# Explore Subtracting Tens

Use [tens block] to find how many are left.

1. 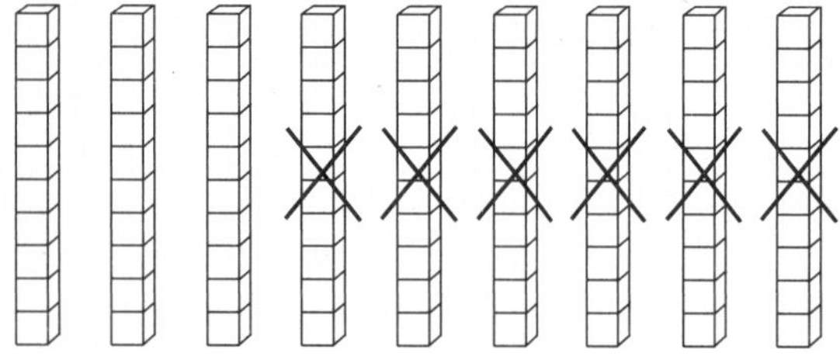

| | |
|---|---|
| 9 tens | 90 |
| − 6 tens | − 60 |
| 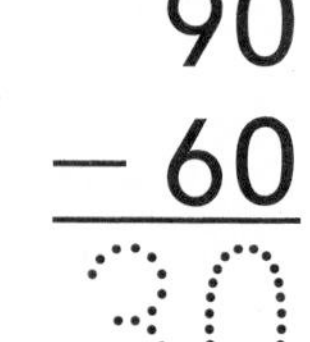 tens |  |

2. 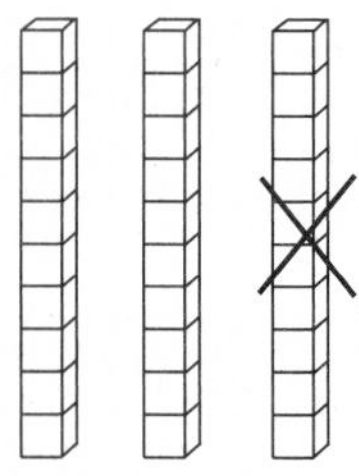

| | |
|---|---|
| 3 tens | 30 |
| − 1 tens | − 10 |

3. 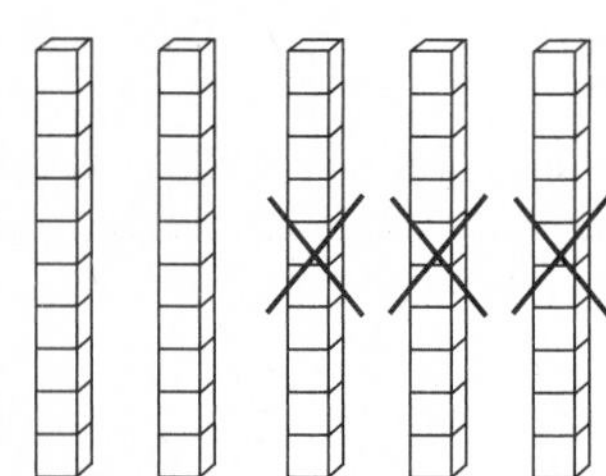
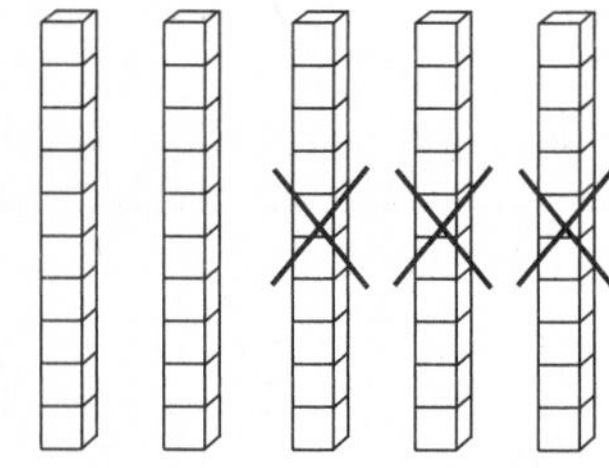

| | |
|---|---|
| 5 tens | 50 |
| − 3 tens | − 30 |

---

Subtract. You can use [tens block] to help.

4.

| | |
|---|---|
| 7 tens | 70 |
| − 2 tens | − 20 |

5.

| | |
|---|---|
| 6 tens | 60 |
| − 4 tens | − 40 |

**Talk About It** How does finding 9 − 6 help you find 90 − 60?



**Notes for Home** Your child explored subtracting tens. *Home Activity:* Ask your child to find 5 tens minus 2 tens and then 50 minus 20. (3 tens, 30)

Name ______________________________

Practice 9-2

# Subtract Tens With a Hundred Chart

Subtract. You can use the hundred chart.

1. 56 − 20 = 36
2. 94 − 50 = ____
3. 35 − 10 = ____
4. 73 − 40 = ____

| 1 | 2 | 3 | 4 | 5 | 6 | 7 | 8 | 9 | 10 |
|---|---|---|---|---|---|---|---|---|---|
| 11 | 12 | 13 | 14 | 15 | 16 | 17 | 18 | 19 | 20 |
| 21 | 22 | 23 | 24 | 25 | 26 | 27 | 28 | 29 | 30 |
| 31 | 32 | 33 | 34 | 35 | 36 | 37 | 38 | 39 | 40 |
| 41 | 42 | 43 | 44 | 45 | 46 | 47 | 48 | 49 | 50 |
| 51 | 52 | 53 | 54 | 55 | 56 | 57 | 58 | 59 | 60 |
| 61 | 62 | 63 | 64 | 65 | 66 | 67 | 68 | 69 | 70 |
| 71 | 72 | 73 | 74 | 75 | 76 | 77 | 78 | 79 | 80 |
| 81 | 82 | 83 | 84 | 85 | 86 | 87 | 88 | 89 | 90 |
| 91 | 92 | 93 | 94 | 95 | 96 | 97 | 98 | 99 | 100 |

5.

| 64 | 27 | 88 | 49 | 61 | 78 | 54 |
|---|---|---|---|---|---|---|
| − 30 | − 10 | − 30 | − 20 | − 40 | − 50 | − 20 |
| ____ | ____ | ____ | ____ | ____ | ____ | ____ |

## Problem Solving Patterns

6. Subtract.

70 − 20 = ____

70 − 30 = ____

70 − 40 = ____

**Write your own** number sentences to make a pattern.

____ − ____ = ____

____ − ____ = ____

____ − ____ = ____



**Notes for Home** Your child subtracted tens on a hundred chart. *Home Activity:* Ask your child to show you how he or she used the hundred chart to subtract tens.

Name ______________________________

# Estimate Two-Digit Differences

Practice 9-3

Find the nearest ten. Estimate the difference.

1.
$$\begin{array}{r} 67 \\ -\ 43 \\ \hline \end{array}$$

Think:
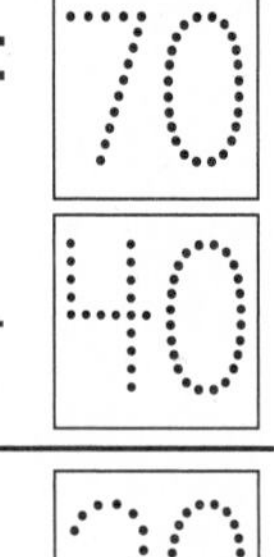


67 − 43 is about 30.

2.
$$\begin{array}{r} 84 \\ -\ 36 \\ \hline \end{array}$$

Think: ☐ − ☐ = ☐

84 − 36 is about ____.

3.
$$\begin{array}{r} 43 \\ -\ 27 \\ \hline \end{array}$$

Think:
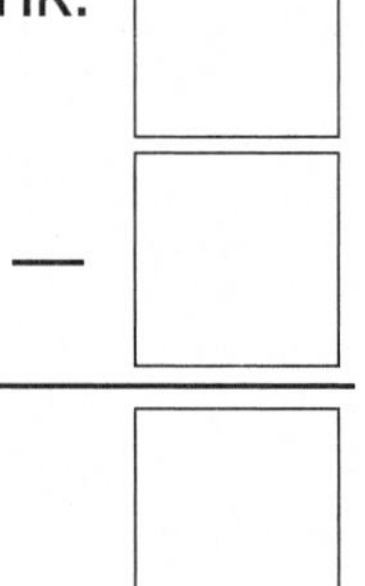

43 − 27 is about ____.

4.
$$\begin{array}{r} 58 \\ -\ 27 \\ \hline \end{array}$$

Think: ☐ − ☐ = ☐

58 − 27 is about ____.

## Problem Solving Estimation

Find the nearest ten. Estimate the difference.

5. The giant squid is about 17 meters long.
The whale shark is about 13 meters long.
About how much longer is the squid than the shark?

About _____ meters



**Notes for Home** Your child used nearest tens to estimate differences. *Home Activity:* Ask your child to tell you how to estimate 81–22. (81 is about 80 and 22 is about 20. 80 minus 20 is 60.)

Name ______________________________

# Explore Subtraction With or Without Regrouping

Samantha counted 40 pennies in her piggy bank.
She gave 9 pennies to her younger brother.
How many pennies does she have now?

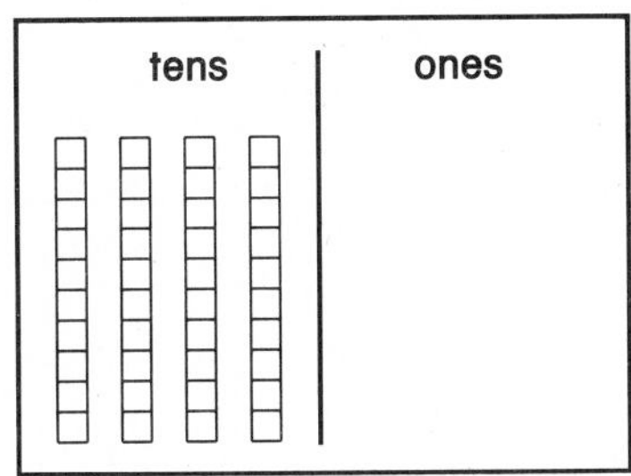


Start with 40.

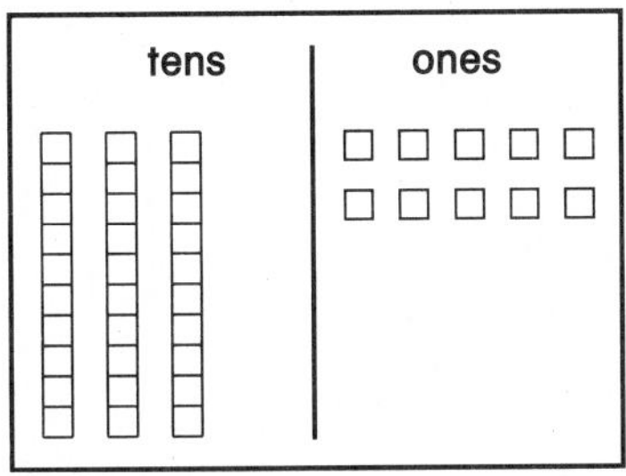


Regroup 1 ten as 10 ones.

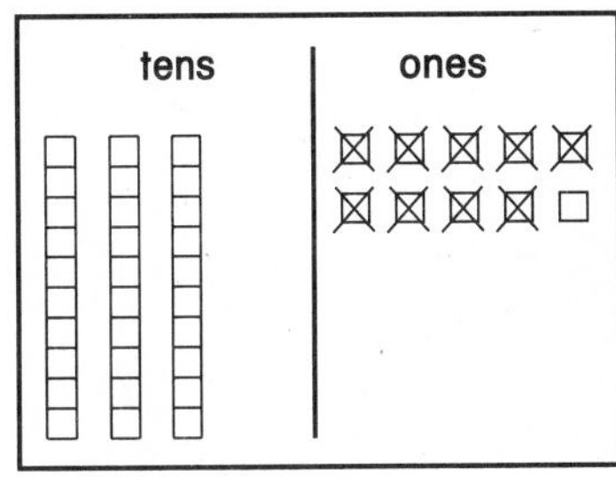


Subtract 9.

_____ pennies

Use [tens | ones], [ten rod], and [unit cube].

Find how many are left.

1. Show 56. Subtract 8.

   __4__ tens __8__ ones

   __48__

2. Show 37. Subtract 9.

   _____ tens _____ ones

   _____

3. Show 73. Subtract 6.

   _____ tens _____ ones

   _____

4. Show 26. Subtract 7.

   _____ tens _____ ones

   _____

**Talk About It** How does regrouping help you subtract?



**Notes for Home** Your child explored regrouping with subtraction. *Home Activity:* Have your child show how he or she regrouped to find the difference for Exercise 2.

Name ____________________

# Subtract With or Without Regrouping

Practice 9-5

Use [tens | ones], [ten rod], and [unit cube].

| | Show this many. | Subtract this many. | Do you need to regroup? | Solve. |
|---|---|---|---|---|
| 1. | 21 | 3 | yes | 21 − 3 = 18 |
| 2. | 56 | 5 | | 56 − 5 = ____ |
| 3. | 27 | 9 | | 27 − 9 = ____ |
| 4. | 35 | 7 | | 35 − 7 = ____ |
| 5. | 44 | 3 | | 44 − 3 = ____ |
| 6. | 18 | 7 | | 18 − 7 = ____ |
| 7. | 42 | 4 | | 42 − 4 = ____ |
| 8. | 33 | 2 | | 33 − 2 = ____ |
| 9. | 11 | 8 | | 11 − 8 = ____ |

## Problem Solving Critical Thinking

10. Which numbers in the first column above can you subtract from 75 without needing to regroup? For which numbers would you need to regroup? How do you know? ____________________

____________________

**Notes for Home** Your child decided when to regroup to subtract. *Home Activity:* Ask your child to show you two subtraction problems, one with regrouping and one without regrouping.

Name ______________________

Practice 9-6

# Record Subtraction

Subtract. You can use [tens | ones mat], [tens block], and [ones cube] to help.

Then circle the difference if you regrouped.

1.

| tens | ones |
|---|---|
| □ | □ |
| 5 | 3 |
| − | 7 |
| 4 | 6 |

| tens | ones |
|---|---|
| □ | □ |
| 6 | 7 |
| − | 6 |
| | |

2.

| tens | ones |
|---|---|
| □ | □ |
| 3 | 2 |
| − | 4 |
| | |

| tens | ones |
|---|---|
| □ | □ |
| 7 | 4 |
| − | 3 |
| | |

| tens | ones |
|---|---|
| □ | □ |
| 6 | 7 |
| − | 8 |
| | |

| tens | ones |
|---|---|
| □ | □ |
| 5 | 3 |
| − | 5 |
| | |

## Problem Solving Patterns

Subtract. What patterns do you see?

3. $67 - 8 =$ ____ $67 - 18 =$ ____ $67 - 28 =$ ____ $67 - 38 =$ ____ $67 - 48 =$ ____



**Notes for Home** Your child regrouped and wrote the differences for subtraction problems. *Home Activity:* Ask your child to explain his or her answer for one of the exercises on this page.

Name ______________________________

# Problem Solving:
## Choose a Computation Method

Choose a strategy. Draw the blocks or write the number sentences.

1. 64 ants marched up the tree. 23 more joined them. Then 39 ants marched away carrying leaves. How many ants are left on the tree?

_____ ants

2. Monica counted 57 pennies in her bank. Her brother gave her 23 pennies. Her father gave her 15 more. How many pennies does Monica have now?

_____ pennies

## Visual Thinking

3. Write a story problem for the picture.

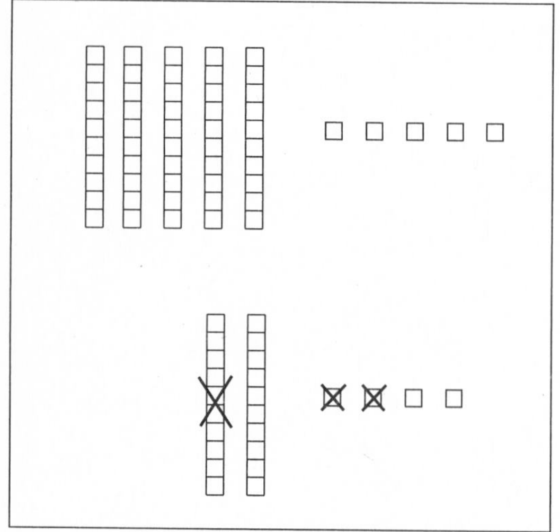

______________________________

______________________________

______________________________

______________________________

______________________________



**Notes for Home** Your child drew pictures, wrote number sentences, and made up a story to solve problems. *Home Activity:* Have your child write two number sentences for Exercise 3. (55 + 24 = 79 and 79 – 12 = 67)

Name ______________________

Practice
Chapter 9
A

# Mixed Practice: Lessons 1–7

Subtract.

1. 6 tens − 4 tens = ____ tens    60 − 40 = ____

2. 9 tens − 7 tens = ____ tens    90 − 70 = ____

Use the chart to subtract.

3. 47 − 10 = ____

4. 36 − 30 = ____

5. 28 − 20 = ____

| 1 | 2 | 3 | 4 | 5 | 6 | 7 | 8 | 9 | 10 |
|---|---|---|---|---|---|---|---|---|---|
| 11 | 12 | 13 | 14 | 15 | 16 | 17 | 18 | 19 | 20 |
| 21 | 22 | 23 | 24 | 25 | 26 | 27 | 28 | 29 | 30 |
| 31 | 32 | 33 | 34 | 35 | 36 | 37 | 38 | 39 | 40 |
| 41 | 42 | 43 | 44 | 45 | 46 | 47 | 48 | 49 | 50 |

## Problem Solving

Choose a way to solve the problem.
Draw the place-value blocks or
write a number sentence.

6. 25 people get on the bus.
At the next stop, 8 get off
and 4 get on. How many
people are on the bus now? ______ people

## Journal

7. Do you need to regroup to subtract?
How do you know?

67 − 6    44 − 7



**Notes for Home** Your child practiced subtracting tens, using a hundred chart, and choosing a strategy to solve a problem. *Home Activity:* Have your child use a different strategy to solve Exercise 3.

Name ______________________________

Practice
Chapters 1–9
A

# Cumulative Review

Draw the clock hands. Write the ending time.

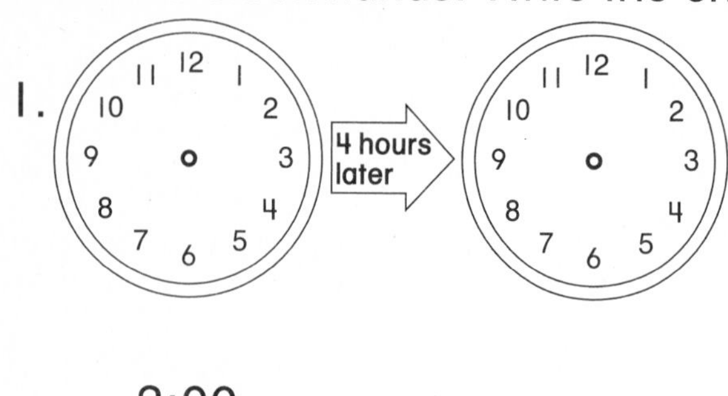


1. 3:00 ________

2. 7 hours later

11:00 ________

## Problem Solving

Circle **add** or **subtract.** Write a number sentence. Solve.

3. 5 children are at the park. 7 more join them. How many children are at the park now?

**add** **subtract**

______________________

______ children

4. 8 horses are running in the field. 3 run away. How many are left?

add subtract

______________________

______ horses

## Test Prep

Fill in ○ for the correct answer.

Add. Regroup if you need to.

5. $\begin{array}{r} 26 \\ +\ 35 \\ \hline \end{array}$ ○ 63 ○ 61 ○ 51 ○ 53

6. $\begin{array}{r} 57 \\ +\ 33 \\ \hline \end{array}$ ○ 80 ○ 90 ○ 89 ○ 70

7. $\begin{array}{r} 34 \\ +\ 54 \\ \hline \end{array}$ ○ 98 ○ 9 ○ 88 ○ 78



**Notes for Home** Your child reviewed telling time, addition and subtraction facts, and writing number sentences. *Home Activity:* Ask your child to explain his or her answer for Exercise 4.

Name ______________________________

Practice 9-8

# Explore Subtracting Two-Digit Numbers

Find 35 − 19.

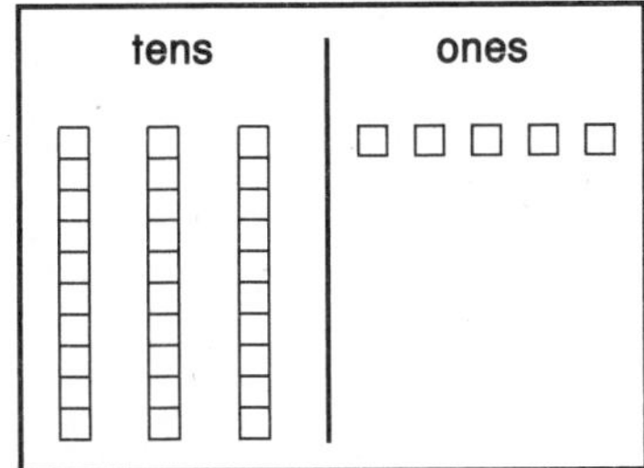


Take 35.

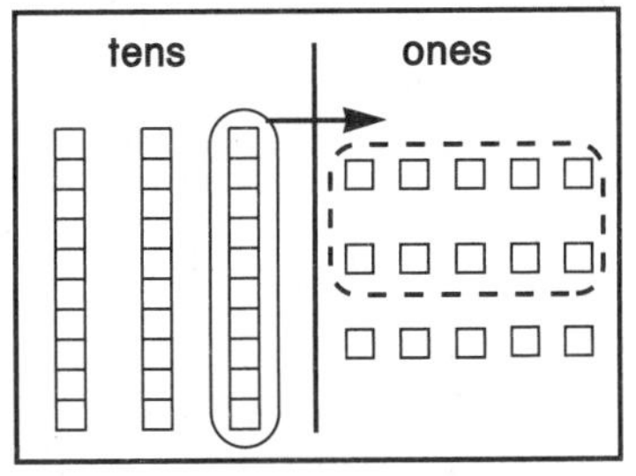


Regroup 1 ten as 10 ones.

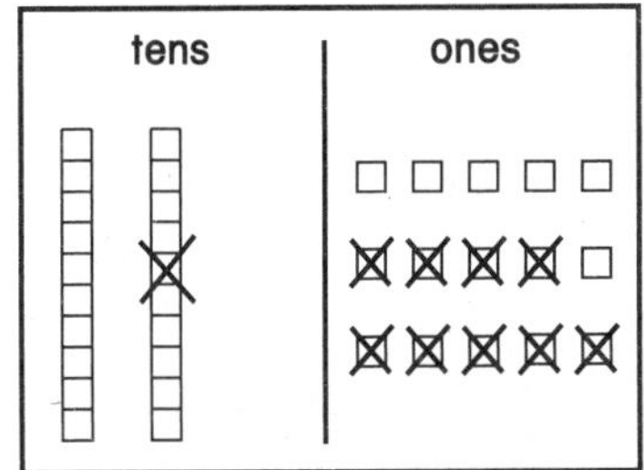


Subtract 19. Write the difference.

35 − 19 = 16

Use tens | ones, ▭▭▭▭▭▭▭▭▭▭, and ▫ to subtract.

| | Show this many. | Subtract this many. | Solve. |
|---|---|---|---|
| 1. | 33 | 27 | 33 − 27 = ____ |
| 2. | 72 | 35 | 72 − 35 = ____ |
| 3. | 48 | 19 | 48 − 19 = ____ |
| 4. | 55 | 38 | 55 − 38 = ____ |
| 5. | 17 | 9 | 17 − 9 = ____ |

## Talk About It

Choose a problem on this page. Tell a classmate how you solved it.



**Notes for Home** Your child subtracted two-digit numbers with regrouping. *Home Activity:* Have your child use dried beans or macaroni to model Exercise 2.

Name ______________________________

Practice 9-9

# Subtract Two- Digit Numbers With or Without Regrouping

Subtract. Use [tens | ones mat], [ten rod], and [one cube].

Regroup if you need to.

1.

| tens | ones |
|---|---|
| 3 | 14 |
| 4 | 4 |
| − 2 | 6 |
| 1 | 8 |

| tens | ones |
|---|---|
| ☐ | ☐ |
| 6 | 8 |
| − 1 | 9 |
| | |

| tens | ones |
|---|---|
| ☐ | ☐ |
| 3 | 2 |
| − 2 | 1 |
| | |

| tens | ones |
|---|---|
| ☐ | ☐ |
| 7 | 5 |
| − 5 | 8 |
| | |

2.

| tens | ones |
|---|---|
| ☐ | ☐ |
| 5 | 1 |
| − 3 | 4 |
| | |

| tens | ones |
|---|---|
| ☐ | ☐ |
| 8 | 3 |
| − 7 | 1 |
| | |

| tens | ones |
|---|---|
| ☐ | ☐ |
| 2 | 6 |
| − 1 | 8 |
| | |

| tens | ones |
|---|---|
| ☐ | ☐ |
| 9 | 1 |
| − 6 | 2 |
| | |

## Problem Solving Visual Thinking

3.

| We started with this: | Now we have this: | Draw what was subtracted. |
|---|---|---|
| 5 tens, 6 ones | 3 tens, 9 ones | |



**Notes for Home** Your child subtracted two-digit numbers with or without regrouping. *Home Activity:* Have your child tell you how to find the difference for 55 minus 37. (Regroup 1 ten for 10 ones. Subtract 7 ones from 15, and 3 tens from 4 tens; 18.)

Name ______________________

Practice 9-10

# Subtract Two-Digit Numbers

Subtract. Regroup if you need to.

| 1. | 5 17<br>~~6~~~~7~~<br>− 48<br>19 | 58<br>− 26 | 33<br>− 16 | 45<br>− 37 | 16<br>− 11 | 27<br>− 19 |
|---|---|---|---|---|---|---|

| 2. | 50<br>− 16 | 48<br>− 39 | 33<br>− 14 | 85<br>− 67 | 10<br>− 7 | 72<br>− 54 |
|---|---|---|---|---|---|---|

Follow the rule. Subtract. Find the rule. Write the missing number.

3.

| Subtract 19. | |
|---|---|
| 70 | |
| 69 | |
| 50 | |
| 39 | |

4.

| Subtract ______ | |
|---|---|
| 90 | 76 |
| 70 | 56 |
| 50 | 36 |
| 30 | 16 |

## Problem Solving Critical Thinking

5. Fill in the missing numbers.

| | 4 | □ |
|---|---|---|
| | □ | 6 |
| − | 3 | □ |
| | □ | 8 |



**Notes for Home** Your child subtracted two-digit numbers. *Home Activity:* Have your child work through the problems in Exercise 3 with you.

Name ______________________________

# Use Addition to Check Subtraction

Practice 9-11

Subtract. Write an addition problem to check.

1.

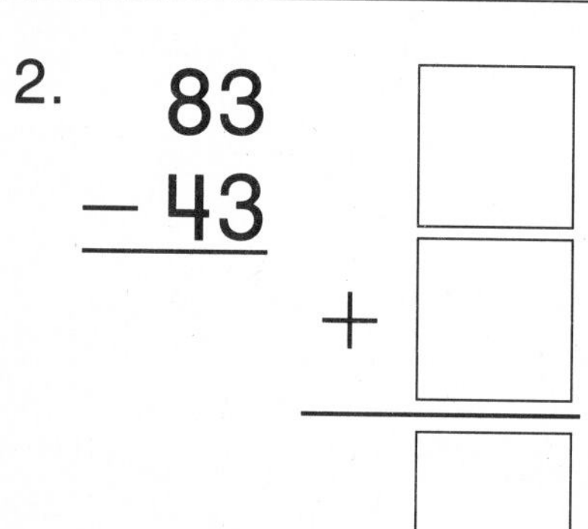

$$\begin{array}{r} 53 \\ -\ 25 \\ \hline \end{array} \qquad \begin{array}{r} \square \\ +\ \square \\ \hline \square \end{array}$$

$$\begin{array}{r} 92 \\ -\ 38 \\ \hline \end{array} \qquad \begin{array}{r} \square \\ +\ \square \\ \hline \square \end{array}$$

2.

$$\begin{array}{r} 83 \\ -\ 43 \\ \hline \end{array} \qquad \begin{array}{r} \square \\ +\ \square \\ \hline \square \end{array}$$

$$\begin{array}{r} 37 \\ -\ 8 \\ \hline \end{array} \qquad \begin{array}{r} \square \\ +\ \square \\ \hline \square \end{array}$$

$$\begin{array}{r} 56 \\ -\ 28 \\ \hline \end{array} \qquad \begin{array}{r} \square \\ +\ \square \\ \hline \square \end{array}$$

3.

$$\begin{array}{r} 24 \\ -\ 13 \\ \hline \end{array} \qquad \begin{array}{r} \square \\ +\ \square \\ \hline \square \end{array}$$

$$\begin{array}{r} 45 \\ -\ 29 \\ \hline \end{array} \qquad \begin{array}{r} \square \\ +\ \square \\ \hline \square \end{array}$$

$$\begin{array}{r} 30 \\ -\ 10 \\ \hline \end{array} \qquad \begin{array}{r} \square \\ +\ \square \\ \hline \square \end{array}$$

## Problem Solving Critical Thinking

4. Lisa did these subtraction problems. Use addition to check her work. Did she do both problems correctly? Explain.

$$\begin{array}{r} 87 \\ -\ 49 \\ \hline 38 \end{array} \qquad \begin{array}{r} 53 \\ -\ 26 \\ \hline 39 \end{array}$$



**Notes for Home** Your child used addition to check subtraction. *Home Activity:* Have your child explain how he or she solved Exercise 4

Name ______________________________

Practice 9-12

# Subtract Money

Subtract.

1. 
| 4 14<br>~~5~~ ~~4~~ ¢<br>− 3 8 ¢<br>1 6 ¢ | 81¢<br>− 63¢ | 27¢<br>− 15¢ | 95¢<br>− 75¢ | 43¢<br>− 26¢ |
|---|---|---|---|---|

2. 
| 32¢<br>− 4¢ | 17¢<br>− 10¢ | 66¢<br>− 57¢ | 54¢<br>− 33¢ | 99¢<br>− 65¢ | 21¢<br>− 15¢ |
|---|---|---|---|---|---|

## Mixed Practice

Add or subtract.

3. 
| 24<br>+ 34 | 48<br>− 26 | 76¢<br>+ 15¢ | 57<br>− 49 | 31¢<br>− 13¢ | 65<br>+ 27 |
|---|---|---|---|---|---|

4. 
| 18¢<br>− 4¢ | 17<br>+ 27 | 52¢<br>− 33¢ | 35<br>+ 22 | 63<br>+ 9 | 94¢<br>− 65¢ |
|---|---|---|---|---|---|

## Problem Solving

Solve.

5. 12 apples are in the basket.
8 children each take one.
How many apples are there now?

______ apples

**Notes for Home** Your child solved addition and subtraction problems involving money. *Home Activity:* Ask your child to subtract 67¢ from 96¢. (29¢)

Name ______________________________

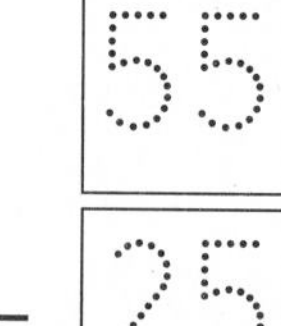


# Problem Solving: Too Much Information

Solve. Cross out the information you do not need.

1. A swan can fly at about 55 miles in one hour. A crow can fly about 25 miles in one hour. An ostrich can run at about 31 miles per hour. How much faster can a swan fly than a crow?

   55
   − 25
   30 miles in one hour

2. The giant salamander is about 4 feet long. A python is the longest snake. It can grow to about 33 feet long. The giant squid can grow to about 56 feet long. How much longer is the python than the giant salamander?

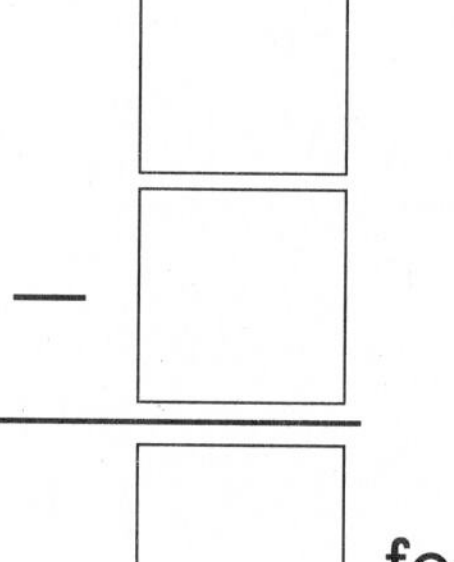

   feet longer

## Journal

3. Write a math problem about playing baseball or basketball with too much information. Have a friend solve it.

______________________________

______________________________

______________________________



**Notes for Home** Your child crossed out the information not needed to solve problems. *Home Activity:* Ask your child to explain his or her reasoning.

Name ______________________

Practice
Chapter 9
B

# Mixed Practice: Lessons 8–13

Subtract. Regroup if you need to.

1.

| tens | ones |
|---|---|
| □ | □ |
| 6 | 6 |
| − 3 | 4 |
| | |

| tens | ones |
|---|---|
| □ | □ |
| 8 | 5 |
| − 6 | 7 |
| | |

2.

$$\begin{array}{r} 52¢ \\ -\ 34¢ \\ \hline \end{array} \qquad \begin{array}{r} 17¢ \\ -\ 12¢ \\ \hline \end{array}$$

Subtract. Write an addition problem to check.

3.

$$\begin{array}{r} 44 \\ -\ 24 \\ \hline \end{array} \quad \begin{array}{r} \square \\ +\ \square \\ \hline \square \end{array} \qquad \begin{array}{r} 83 \\ -\ 65 \\ \hline \end{array} \quad \begin{array}{r} \square \\ +\ \square \\ \hline \square \end{array} \qquad \begin{array}{r} 26 \\ -\ 17 \\ \hline \end{array} \quad \begin{array}{r} \square \\ +\ \square \\ \hline \square \end{array}$$

## Problem Solving

Solve. Cross out the information you do not need.

4. Maritza collected 57 stickers. It took her 6 months. Felipé collected 39 stickers. It took him 4 months. How many more stickers does Maritza have than Felipé?

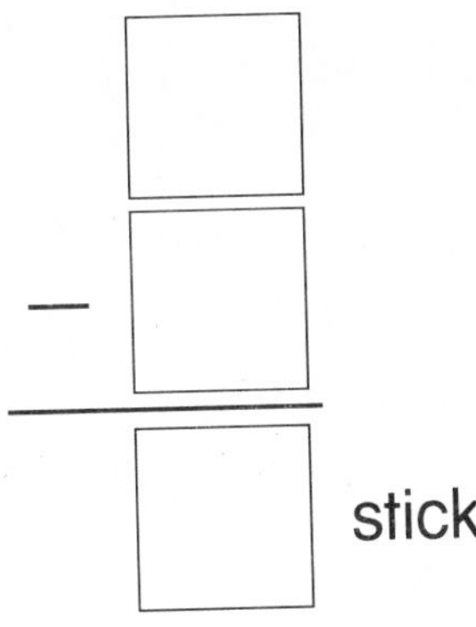


## Journal

5. Write an addition problem to check this problem: 44 − 26 = 18. How do you know if it's correct? Explain.



**Notes for Home** Your child practiced subtracting two-digit numbers with and without regrouping, checking subtraction with addition, and crossing out information not needed in problems. *Home Activity:* Ask your child to explain his or her answers for Exercise 1.

Name ____________________

# Cumulative Review

Practice Chapters 1–9 B

Write the time.

1. 

_____ o'clock

_____ : _____

2. 

_____ : _____

3. 

_____ : _____

## Problem Solving

Use the chart.

| Marble colors | Tally | Totals |
|---|---|---|
| Green | ~~////~~ //// | 9 |
| Orange | ~~////~~ ~~////~~ | 10 |
| Blue | ~~////~~ / | 6 |

4. How many more green marbles are there than blue marbles?

_____ more

5. What color marble is there fewest of in the jar? _____

## Test Prep

Fill in the ○ for the correct answer.

Use mental math to add.

6. 46 + 40 = _____

○ 56 ○ 67 ○ 86 ○ 76

7. 23 + 60 = _____

○ 73 ○ 83 ○ 63 ○ 93



**Notes for Home** Your child reviewed telling time, solving problems, and adding. *Home Activity:* Ask your child to use mental math to add 33 and 60. (93)

Name ______________________

Practice 10-1

# Explore Hundreds

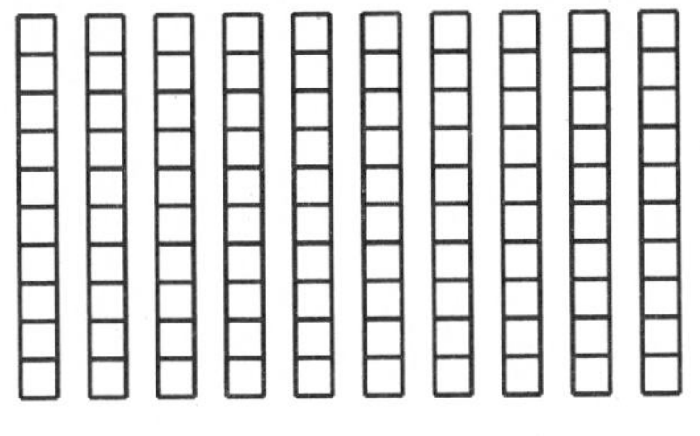

10 tens

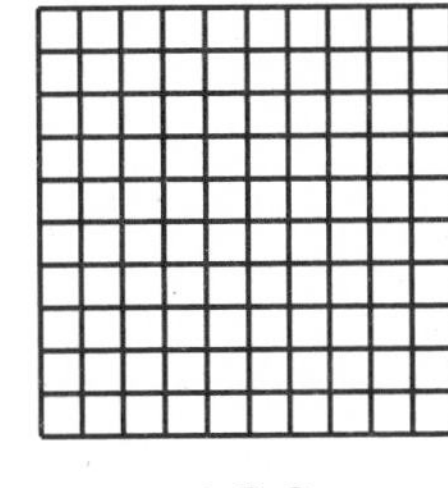

100

10 tens = 1 hundred

Write how many hundreds.
Write the number.

| | | How many hundreds? | Write the number. |
|---|---|---|---|
| 1. | | ____ hundred | ______ |
| 2. | | ____ hundreds | ______ |
| 3. | | ____ hundreds | ______ |
| 4. | | ____ hundreds | ______ |
| 5. | | ____ hundreds | ______ |
| 6. | | ____ hundreds | ______ |

## Journal

7. Write 2 things that you think might come packaged in hundreds.



**Notes for Home** Your child wrote how many hundreds and the number. *Home Activity:* Ask your child how many hundreds are in 700. (7 hundreds)

Name ______________________

Practice 10-2

# Identify Hundreds

Use 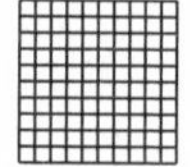 to complete the chart.

| | Show this many. Write the number. | Show 200 less. Write the number. | Show 200 more. Write the number. |
|---|---|---|---|
| 1. | 200 | 0 | 400 |
| 2. | ______ | ______ | ______ |
| 3. | ______ | ______ | ______ |

## Problem Solving Visual Thinking

4. Yani needs 800 cubes.
   Circle bags to show 800.

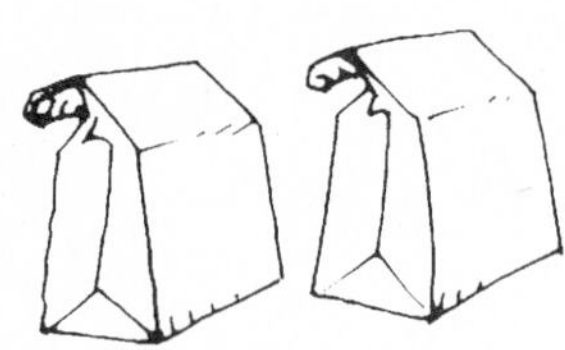

100 in each small bag

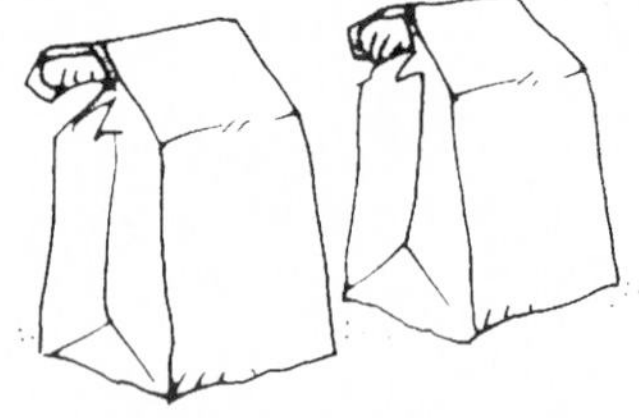

200 in each medium bag

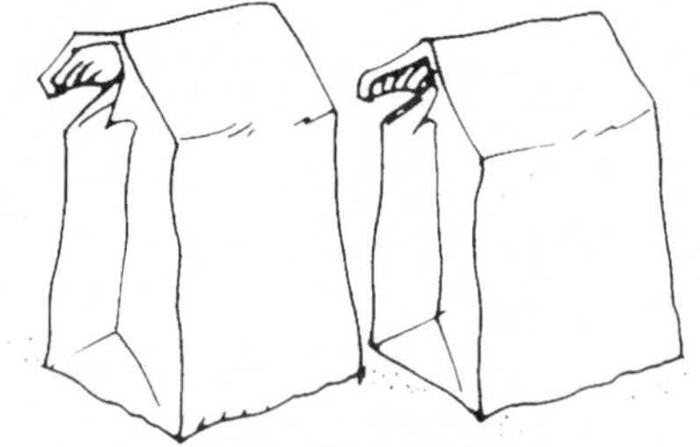

400 in each large bag



**Notes for Home** Your child practiced writing numbers for groups of 100. *Home Activity:* Ask your child to write the number that is 200 less than 900 and the number that is 200 more than 100. (700 and 300)

Name ______________________________

Practice 10-3

# Write Three-Digit Numbers

Write how many hundreds, tens, and ones.
Write the number.

You can use

| hundreds | tens | ones |
| --- | --- | --- |
| | | |

and 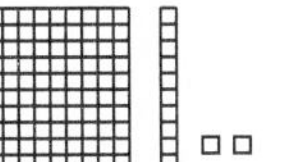.

1. 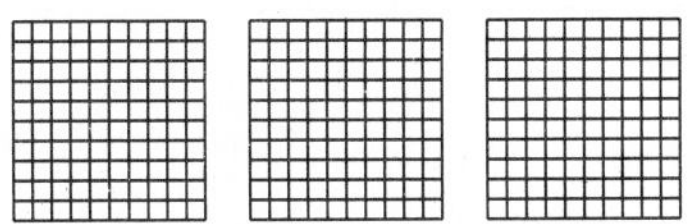

| hundreds | tens | ones |
| --- | --- | --- |
| 3 | 0 | 5 |

______

2. 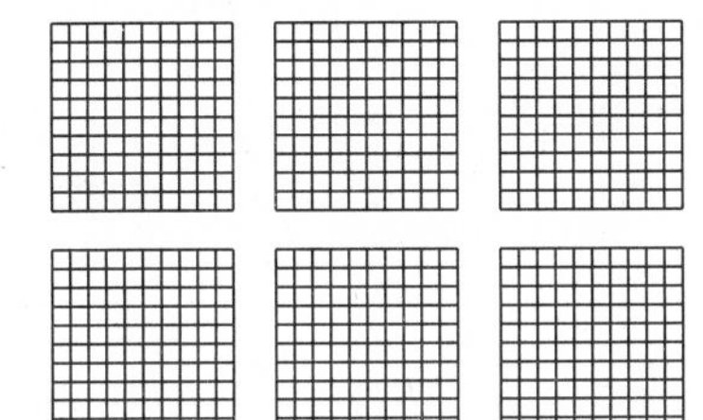 

| hundreds | tens | ones |
| --- | --- | --- |
| | | |

______

**Write your own.** Choose your own number. Draw the hundreds, tens, and ones.
Then write the number.

3.

| hundreds | tens | ones |
| --- | --- | --- |
| | | |

______

## Problem Solving Patterns

Find each answer. What pattern do you see?

4. How many  in 400? ______
How many tens in 400? ______
How many ones in 400? ______

5. How many hundreds in 800? ______
How many tens in 800? ______
How many ones in 800? ______



**Notes for Home** Your child wrote three-digit numbers. *Home Activity:* Have your child look in a newspaper, magazine, or book for a three-digit number and tell you how many hundreds, tens, and ones are in the number. (Hint: Page numbers in books frequently run to three digit numbers.)

Name ______________________

Practice 10-4

# Before, After, Between

Write the number that comes one before.

1. 154, 155 ____, 121 ____, 186
2. ____, 378 ____, 599 ____, 701
3. ____, 411 ____, 600 ____, 259

Write the number that comes one after.

4. 734, 735 551, ____ 287, ____
5. 414, ____ 880, ____ 699, ____
6. 108, ____ 348, ____ 99, ____

Write the number that comes between.

7. 214, 215, 216 589, ____, 591
8. 777, ____, 779 305, ____, 307
9. 880, ____, 882 98, ____, 100

## Problem Solving

10. Write all the even numbers between 515 and 535.

516, 518, ______________________

______________________

**Notes for Home** Your child identified numbers that are one before, one after, and between other numbers. *Home Activity:* Pick 3 numbers between 100 and 500. For each, ask your child to say the number that comes one before it and the number that comes one after it.

Name ______________________________

Practice 10-5

# Compare Numbers

Compare the numbers.
Write >, <, or =.

> is greater than
< is less than
= is equal to

1. 521  542      835  816

2. 681  914      315  315

3. 130 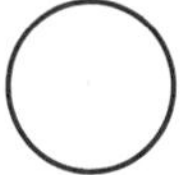 119      725  735

**Write your own** numbers between 300 and 400 to make true statements.

4. ________  ________      ________  ________

5. ________  ________      ________  ________

6. ________ 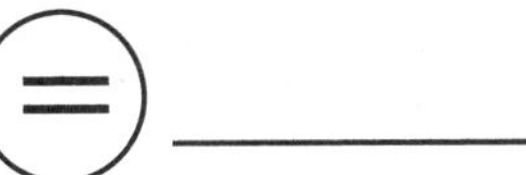 ________      ________  ________

## Problem Solving Critical Thinking

Solve the riddle.

7. I am a number less than 250 and greater than 245. I have 7 ones. What number am I?

________

8. I am an even number between 624 and 630. I have more than 6 ones. What number am I?

________



**Notes for Home** Your child compared numbers. *Home Activity:* Choose two numbers between 100 and 500. Ask your child to write the numbers and symbols to show "is greater than" and "is less than." (Possible choice and answers: 350 and 375; 350 < 375, 375 > 350.)

Name ______________________________

Practice 10-6

# Order Numbers

Write the numbers in order from least to greatest.

1. 225, 98, 187, 309 98, ____, ____, ____
2. 470, 417, 428, 459 ____, ____, ____, ____

Write the numbers in order from greatest to least.

3. 518, 377, 801, 495 801, ____, ____, ____
4. 350, 96, 606, 428 ____, ____, ____, ____
5. 770, 765, 707, 777 ____, ____, ____, ____

## Write your own.

6. List four numbers in order from least to greatest. Choose numbers between 200 and 300. ____, ____, ____, ____

7. List four numbers in order from greatest to least. Choose numbers between 800 and 900. ____, ____, ____, ____

## Problem Solving Estimation

8. These stacks of crayons will be sent to different schools. Draw lines to match each number to a stack. Then write the numbers in order from least to greatest.

264 216 288 240

____, ____, ____, ____



**Notes for Home** Your child put numbers in order. *Home Activity:* Ask your child where he or she would place a stack of 228 crayons in Exercise 8. (Between 216 and 240.)

Name ______________________________

Practice 10-7

# Problem Solving:
## Group Decision Making

Work with your group to solve the problem.

1. Roy and Reba are buying shells to make jewelry. They need 60 shells in all for their projects. Roy buys 12 shells. Reba buys 18 shells. How many more shells do they need to buy?

**Understand** What does the problem ask? How many more shells do Roy and Reba need to buy?

**Plan** How can you solve the problem? ______________________________

______________________________

**Solve** Solve the problem. ______________________________

______________________________

**Look Back** Check your work. ______________________________

______________________________

**Write your own.**

2. Work as a group to write a problem for another group to solve.

______________________________

______________________________



**Notes for Home** Your child used the Problem Solving Guide. *Home Activity:* Ask your child what way his or her group used to find, and then check, the answer to the problem.

Name ______________________________

# Mixed Practice: Lessons 1–7

Write 100 less and 100 more. You can use [hundred flat].

| | Show this many. Write the number. | Show 100 less. Write the number. | Show 100 more. Write the number. |
|---|---|---|---|
| 1. | [2 hundreds] ______ | ______ | ______ |

Write how many hundreds, tens, and ones. Then write the number.

2. [2 hundreds, 4 tens, 7 ones]

| hundreds | tens | ones |
|---|---|---|
| | | |

______

Write the number one before, one after, or between.

3. ______, 148    589, ______    399, ______, 401

Compare. Write >, <, or =.

4. 380 ◯ 320    540 ◯ 540    793 ◯ 801

## Problem Solving

Solve. Use the Problem Solving Guide to help.

5. Sabrina brought a box of 200 buttons for a project. Later she brought a box of 500 buttons. She used 190 buttons. How many buttons does she have now? ______ buttons

**Notes for Home** Your child practiced writing and comparing three-digit numbers. *Home Activity:* Ask your child what page in a book comes before and after page 381. (380 and 382)

Name ______________________________



# Cumulative Review

Count the money.

Write the total amount.

1.        ______

## Problem Solving

Use the graph to answer the questions.

| Coin Collections | |
|---|---|
| Tao | O O O |
| Jin | O O |
| Lee | O O O O |
| Each O means 10 coins. | |

2. How many more coins does Tao have than Jin?

   ______ coins

3. How many coins in all do Tao, Jin, and Lee have?

   ______ coins

## Test Prep

Fill in the ○ for the correct answer.

Subtract.

4. $\begin{array}{r} 80 \\ -\ 45 \\ \hline \end{array}$

   ○ 45 ○ 35 ○ 65 ○ 25

5. $\begin{array}{r} 92 \\ -\ 60 \\ \hline \end{array}$

   ○ 30 ○ 32 ○ 20 ○ 22



**Notes for Home** Your child reviewed counting money, using a graph to solve problems, and subtracting. *Home Activity:* Ask your child to look at the graph and tell how many fewer coins Jin has than Lee. (20 fewer coins)

Name ______________________________

Practice 10-8

# Add and Subtract Mentally

Add or subtract. Use mental math.

1. $60 + 30 = 90$    $400 + 200 =$    $300 + 100 =$    $50 + 20 =$    $300 + 500 =$

2. $70 - 10 =$    $800 - 300 =$    $600 - 200 =$    $80 - 30 =$    $40 - 30 =$

Follow the rule.

3.

| Add 100 | |
|---|---|
| 200 | |
| 500 | |
| 100 | |
| 600 | |

4.

| Subtract 10 | |
|---|---|
| 340 | |
| 410 | |
| 790 | |
| 950 | |

5.

| Add 30 | |
|---|---|
| 800 | |
| 620 | |
| 270 | |
| 440 | |

## Problem Solving Patterns

Add or subtract. What patterns do you see?

6. $3 + 6 =$    $33 + 66 =$    $333 + 666 =$

7. $8 - 2 =$    $88 - 22 =$    $888 - 222 =$



**Notes for Home** Your child added and subtracted using mental math. *Home Activity:* Ask your child to explain how to use mental math to subtract 500 – 200. (5 – 2 = 3; 500 – 200 = 300)

Name ____________________

Practice 10-9

# Add Three-Digit Numbers

Show each number. Add.

You can use a hundreds | tens | ones chart and place-value blocks.

1.

| hundreds | tens | ones |
|---|---|---|
| 2 | 4 | 6 |
| + 2 | 1 | 3 |
| 4 | 5 | 9 |

| hundreds | tens | ones |
|---|---|---|
| 3 | 5 | 1 |
| + 1 | 0 | 7 |
| | | |

| hundreds | tens | ones |
|---|---|---|
| 6 | 0 | 4 |
| + 2 | 6 | 3 |
| | | |

2. $231 + 137$    $125 + 64$    $726 + 203$    $205 + 381$    $523 + 263$

3. $146 + 132$    $219 + 260$    $307 + 92$    $115 + 151$    $430 + 305$

## Problem Solving

4. Fill in the missing numbers.

| hundreds | tens | ones |
|---|---|---|
| ☐ | 2 | ☐ |
| + 3 | ☐ | 5 |
| 4 | 7 | 9 |

| hundreds | tens | ones |
|---|---|---|
| 4 | ☐ | 5 |
| + ☐ | 7 | ☐ |
| 5 | 9 | 5 |

| hundreds | tens | ones |
|---|---|---|
| ☐ | 6 | ☐ |
| + 3 | ☐ | 4 |
| 8 | 7 | 6 |



**Notes for Home** Your child added three-digit numbers. *Home Activity:* Ask your child to tell you what the missing three-digit number is in 352 + ___ = 586. (234)

Name ______________________________

# Add Three-Digit Numbers With or Without Regrouping

Add. Regroup if you need to.

You can use 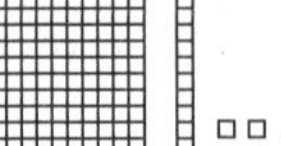 and ▦ ▯ ▫▫.

1.

| hundreds | tens | ones |
|---|---|---|
| □ | □ (1) | |
| 3 | 2 | 5 |
| + 2 | 4 | 7 |
| 5 | 7 | 2 |

| hundreds | tens | ones |
|---|---|---|
| □ | □ | |
| 4 | 6 | 8 |
| + 3 | 0 | 7 |
| | | |

| hundreds | tens | ones |
|---|---|---|
| □ | □ | |
| 6 | 7 | 3 |
| + 2 | 7 | 5 |
| | | |

2. $335 + 48$ $\qquad 619 + 124$ $\qquad 380 + 65$ $\qquad 155 + 793$ $\qquad 518 + 291$

3. $258 + 327$ $\qquad 775 + 19$ $\qquad 406 + 285$ $\qquad 670 + 86$ $\qquad 189 + 150$

## Problem Solving

Solve.

4. Jose made 125 cat pins for the craft fair. Martina made 148 dog pins. How many pet pins did they make in all?

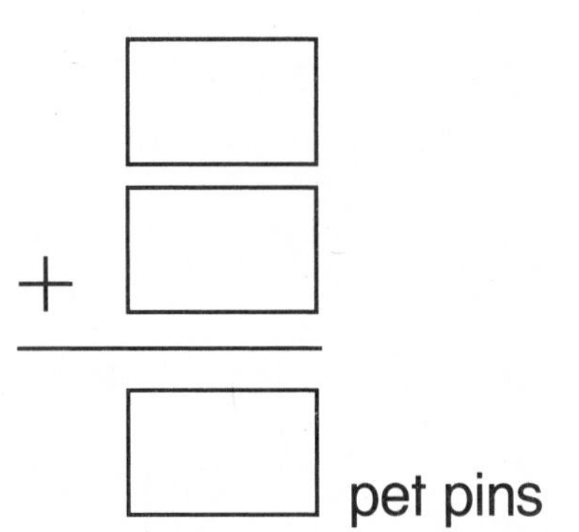




**Notes for Home** Your child added with and without regrouping. *Home Activity:* Pick a number between 100 and 500. Have your child pick another number between 100 and 500. Ask your child to tell you whether he or she must regroup to add the two numbers. (Examples: 326, 142, no; 326, 184, yes.)

Name ______________________________



# Subtract Three-Digit Numbers

Show each number. Subtract.

You can use [hundreds | tens | ones mat] and [place-value blocks].

1.

| | hundreds | tens | ones |
|---|---|---|---|
| | 6 | 4 | 8 |
| − | 3 | 1 | 5 |
| | 3 | 3 | 3 |

| | hundreds | tens | ones |
|---|---|---|---|
| | 8 | 9 | 5 |
| − | 1 | 0 | 2 |
| | | | |

| | hundreds | tens | ones |
|---|---|---|---|
| | 7 | 4 | 6 |
| − | 6 | 1 | 5 |
| | | | |

2. $\begin{array}{r} 745 \\ -\,234 \\ \hline \end{array}$ $\begin{array}{r} 386 \\ -\,62 \\ \hline \end{array}$ $\begin{array}{r} 942 \\ -\,301 \\ \hline \end{array}$ $\begin{array}{r} 555 \\ -\,43 \\ \hline \end{array}$ $\begin{array}{r} 489 \\ -\,115 \\ \hline \end{array}$

3. $\begin{array}{r} 678 \\ -\,26 \\ \hline \end{array}$ $\begin{array}{r} 896 \\ -\,143 \\ \hline \end{array}$ $\begin{array}{r} 357 \\ -\,245 \\ \hline \end{array}$ $\begin{array}{r} 779 \\ -\,320 \\ \hline \end{array}$ $\begin{array}{r} 935 \\ -\,20 \\ \hline \end{array}$

## Write a math story.

4. Use these numbers to write a math story. Then solve.

$\begin{array}{r} 745 \\ -\,234 \\ \hline \end{array}$

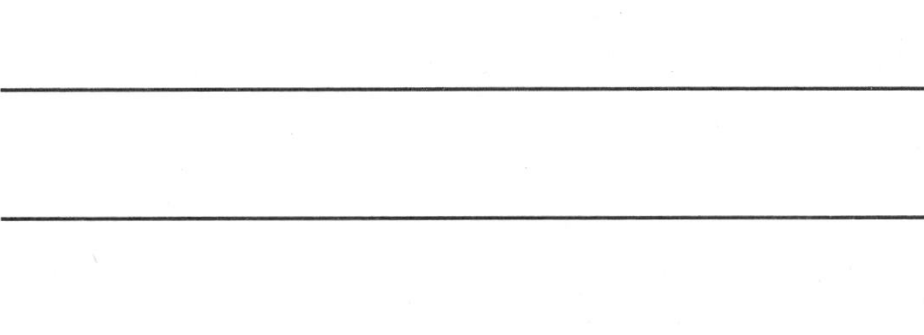



**Notes for Home** Your child subtracted three-digit numbers. *Home Activity:* Ask your child to estimate the answer then check the estimate on paper for the problem 678 – 214. (Estimates will vary. Sample estimate is 700 – 200, or 500. Answer is 464.)

Name ______________________________

# Subtract Three-Digit Numbers With or Without Regrouping

Subtract. Regroup if you need to.

You can use hundreds | tens | ones and ▦ ▯ ▫▫.

1.

| hundreds | tens | ones |
|---|---|---|
| | 3 | 12 |
| 6 | ~~4~~ | ~~2~~ |
| − | 2 | 8 |
| 6 | 1 | 4 |

| hundreds | tens | ones |
|---|---|---|
| | | |
| 4 | 2 | 9 |
| − 1 | 5 | 6 |
| | | |

| hundreds | tens | ones |
|---|---|---|
| | | |
| 8 | 4 | 0 |
| − 4 | 1 | 5 |
| | | |

2.

| 562 | 864 | 318 | 624 | 295 |
|---|---|---|---|---|
| − 147 | − 329 | − 42 | − 273 | − 76 |

3.

| 480 | 709 | 593 | 854 | 666 |
|---|---|---|---|---|
| − 126 | − 225 | − 328 | − 309 | − 107 |

## Problem Solving Critical Thinking

4. You need to regroup twice. What could the missing numbers be?

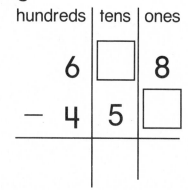

| hundreds | tens | ones |
|---|---|---|
| 6 | ☐ | 8 |
| − 4 | 5 | ☐ |
| | | |



**Notes for Home** Your child subtracted three-digit numbers with regrouping. *Home Activity:* Ask your child to write a subtraction problem that needs regrouping and a problem that does not need regrouping. Then have him or her show you how to solve the problems.

Name ______________________

# Problem Solving:
## Use Data from a Picture

1. Kris puts the tub of stones in the box. What else can he put in?

   ______________________

2. Sarah puts 570 items in the box. What did she put in?

   ______________________

3. Leon put the buttons in the box. What else can he put in?

   ______________________

4. Lana put 500 items in the box. What did she put in?

   ______________________

5. Dana puts 540 items in the box. What did she put in?

   ______________________

## Critical Thinking

6. Are there any 3 tubs that could be put in the box together? Explain your answer.

   ______________________

   ______________________



**Notes for Home** Your child used the numbers in the picture to solve problems. *Home Activity:* Ask your child which two tubs together hold the least number of items. (Shells and beads)

Name ______________________________

# Mixed Practice: Lessons 8–13

Add or subtract. Use mental math.

1. $\begin{array}{r} 400 \\ +\,300 \\ \hline \end{array}$ $\begin{array}{r} 700 \\ +\,200 \\ \hline \end{array}$ $\begin{array}{r} 60 \\ -\,40 \\ \hline \end{array}$ $\begin{array}{r} 800 \\ -\,200 \\ \hline \end{array}$ $\begin{array}{r} 55 \\ +\,33 \\ \hline \end{array}$

Add or subtract. Regroup if you need to.

2. $\begin{array}{r} 463 \\ +\,26 \\ \hline \end{array}$ $\begin{array}{r} 748 \\ -\,153 \\ \hline \end{array}$ $\begin{array}{r} 537 \\ +\,281 \\ \hline \end{array}$ $\begin{array}{r} 638 \\ -\,18 \\ \hline \end{array}$ $\begin{array}{r} 370 \\ +\,426 \\ \hline \end{array}$

## Problem Solving

Use the picture to answer the questions.

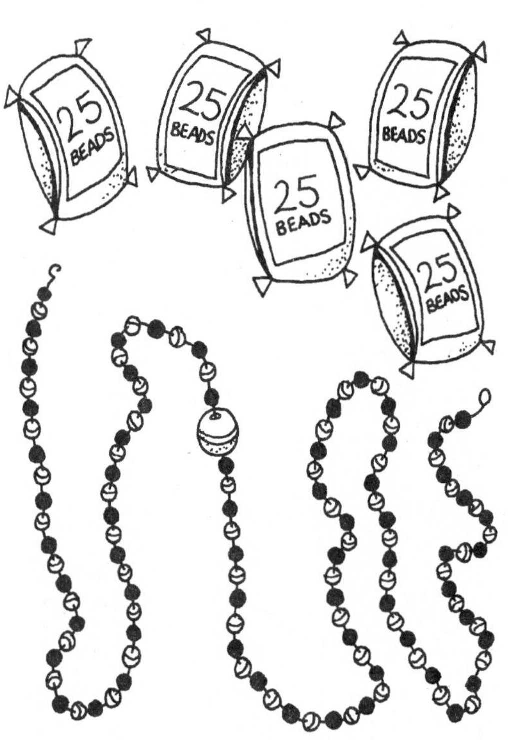


3. Doreen needs 125 beads to make a Navaho necklace. How many bags of beads does she need?

   ______ bags of beads

4. Donny has 2 bags of beads. How many more bags of beads does he need to make a Navaho necklace?

   ______ bags of beads

## Journal

5. How did the pictures help you answer the problems?



**Notes for Home** Your child practiced the skills and concepts from this section. *Home Activity:* Ask your child how many bags of beads would be needed if it takes 150 beads to make a different necklace. (6 bags of beads)

 Use with page 389.

Name ______________________________



# Cumulative Review

Write the number of tens and ones.
Then write the number.

1. 

_____ tens and _____ ones

_____

2. 

_____ tens and _____ ones

_____

Does the activity take less or more than one minute?
Circle **less** or **more.**

3. eating dinner

less more

4. closing a door

less more

5. sneezing

less more

6. cleaning your room

less more

## Test Prep

Fill in the ○ for the correct answer.
Add.

7.
$$\begin{array}{r} 46¢ \\ +\ 23¢ \\ \hline \end{array}$$

69¢ ○  79¢ ○  13¢ ○  23¢ ○

8.
$$\begin{array}{r} 38¢ \\ +\ 15¢ \\ \hline \end{array}$$

43¢ ○  53¢ ○  23¢ ○  48¢ ○



**Notes for Home** Your child reviewed identifying and writing tens and ones, estimating if activities take more or less than one minute, and adding amounts of money. *Home Activity:* Ask your child to tell you the fewest number of coins that make 43¢. (1 quarter, 1 dime, 1 nickel, 3 pennies)

Name ______________________________

**Practice 11-1**

# Explore Nonstandard Units

Estimate the lengths. Use Snap Cubes to measure. Write the numbers.

1.

Estimate: about 3 Snap Cubes

Measure: about ______ Snap Cubes

2.

Estimate: about ______ Snap Cubes

Measure: about ______ Snap Cubes

3.

Estimate: about ______ Snap Cubes

Measure: about ______ Snap Cubes

## Problem Solving Critical Thinking

4. Militа measured the length of her arm.
First she measured with connecting cubes.
Then she measured with new crayons.
Did Milita need more cubes or more crayons?

______________

**Notes for Home** Your child estimated and measured the lengths of objects using cubes. *Home Activity:* Ask your child to use a spoon to measure the length of a table in your home.

Name ______________________________

**Practice 11-2**

# Inches and Feet

Estimate about how many inches.

Measure with your inch ruler.

1.

| What to Measure | Estimate | Measurement |
|---|---|---|
| width of your hand | about _____ inches | about _____ inches |

Estimate about how many feet.

Measure with your yardstick.

2.

| What to Measure | Estimate | Measurement |
|---|---|---|
| width of a door | about _____ inches | about _____ inches |

## Write your own.

Draw or write what you will measure.

Use inches or feet to measure.

3.

| What to Measure | Estimate | Measurement |
|---|---|---|
| | about _____ | about _____ |

## Problem Solving Visual Thinking

4. Look at the two ant paths.
   Circle the path you think is longer.
   Explain. You can use string to check.

**Notes for Home** Your child practiced estimating and measuring lengths in inches and feet. *Home Activity:* Ask your child to estimate and measure the width of a window in your home and tell you the measurement.

Name ______________________________



# Inches, Feet, and Yards

Complete the chart.

| | Estimate. Find an object about this long. | Write or draw the object. | Measure length to check. |
|---|---|---|---|
| 1. | about 2 inches | | about ______ |
| 2. | about 2 feet | | about ______ |
| 3. | about 2 yards | | about ______ |

## Problem Solving Estimation

Circle the best estimate of length.

4. 

about 1 inch

about 1 foot

about 1 yard

5. 

about 1 inch

about 1 foot

about 1 yard

6. 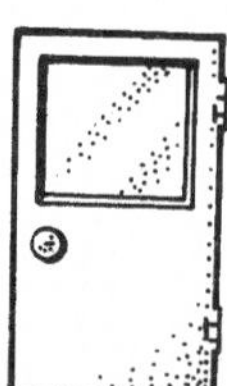

about 1 inch

about 1 foot

about 1 yard



**Notes for Home** Your child found and measured objects that were about 1 inch, 1 foot, and 1 yard long. *Home Activity:* Give your child a measurement, such as 3 inches, and have him or her find an object around home that is about that long.

Name ______________________________

Practice 11-4

# Centimeters and Meters

Estimate about how many meters.

Measure with a meter stick.

| | What to Measure | Estimate | Measure |
|---|---|---|---|
| 1. | width of a window | about ______ meters | about ______ meters |
| 2. | height of a door | about ______ meters | about ______ meters |
| 3. | distance from the front wall of your classroom to the rear wall | about ______ meters | about ______ meters |

## Mental Math

4. Solve.

Jon is 132 centimeters tall. Jennie is 128 centimeters tall. How much taller is Jon?

______ centimeters taller



**Notes for Home** Your child estimated and measured length and height in meters. *Home Activity:* Ask your child to estimate the width of a room in your home in meters.

Name ______________________________



# Perimeter

1. Mark an X on the shape that you estimate has the greatest perimeter. Measure the lengths of the sides. Add to find the perimeter. Circle the shape with the greatest perimeter.

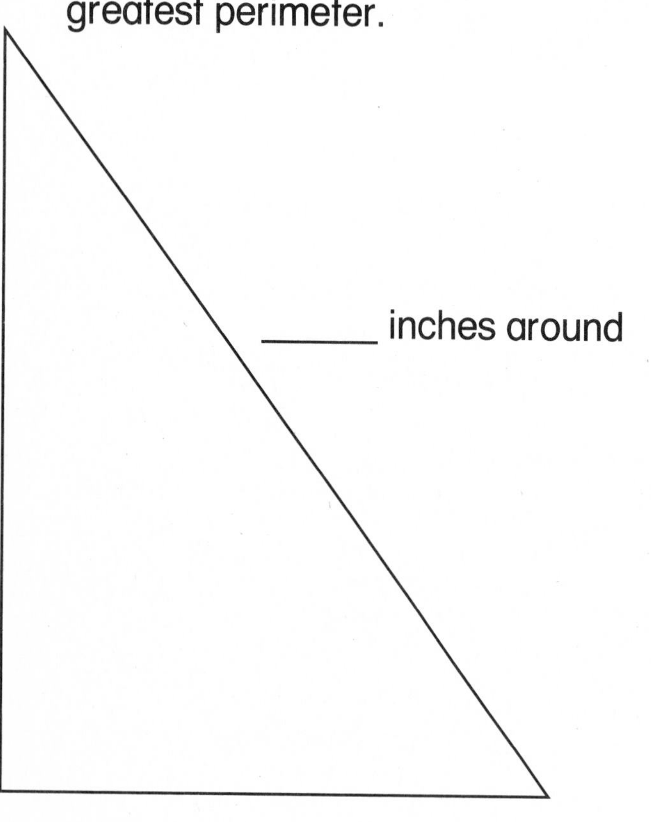

_____ inches around

_____ inches around

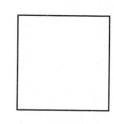

_____ inches around

## Problem Solving Visual Thinking

2. Do not measure. Which has the greater perimeter, the square or the rectangle. How do you know?

_______________________________________________

_______________________________________________



**Notes for Home** Your child practiced finding the perimeter of different shapes and objects. *Home Activity:* Give your child a book or magazine and ask him or her to find the perimeter.

Name ____________________

Practice 11-6

# Explore Area

Estimate how many [Snap Cube] will cover the shape.
Draw square units to show what you did.

1. Estimate: ______ Snap Cubes

   Measure: ______ square units

2. Estimate: ______ Snap Cubes

   Measure: ______ square units

Estimate how many [Snap Cube] will cover each of these objects.

Use [Snap Cube] to check your estimate.

3. top of a chalkboard eraser

   Estimate: ______ Snap Cubes

   Measure: ______ Snap Cubes

4. this piece of paper

   Estimate: ______ Snap Cubes

   Measure: ______ Snap Cubes

## Problem Solving Critical Thinking

5. Each side of the large square is twice as long as a side of the small square. Which would you need fewer of to cover the top of your desk? Why? Circle your answer. ______________________________

   ______________________________

**Notes for Home** Your child practiced using Snap Cubes to cover the area of different shapes.
*Home Activity:* Ask your child to tell you how he or she would use a Snap Cube to find the area of a table top.

Name ______________________________

# Problem Solving:
## Use Objects

Use centimeter cubes to make each shape.
Color the grid to show the shape.

1. Make a rectangle that covers 8 square units inside and has a perimeter of 12 units around the outside.

2. Make a rectangle that covers 14 square units inside and has a perimeter of 18 units around the outside.

## Write your own.

3. Draw your own shape.
Tell about your shape.

My shape:
is ______________________.
has a perimeter of ______ units.
has ______ square units inside.

## Journal

4. Make some shapes that have the same number of square units inside, but different perimeters. Draw the shapes. Tell about them.



**Notes for Home** Your child solved problems involving area and perimeter. *Home Activity:* Work with your child to make a chart that shows the perimeters of different rectangles that have an area of 16 square units. You may find something interesting about the one with the smallest perimeter.

Name ___________________________

Practice
Chapter 11
A

# Mixed Practice: Lessons 1–7

Estimate the length. Measure with a centimeter ruler.

1. Estimate: about _____ centimeters long

Measure: about _____ centimeters long

Estimate the perimeter and area. Measure with an inch ruler and use [square] to cover the shape.

2. Perimeter

Estimate: _____ inches around

Measure: _____ inches around

3. Area

Estimate: _____ square units

Measure: _____ square units

## Problem Solving

Draw a different shape with the same area.

4. Area: _____ square units

Perimeter: _____ units

5. Area: _____ square units

Perimeter: _____ units

## Journal

6. Draw a shape. Label it A. Draw another shape with the same area as A but a different perimeter. Draw another shape with the same perimeter as A but a different area.



**Notes for Home** Your child practiced estimating and measuring length, perimeter, and area. *Home Activity:* Have your child find the perimeter of an object such as a book or magazine. Then have him or her find another object in your home with a greater perimeter.

Name ______________________

# Cumulative Review

**Practice**
Chapters 1–11
**A**

Add

1.

| 47 | 60 | 72 | 14 | 28 | 53 |
|---|---|---|---|---|---|
| + 24 | + 38 | + 8 | + 13 | + 35 | + 24 |

Write how many hundreds, tens, and ones.
Then write the number.

2. 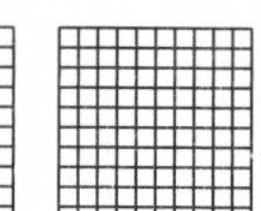 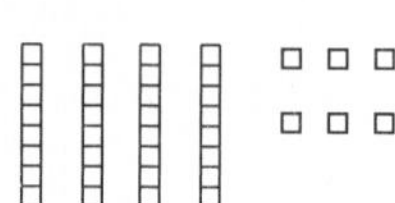

| hundreds | tens | ones |
|---|---|---|
| | | |

______

## Problem Solving

Solve.

3. Penny packs 16 cartons with soda crackers. Then she packs 14 cartons with cheese crackers. How many cartons did Penny pack?

______ cartons

4. Pete packs 28 bags of peppers in the morning. He packs 32 bags in the afternoon. How many bags did Pete pack?

______ bags

## Test Prep

Fill in the ○ for the correct answer.

5. Choose the number that comes just before 749.

○ 750 ○ 748 ○ 794

6. Choose the number that comes just after 519.

○ 518 ○ 529 ○ 520



**Notes for Home** Your child reviewed 2-digit addition, writing large numbers, and using addition to solve problems. *Home Activity:* Ask your child to make up an addition problem. Then have him or her tell you how to solve it and give the sum.

Name ____________________

Practice 11-8

# Explore One Pound

Is each object **heavier than, lighter than,** or **about** 1 pound? Estimate. Then use a pound weight to check. Complete the chart.

| | Object | Estimate | Measure |
|---|---|---|---|
| 1. | TELEPHONE | ______ 1 pound | ______ 1 pound |
| 2. | | ______ 1 pound | ______ 1 pound |
| 3. | | ______ 1 pound | ______ 1 pound |
| 4. | | ______ 1 pound | ______ 1 pound |
| 5. | JUICE | ______ 1 pound | ______ 1 pound |

## Tell a Math Story

6. Write a math story about something that is heavier than a pound and something that is lighter than a pound.

**Notes for Home** Your child estimated whether objects weigh more or less than 1 pound. *Home Activity:* Visit a food store with your child and check the labels on different foods. Explain that 16 oz (ounces) is a pound, anything over 16 oz is heavier than a pound and anything under 16 oz is lighter than a pound. Have him or her make lists of the foods over, about, or under a pound.

Name ______________________________

# Kilograms

**Practice 11-9**

1. Circle in red the objects that are lighter than 1 kilogram
2. Circle in blue the objects that are heavier than 1 kilogram.

**Write your own.** Choose an object. Is your object lighter or heavier than 1 kilogram?

My object:__________ __________ than a kilogram

## Problem Solving Critical Thinking

3. Which weighs more, a football or a bowling ball? Explain. _______

______________________________________________

**Notes for Home** Your child identified objects that are lighter or heavier than 1 kilogram. *Home Activity:* Ask your child to make a list of 5 objects that are heavier than a kilogram and 5 objects that are lighter than a kilogram. (A kilogram is about 2 1/5 pounds.)

Name ______________________________

# Cups, Pints, and Quarts

Solve.

1. Larry has 3 pints of milk.
   Color the number of cups
   he could fill.

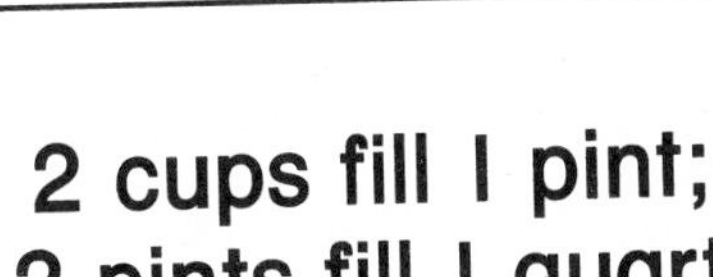
2 cups fill 1 pint;
2 pints fill 1 quart

2. Shelly buys 2 pints of milk.
   Color the number of cups
   she could fill.

3. Ms. Ito has 1 quart of milk.
   Color the number of cups
   she could fill.

4. Indra wants 6 pints of juice.
   Color the number of quarts
   that hold the same amount.

5. Sani wants 3 quarts of juice.
   Color the number of pints
   that hold the same amount.

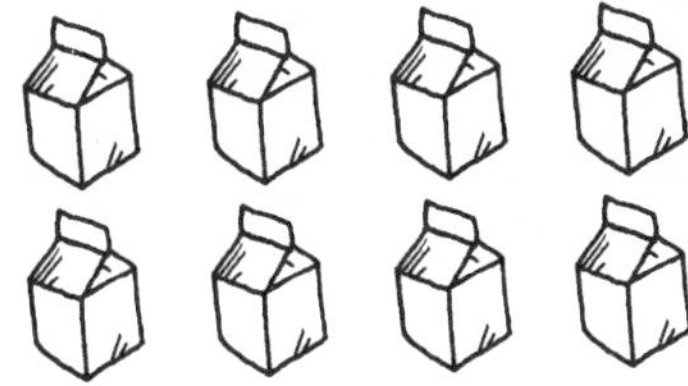

## Problem Solving Visual Thinking

6. Draw cups to solve.
   Raul has 3 quarts of juice.
   Rita has 10 cups of juice. Who has more?

   ________________ has more.

**Notes for Home** Your child solved problems about cups, pints, and quarts. *Home Activity:* Give your child a measuring cup and some empty containers. Have him or her find the number of cups that each container can hold.

Name ______________________________



# Liters

1. Which things hold less than one liter?
   Circle them.

2. Which things hold more than one liter?
   Mark an X on them.

## Mental Math

3. A keg holds eight liters of cider.
   How many liters will ten kegs hold?

   ______ liters



**Notes for Home** Your child identified containers that hold more or less than one liter. *Home Activity:* When you visit a grocery store, ask your child to identify containers that hold more than, less than, and about one liter.

Name ________________________________

# Problem Solving:
## Group Decision Making

Make your own recipe for punch.
You need to make 40 cups.

1. Write your recipe on this card.
   Write a name for your punch.

| Our Recipe: ______________________ | |
|---|---|
| How much? | What kind of juice? |
| | |
| | |
| | |
| | |

Answer these questions about your punch recipe.

2. How many cups of punch does your recipe make? 40
3. How many pints of punch does your recipe make? ____
4. How many quarts of punch does your recipe make? ____

## Journal

5. Write a punch recipe for your family.
   Make enough for each person to have 2 cups.

**Notes for Home** Your child explored making decisions with a group to create recipes. *Home Activity:* Ask your child to tell you how many cups of each kind of juice would be needed in his or her family recipe if each member wanted 4 cups. (Double each ingredient.)

Name ______________________________

Practice 11-13

# Temperature

Color to show the temperature.

1. 

10° F

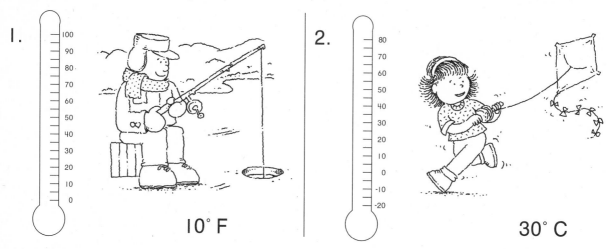

2. 80 70 60 50 40 30 20 10 0 -10 -20

30° C

## Write your own.

Choose and write a temperature. Color in the thermometer.

Draw a picture to show an activity you might do at that temperature.

3. 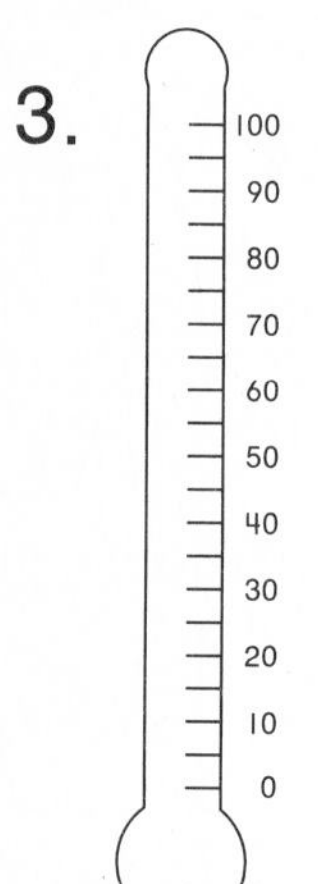


_____ °F

4. 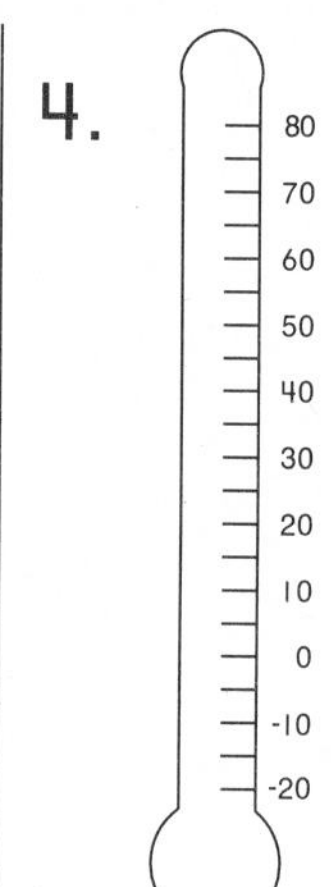


_____ °C

## Problem Solving Critical Thinking

5. It is 20° Celsius outside today. You must walk to school. Should you wear a heavy coat or just a light sweater? Why?



**Notes for Home** Your child practiced showing different temperatures on thermometers. *Home Activity:* Ask your child when the temperature in Celsius and Fahrenheit will be cool enough outside for you to want to wear a coat. (At about $50^{\circ}$ Fahrenheit and $10^{\circ}$ Celsius, you might want to wear a coat, or at least a sweater, outside.)

Name ______________________________

Practice
Chapter 11
B

# Mixed Practice: Lessons 8–13

1. Color to show the temperature.

86° F

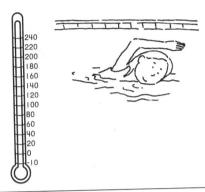

240 220 200 180 160 140 120 100 80 60 40 20 0 -10

2° F

240 220 200 180 160 140 120 100 80 60 40 20 0 -10

2. Is the pencil heavier or lighter than 1 pound? Write **heavier** or **lighter.**

A pencil is ______________

3. Is the TV heavier or lighter than 1 kilogram? Write **heavier** or **lighter.**

A TV is ______________

## Problem Solving

Solve.

PUNCH

4 pints of grape juice
2 quarts of apple juice
8 cups of lemonade

4. You need to make 2 cups of punch for each of 10 party guests. Do you have enough? Circle **yes** or **no.**

yes no

5. Which juice do you need more of in this recipe?

______________________________

**Journal**

6. Keep track of the **temperature** at the same time each evening. Write about what you find.



**Notes for Home** Your child practiced finding temperatures, the weights of objects using kilograms and pounds, and amounts of liquids. *Home Activity:* Ask your child to estimate how much different objects around the home weigh. Weigh each object and compare the result with the estimate.

Name ___________________________

Practice
Chapters 1–11
B

# Cumulative Review

Use the hundred chart to subtract.

1. 58 − 30 = ____
2. 34 − 10 = ____
3. 85 − 40 = ____
4. 62 − 50 = ____
5. 42 − 40 = ____
6. 98 − 60 = ____

| 1 | 2 | 3 | 4 | 5 | 6 | 7 | 8 | 9 | 10 |
|---|---|---|---|---|---|---|---|---|---|
| 11 | 12 | 13 | 14 | 15 | 16 | 17 | 18 | 19 | 20 |
| 21 | 22 | 23 | 24 | 25 | 26 | 27 | 28 | 29 | 30 |
| 31 | 32 | 33 | 34 | 35 | 36 | 37 | 38 | 39 | 40 |
| 41 | 42 | 43 | 44 | 45 | 46 | 47 | 48 | 49 | 50 |
| 51 | 52 | 53 | 54 | 55 | 56 | 57 | 58 | 59 | 60 |
| 61 | 62 | 63 | 64 | 65 | 66 | 67 | 68 | 69 | 70 |
| 71 | 72 | 73 | 74 | 75 | 76 | 77 | 78 | 79 | 80 |
| 81 | 82 | 83 | 84 | 85 | 86 | 87 | 88 | 89 | 90 |
| 91 | 92 | 93 | 94 | 95 | 96 | 97 | 98 | 99 | 100 |

## Problem Solving

Write each number sentence. Solve.

7. 26 pumpkins are on the wagon.
   8 more pumpkins are loaded on. ____________ pumpkins

   At the first store, 10 pumpkins are unloaded. How many pumpkins are on the wagon now? ____________ pumpkins

## Test Prep

Fill in the ○ for the correct answer.

8. 418 + 152

   ○ 266
   ○ 562
   ○ 560
   ○ 570

9. 256 + 183

   ○ 439
   ○ 336
   ○ 339
   ○ 133

**Notes for Home** Your child reviewed subtracting tens, multiple-step problems, and adding and subtracting large numbers. *Home Activity:* Ask your child to choose a number between 30 and 70, add 10 to the number, subtract 20 from the result and tell you the new number. (The new number will be 10 less than the number your child chose.)

Name ________________________________

Practice 12-1

# Explore Solid Figures

Use solid figures. Find how many faces, corners, and edges.

| | Solid | Name | Faces | Corners | Edges |
|---|---|---|---|---|---|
| 1. | | | | | |
| 2. | | | | | |
| 3. | | | | | |
| 4. | | | | | |
| 5. | | | | | |

## Problem Solving Critical Thinking

What is the same about these solids?

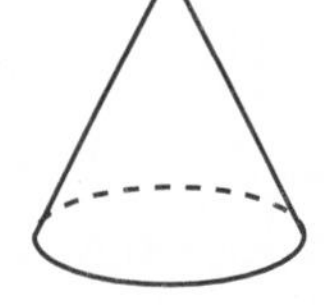

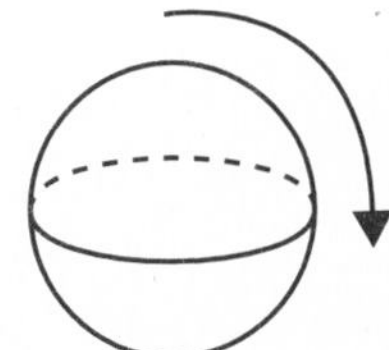

What can they do? ______________________

Draw another shape that belongs.

**Notes for Home** Your child explored the properties of solid figures. *Home Activity:* Ask your child to look through your kitchen cabinets to find containers that roll and containers that stack.

Name ______________________________

Practice 12-2

# Explore Solid and Plane Figures

Circle a shape you would make if you traced the face the object is sitting on.

1.   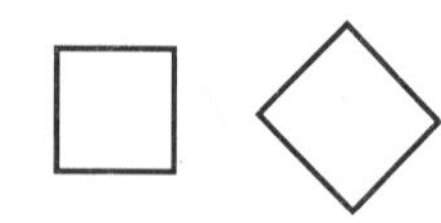

2.   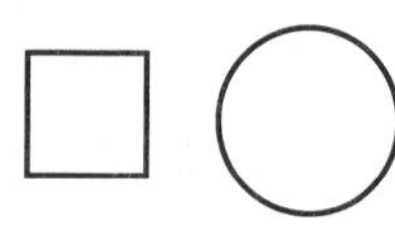

3. 

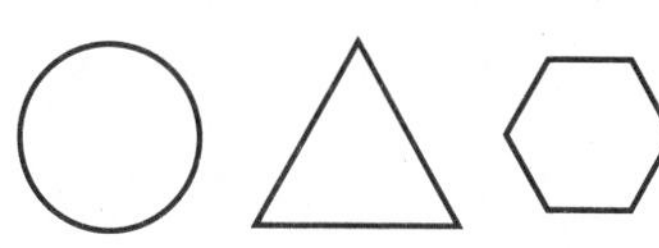

4.    

## Problem Solving Visual Thinking

5. Write the name of the solid shape you could make with the pieces.

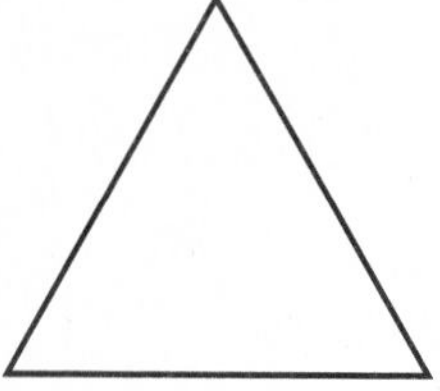 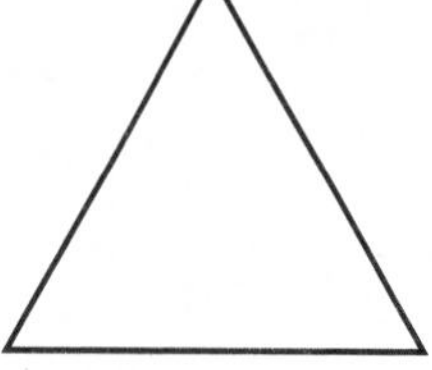

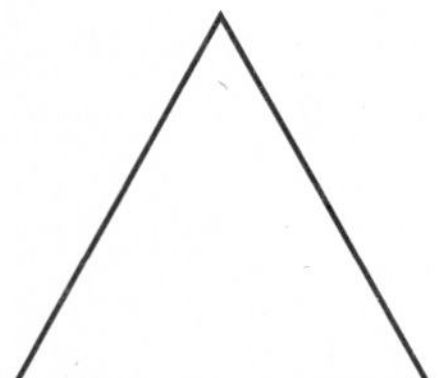 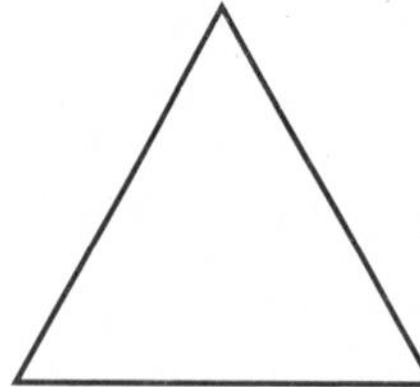

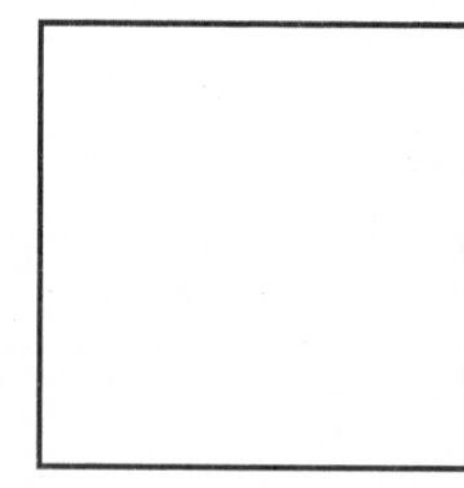

______________________________



**Notes for Home** Your child explored tracing the faces of solid shapes to make plane figures. *Home Activity:* Ask your child to trace some different shapes from a cereal or cracker box.

Name ___________________________

Practice 12-3

# Make Shapes

Write your own. Use pattern blocks.

Make new shapes.

Complete the chart.

| | Blocks I Used | New Shape I Made | How many sides? | How many corners? |
|---|---|---|---|---|
| 1. | | | | |
| 2. | | | | |

## Problem Solving Patterns

3. Draw what comes next.

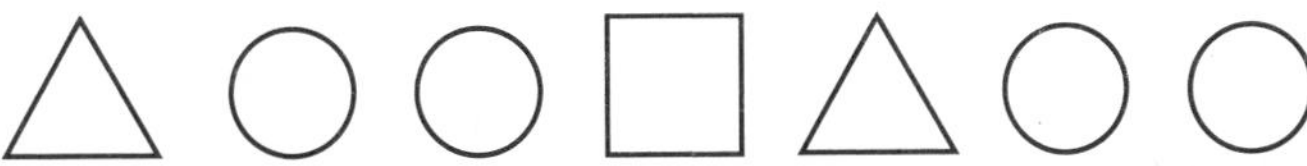

**Notes for Home** Your child used pattern blocks to make new shapes and found the number of sides and corners for the new shape. *Home Activity:* Using objects such as napkins or paper, ask your child to match the edges to make a new shape and to count the number of sides and corners.

Name ______________________________

# Congruent Shapes

Practice 12-4

Draw a shape that is congruent.

1. 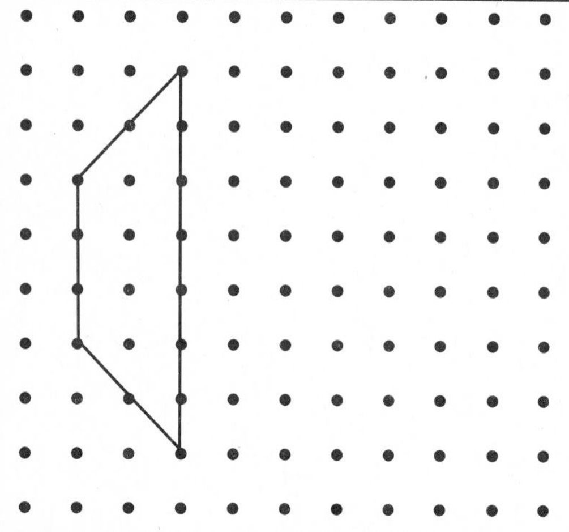

2. 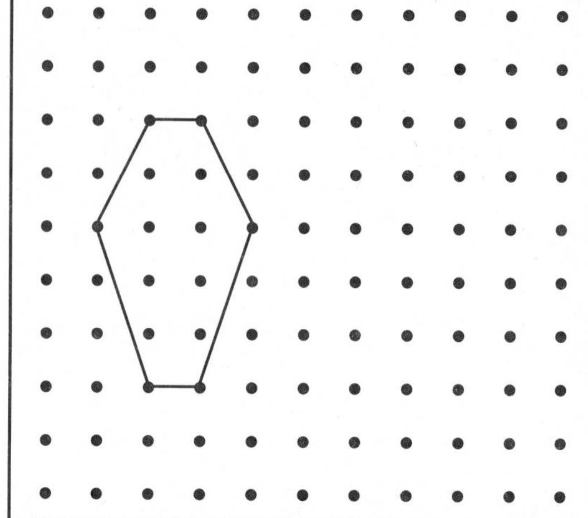

**Write your own.** Draw a shape. Then have a friend draw a shape that is congruent to your shape..

3. 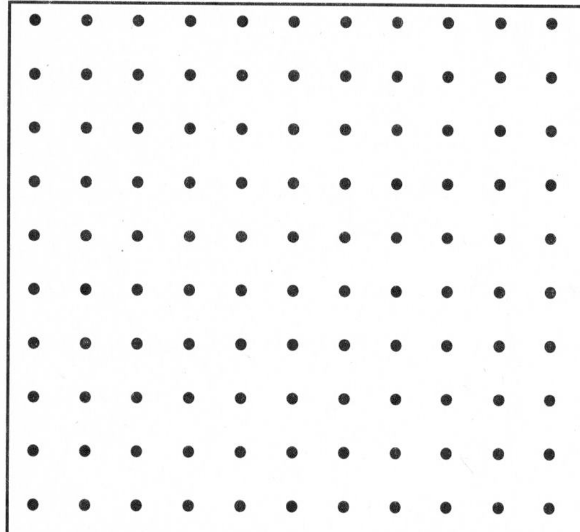

4. 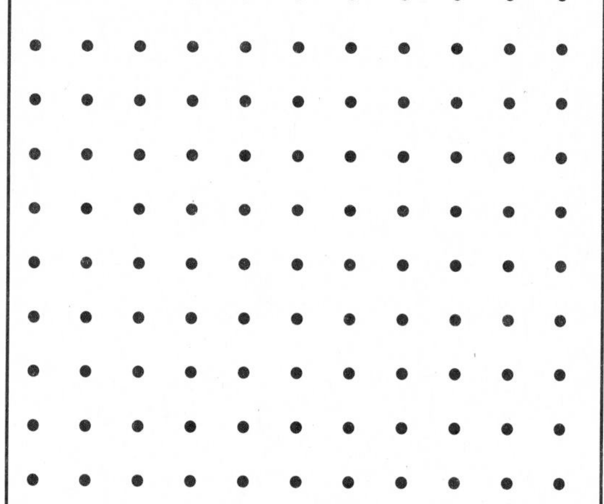

## Problem Solving Visual Thinking

5. Draw a shape so there are 5 dots inside and 8 dots on the lines.

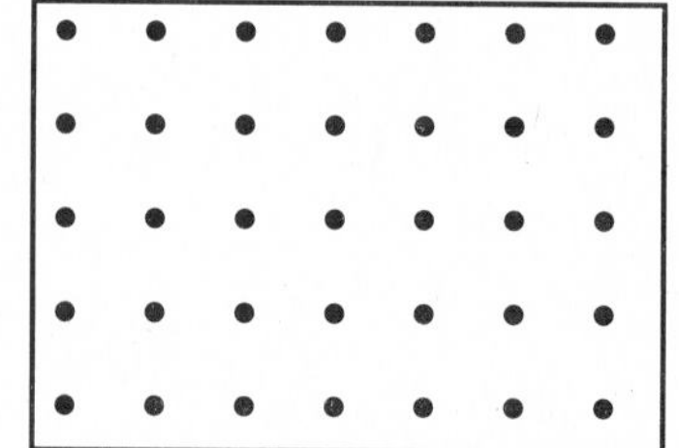



**Notes for Home** Your child practiced drawing figures that are the same size and the same shape. *Home Activity:* Ask your child to look in bureau drawers and on kitchen shelves to find sets of objects that are congruent.

Name ____________________________________

Practice 12-5

# Slides, Flips, and Turns

Write **slide, flip** or **turn.** Use pattern blocks to check.

1. ____________________

2. ____________________

3. ____________________

4. ____________________

## Problem Solving

5. How many of each shape do you need to make a hexagon?
Use pattern blocks to help you.

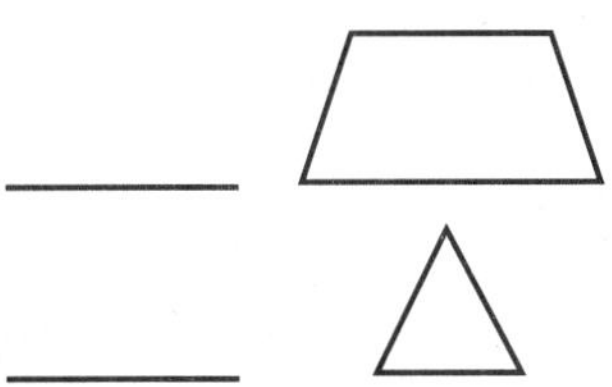

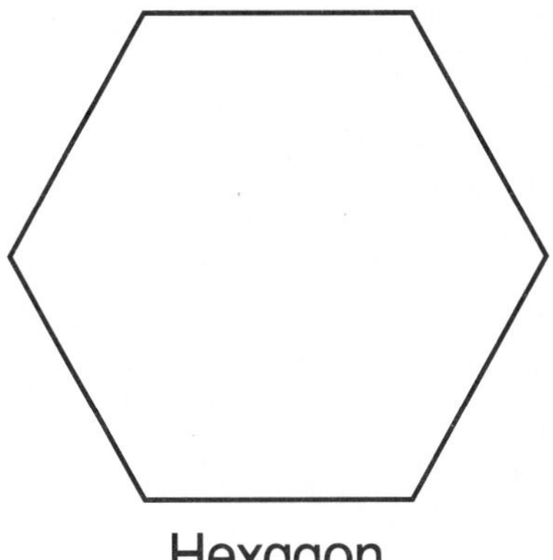

Hexagon



**Notes for Home** Your child used pattern blocks to tell whether a shape changed by sliding, flipping, or turning. *Home Activity:* Ask your child to use an irregular shape, such as a puzzle piece or spoon, and demonstrate three ways of moving it.

Name ________________________________

# Symmetry

**Practice 12-6**

Make the shapes show symmetry.
Draw to show the matching part.

1.

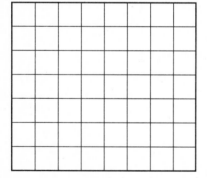

2. 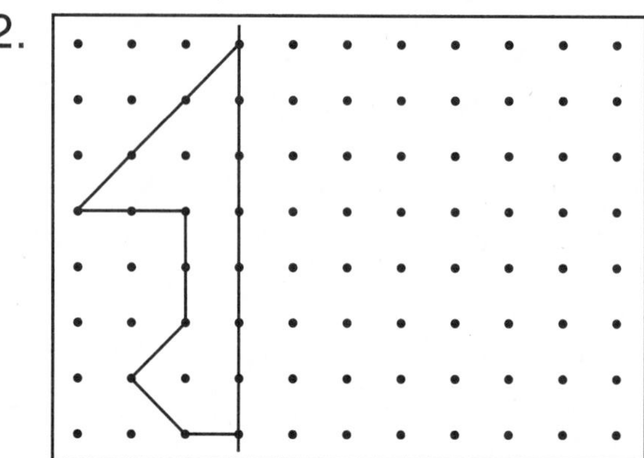

## Mixed Practice

Trace each shape. Flip the pattern block. Trace again.
Draw one line of symmetry for the new shape.

3. Use □.

4. Use ◇.

## Problem Solving Visual Thinking

5. Draw a different line of symmetry on each shape.

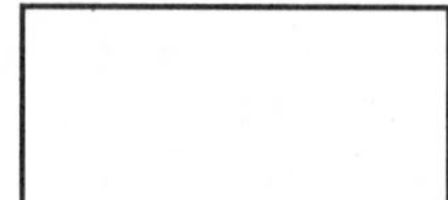

**Notes for Home** Your child completed shapes to show matching parts and drew lines of symmetry. *Home Activity:* Ask your child to draw one picture that has symmetry and another picture that has no line of symmetry.

Name ______________________________

Practice 12-7

# Problem Solving: Use Logical Reasoning

Solve the riddles. Cross out pictures that don't match the clues. Circle the answers.

1. Which plate am I?
   I have a congruent partner.
   I have no stripes.

2. Which sticker am I?
   If you traced around a cube, you would draw my shape.
   I am greater than 3.

3. Which paper hat am I?
   My shape shows symmetry.
   I have more than 3 corners.

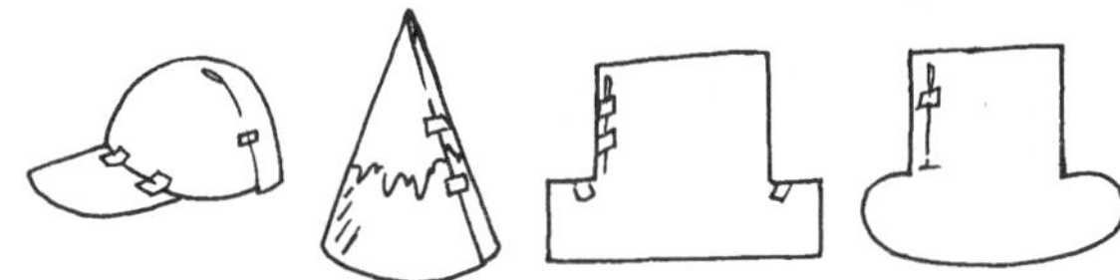

## Write About It

4. Write your own riddle.

______________________________

______________________________

______________________________

______________________________

______________________________

Draw your shapes.



**Notes for Home** Your child practiced using logical reasoning to solve and make riddles. *Home Activity:* Ask your child to solve this riddle: "I have sides. I have 4 corners. What shape am I—a circle, a triangle, or a square?" (a square)

Name ______________________________

# Mixed Practice: Lessons 1–7

Write how many faces, corners, and edges for this solid.

1. ______ faces 2. ______ corners 3. ______ edges

4. Draw a shape that is congruent.

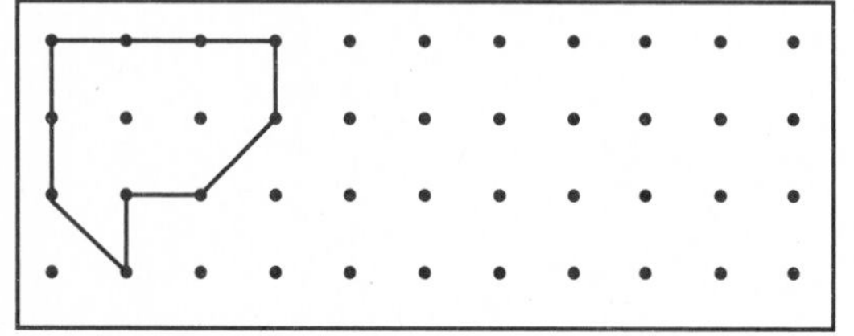

5. Write **slide**, **flip**, or **turn**.

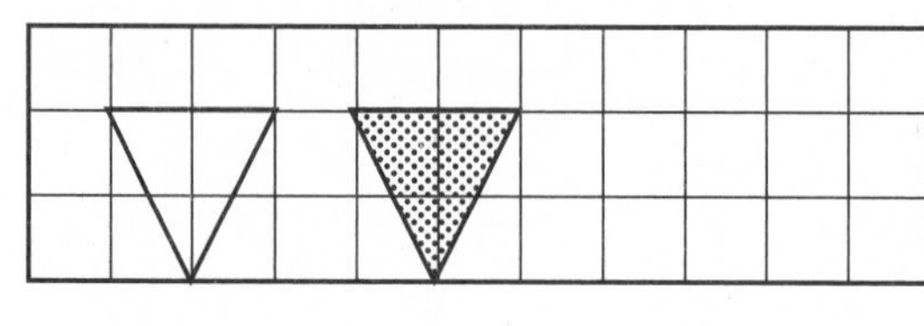

______________

Make the shapes show symmetry. Draw matching parts.

6.

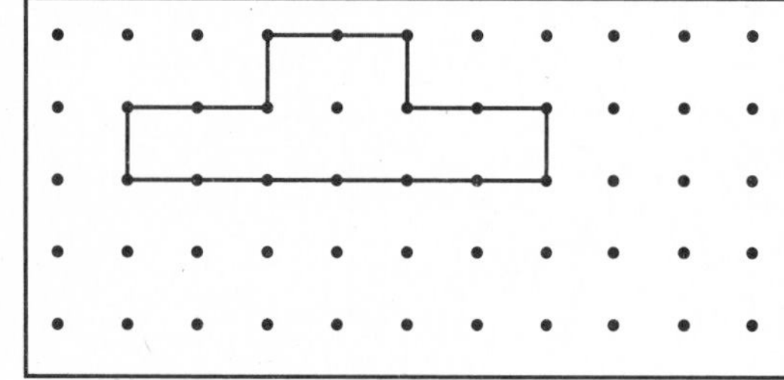

7.

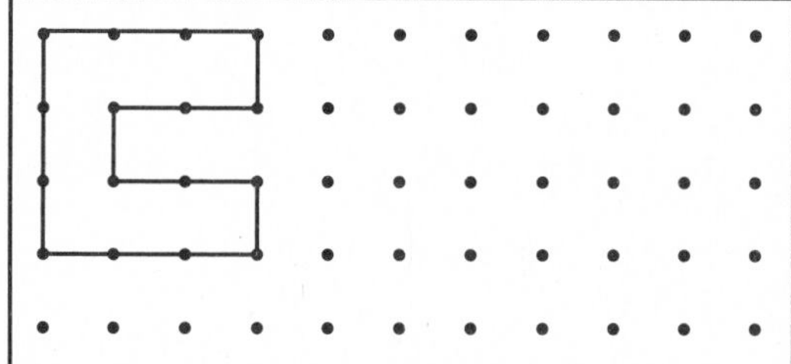

## Problem Solving

Solve the riddle. As you read the riddle, cross out the pictures that don't match the clues. Circle the answer.

8. I am a rectangle.
I have more than 1 line of symmetry.
I have 4 equal sides.

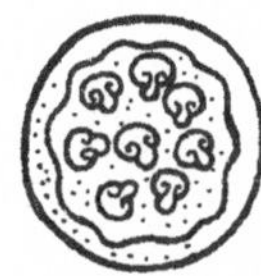

## Journal

9. Draw 2 squares. Draw a different line of symmetry on each square.



**Notes for Home** Your child practiced identifying and drawing shapes. *Home Activity:* Play "I Spy" with your child. Look for examples of circles, squares, rectangles, and triangles, and include clues about the number of sides and corners each shape has.

Name ______________________________

Practice
Chapters 1–12
A

# Cumulative Review

Write the number.

1. forty-eight ______ 2. ninety ______ 3. eighty-one ______

Find the nearest ten. Estimate the sum.

4. 22 + 57 = ____

Think:

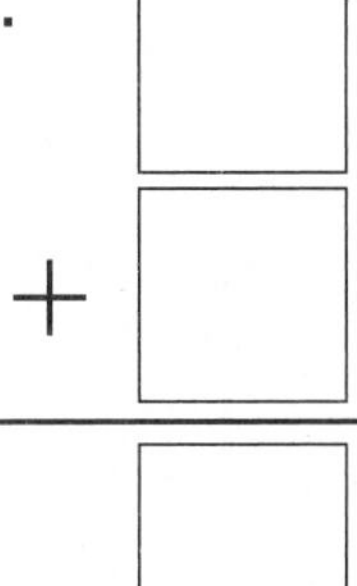

22 + 57 is about ____

5. 38 + 19 = ____

Think:

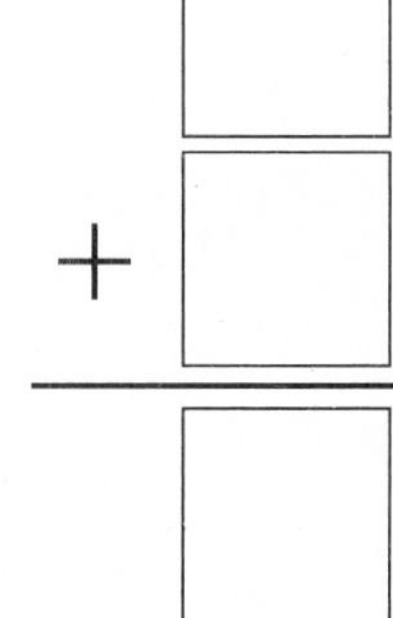

38 + 19 is about ____

## Problem Solving

Solve.

6. Jack poured 14 glasses of juice and 27 glasses of lemonade. How many glasses did he pour?

______ glasses

7. Lemonade costs 35¢. A sandwich costs 48¢. How much would you pay for for lemonade and a sandwich?

______ ¢

## Test Prep

Fill in the ○ for the correct answer.

8. Find the length in inches.

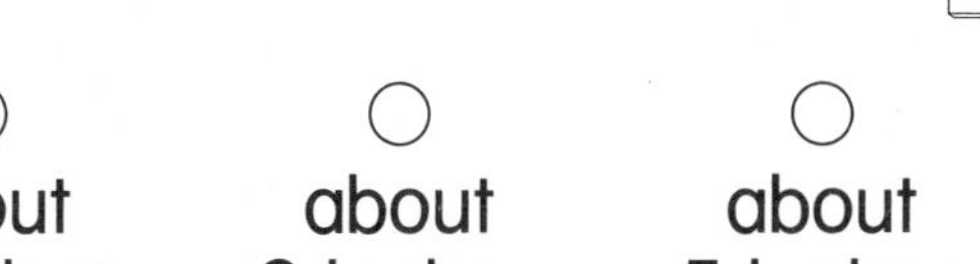


○ about 8 inches ○ about 3 inches ○ about 5 inches ○ about 6 inches



**Notes for Home** Your child reviewed reading and writing numbers, estimating sums, solving problems, and estimating lengths. *Home Activity:* Ask your child to estimate the sum of 19 + 32. (About 50)

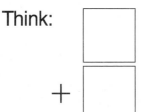

Name ______________________________

Practice 12-8

# Equal and Unequal Parts

How many equal parts in each shape?

1. 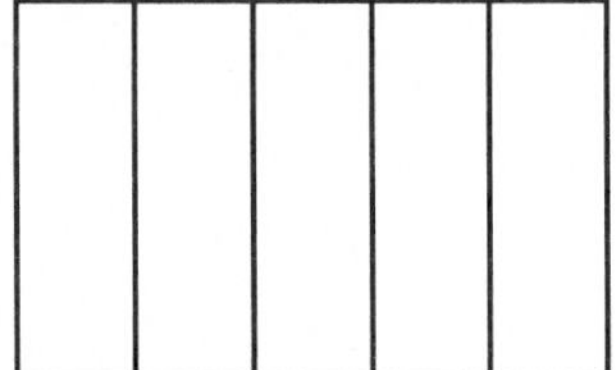 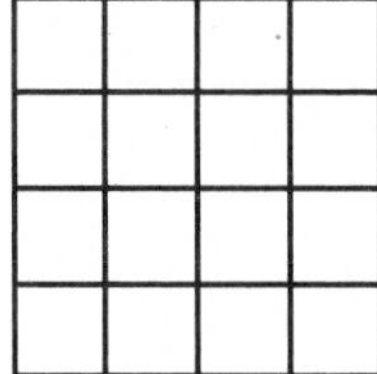

_____ equal parts _____ equal parts _____ equal parts

Draw equal parts. Color each part a different color.

2. 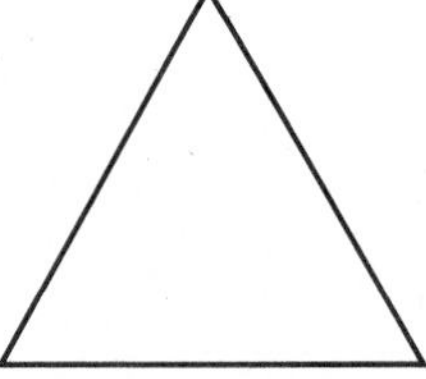 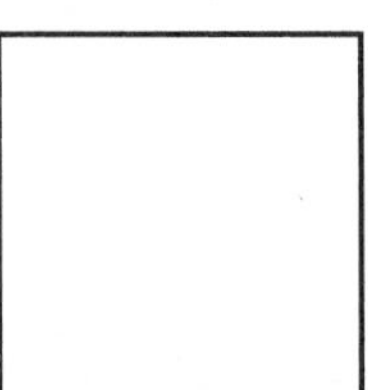 

2 equal parts 4 equal parts 3 equal parts

3. 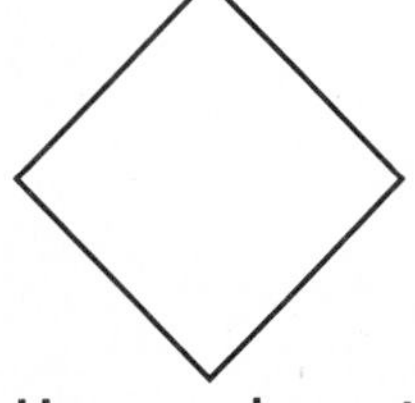 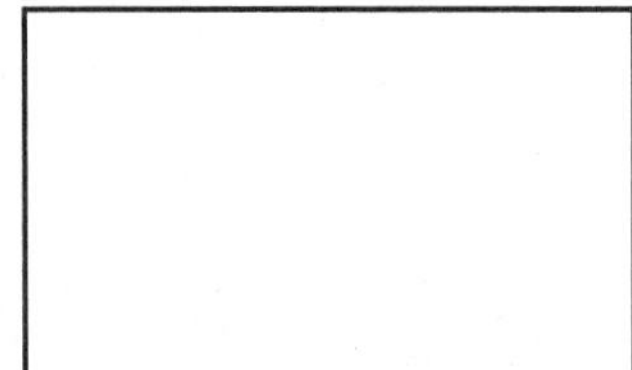 

4 equal parts 3 equal parts 6 equal parts

## Problem Solving Visual Thinking

Use pattern blocks to make this shape.
Make the shape the same size.
Trace to show the blocks you used.

How many equal parts did you make? _____

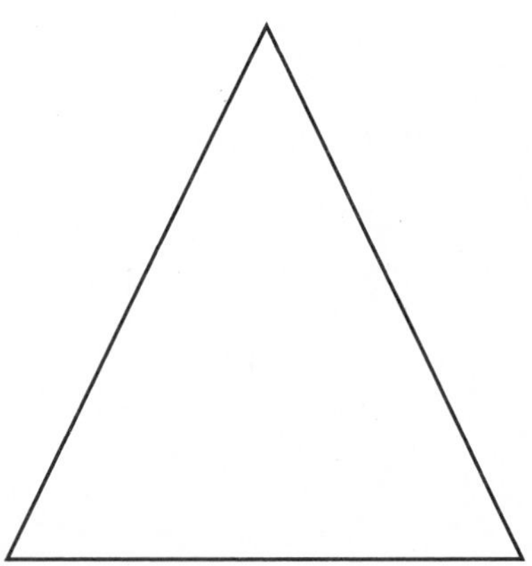



**Notes for Home** Your child practiced identifying and drawing equal parts. *Home Activity:* Ask your child to show how he or she would divide a food item, such as a pizza, loaf of bread, or stalk of celery, into four equal parts.

Name ________________________________



# Unit Fractions

Write the fraction for the shaded part.

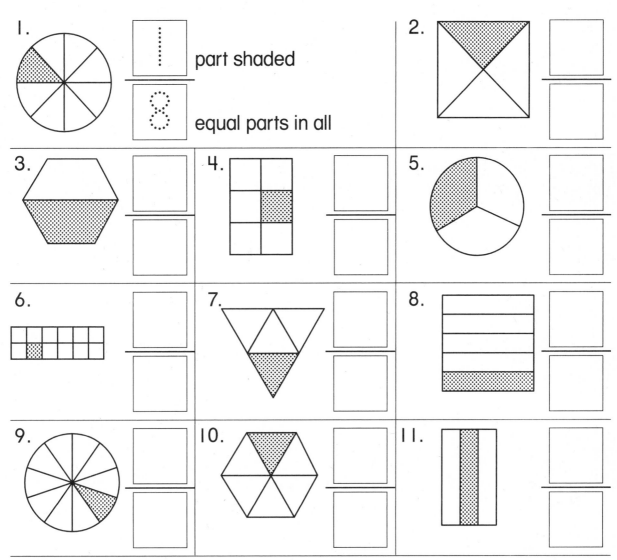

1. $\frac{1}{8}$ — 1 part shaded, 8 equal parts in all

2.

3.

4.

5.

6.

7.

8.

9.

10.

11.

## Problem Solving Critical Thinking

12. Is $\frac{1}{3}$ of Jim's fruit pie the same size as $\frac{1}{3}$ of Gina's pie? Why or why not?

Jim's Pie

Gina's Pie

______________________________________________



**Notes for Home** Your child practiced writing different fractions. *Home Activity:* Draw a circle and ask your child how he or she would draw a line to cut the "pie" into fair shares for 4 people. (Draw two lines to divide the pie into fourths.]

Name ______________________

# Fractions

Practice 12-10

Shade some of the equal parts.
Write the fraction for parts that are shaded.

1. Shade 2 parts.

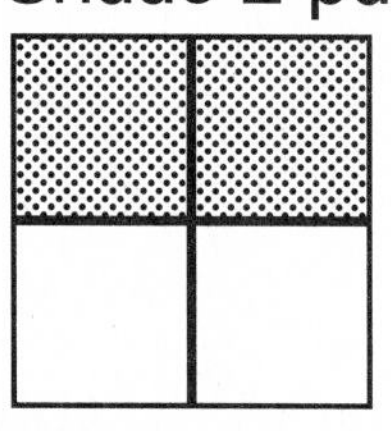

$\frac{2}{4}$

2. Shade 1 part.

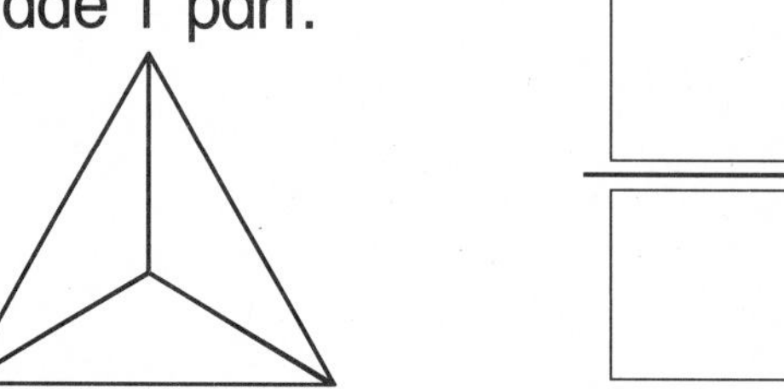

3. Shade 5 parts.

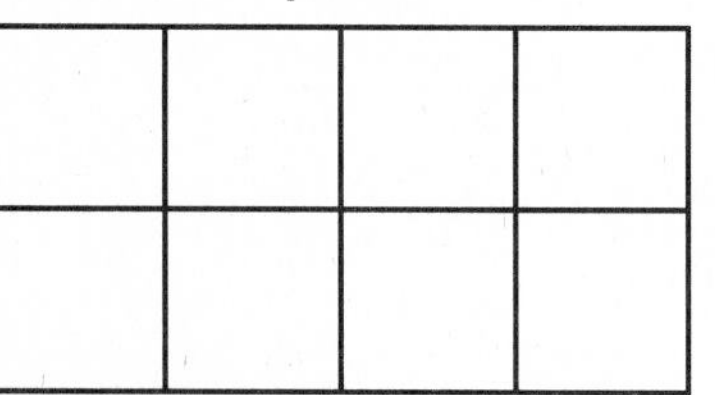

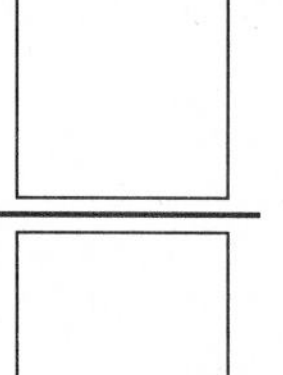

4. Shade 3 parts.

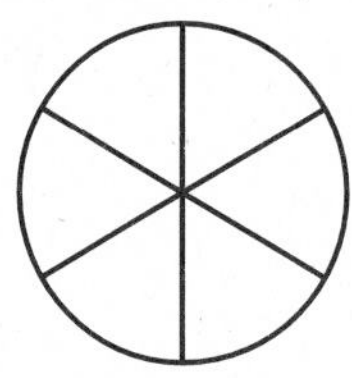

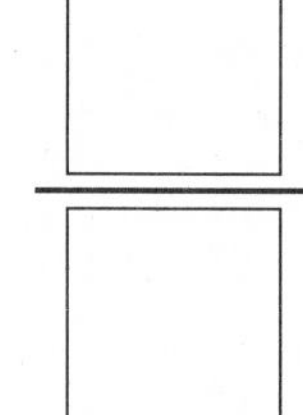

5. Shade 4 parts.

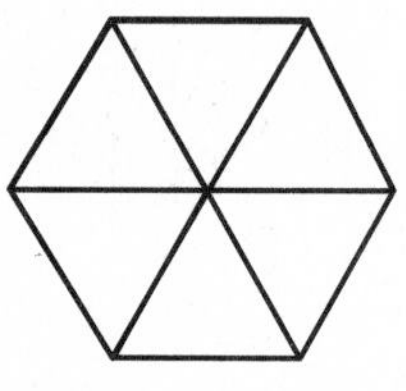

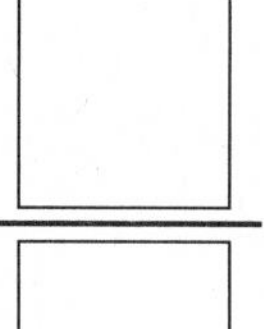

6. Shade 2 parts.

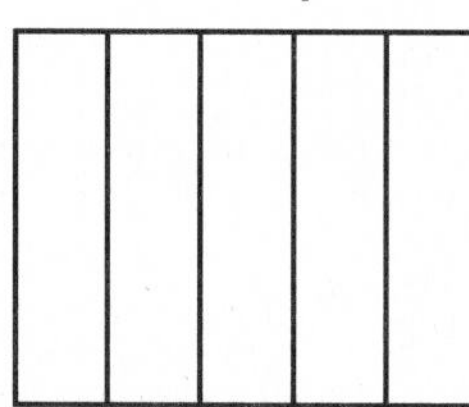

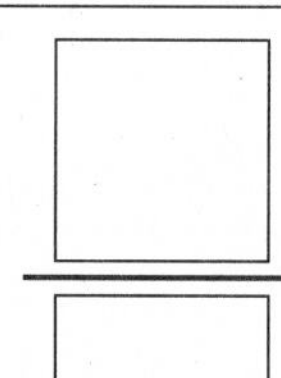

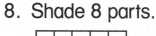

7. Shade 1 part.

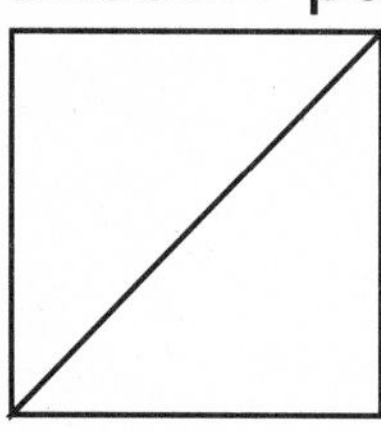

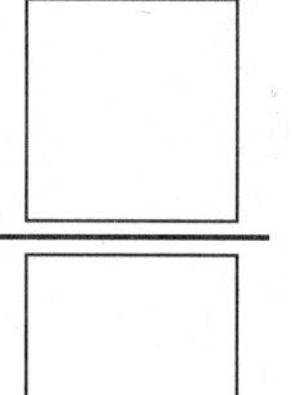

8. Shade 8 parts.

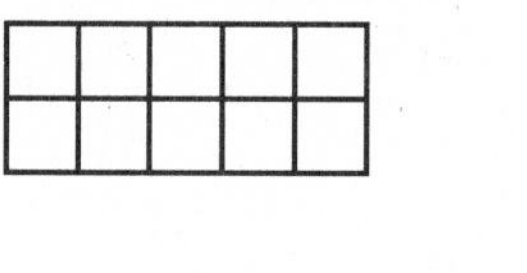

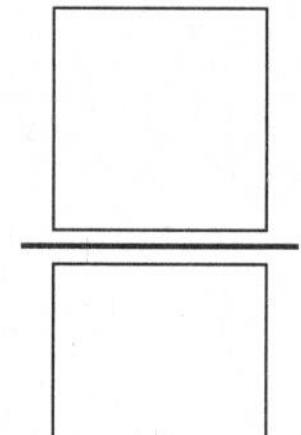

## Problem Solving

9. Solve.
You ate $\frac{2}{4}$ of a sandwich. Do you have $\frac{1}{2}$ a sandwich left? ______

**Write your own** problem about a fraction of a sandwich. Have a friend solve it.

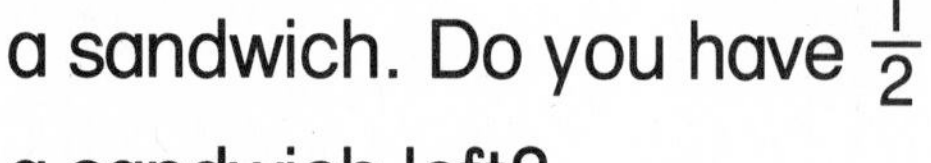

______________________

______________________



**Notes for Home** Your child practiced writing fractions. *Home Activity:* Ask you child to shade 2 more parts in exercise 6 and name the fraction. (4/5 — four fifths)

Name ______________________________

Practice 12-11

# Estimate Parts of a Whole

How much is **left**? Circle the best estimate.

1.

glass of milk

about $\frac{3}{4}$

about $\frac{1}{8}$

about $\frac{1}{3}$

2.

pita bread

about $\frac{2}{3}$

about $\frac{1}{2}$

about $\frac{5}{6}$

How much **was eaten**? Circle the best estimate.

3.

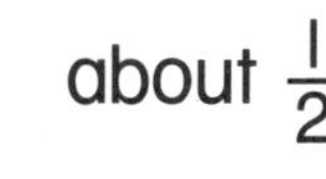

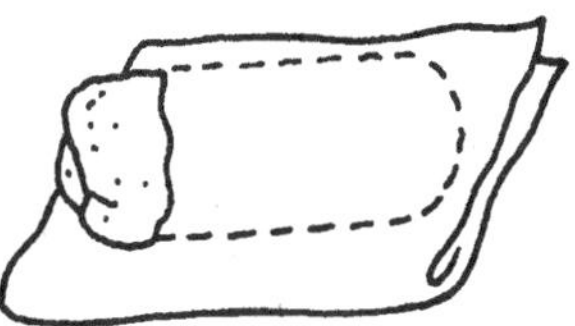

spring roll

about $\frac{1}{2}$

about $\frac{7}{8}$

about $\frac{3}{4}$

4.

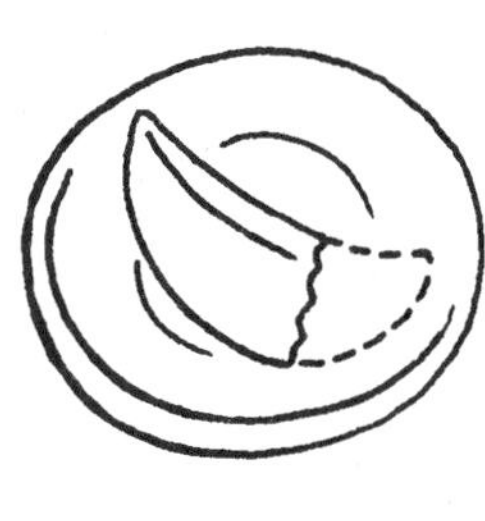

papaya

about $\frac{9}{10}$

about $\frac{1}{3}$

about $\frac{1}{4}$

## Problem Solving Visual Thinking

5. Ana filled two glasses from the pitcher. About how many more glasses can she fill?

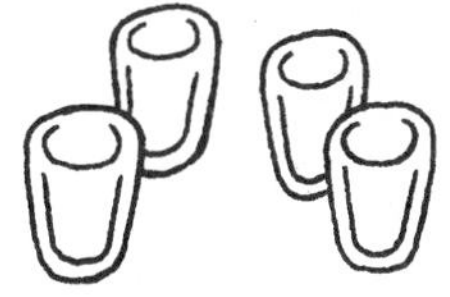

about ______ glasses



**Notes for Home** Your child used pictures to estimate fractions. *Home Activity:* Ask your child to draw half an apple and tell you the part that is left and the part that is missing. (1/2 is left, 1/2 is missing.)

Name ___________________________

Practice 12-12

# Explore a Fraction of a Set

What fraction of each group is striped?

Write the fraction.

1.

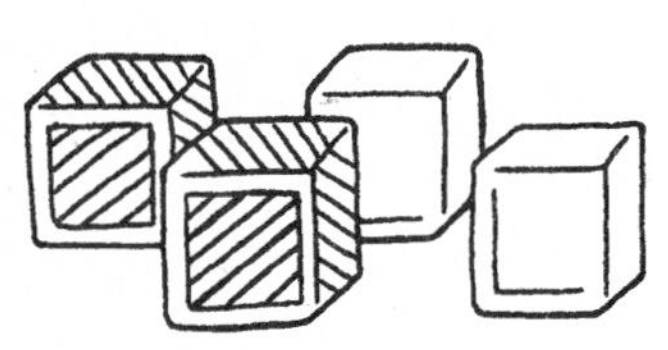

_____ striped blocks

_____ blocks in all

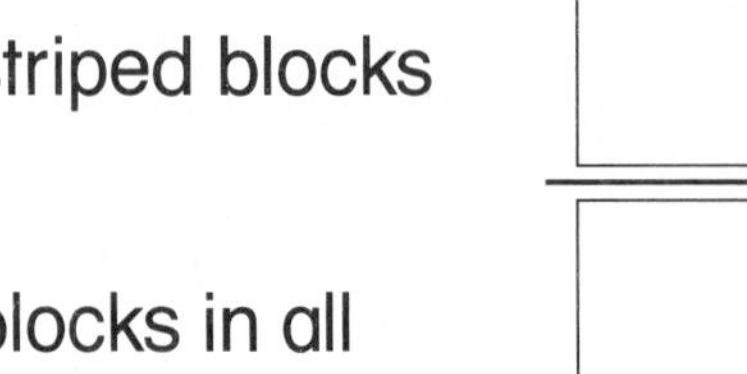

are striped.

2.

_____ striped

_____ balls in all

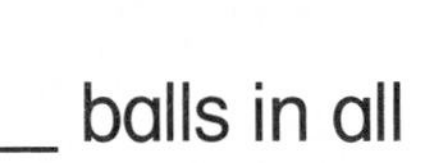

are striped.

3.

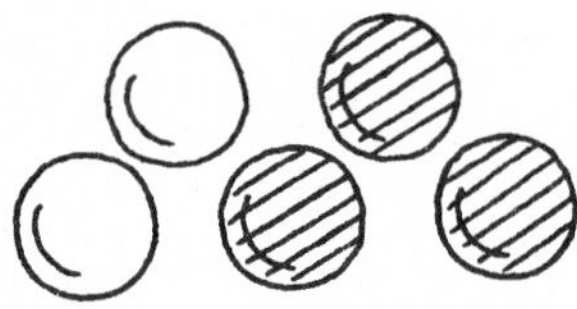

_____ striped

_____ marbles in all

are striped.

4.

_____ striped

_____ blocks in all

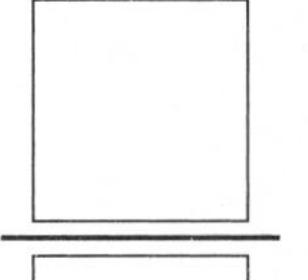

are striped.

## Problem Solving

5. Draw 5 tennis balls. Color some green.
   Color the rest yellow.
   What fraction is yellow?

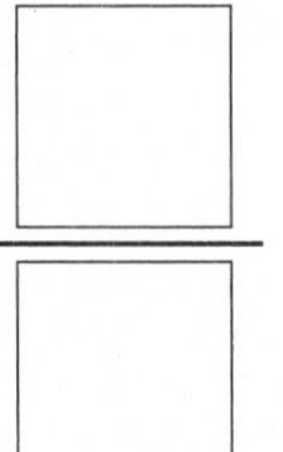



**Notes for Home** Your child used pictures to write the fraction of a set. *Home Activity:* Display a set of 2 dimes and 4 nickels and ask: "What fraction of the coins are dimes?" (2/6 — two sixths)

Name ______________________



# Fraction of a Set

1. Draw a group of buttons.

   Color $\frac{2}{5}$ blue. Color $\frac{3}{5}$ orange.

2. Draw a group of beads.

   Color $\frac{1}{4}$ red. Color $\frac{3}{4}$ black.

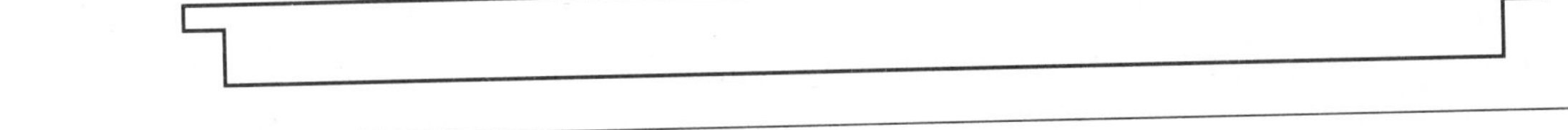

3. Draw a group of rings.

   Color $\frac{5}{6}$ green. Color $\frac{1}{6}$ yellow.

## Mental Math

Solve.

4. $\frac{1}{4}$ of my bracelets are cotton.
   The rest of my bracelets are plastic.
   What fraction of my bracelets are plastic?

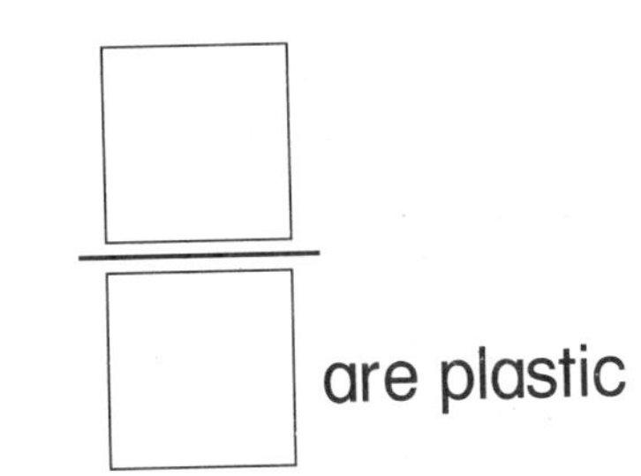

are plastic

How many bracelets are plastic? ______



**Notes for Home** Your child practiced drawing and coloring a group to show a fraction. *Home Activity:* Ask your child to draw and color to show this group: 1/3 of the apples are green. 2/3 of the apples are red. (Draw 1 green and 2 red apples.)

Name ______________________________

# Explore Probability

**Practice 12-14**

Reach in the bag and pick 1 cube at a time.
Write what color you pick on a piece of paper.
Put the cube back in the bag. Pick 10 times in all.

1. Put red, blue, and yellow cubes in a bag. Make the red cubes more likely to be picked. Use 30 cubes in all.

   Do the activity.

| Number of cubes in my bag. | My results. |
|---|---|
| R ____ | R ____ |
| B ____ | B ____ |
| Y ____ | Y ____ |

2. Put red, blue, and yellow cubes in a bag. Make the yellow cubes more likely to be picked. Use 30 cubes in all.

   Do the activity.

| Number of cubes in my bag. | My results. |
|---|---|
| R ____ | R ____ |
| B ____ | B ____ |
| Y ____ | Y ____ |

## Journal

3. Why are you more likely to pick blue if you have 10 blue cubes, 5 red cubes, and 5 yellow cubes in a bag? Explain.



**Notes for Home** Your child made up and completed a probability activity. *Home Activity:* Ask your child to collect a group of 2 different kinds of objects so that one kind of object is more likely to be picked, and then show you how to complete a probability experiment like the one above.

Name ______________________________



# Problem Solving: Make a Prediction

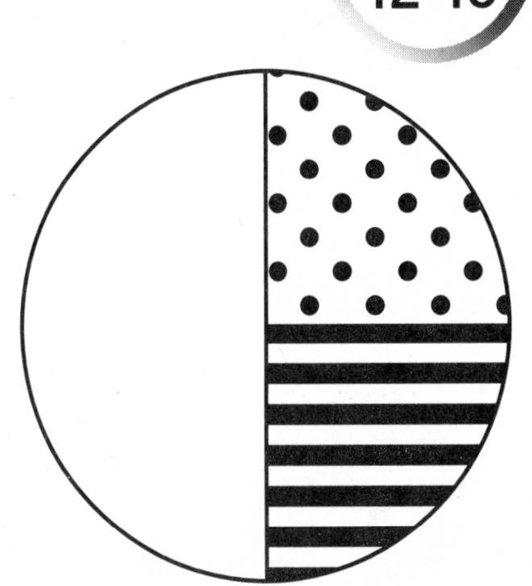

1. Predict. If you were to spin once, would this spinner be more likely to land on plain, dots, or stripes?

   What makes you think so?

   ______________________

   ______________________

2. Predict. If you were to spin 12 times, how many times would the spinner land on plain? _____ On dots? _____ On stripes? _____

3. Spin 12 times. Color a square for each spin. Write the results.

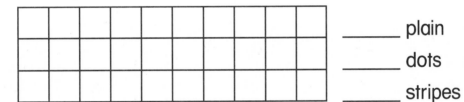

_____ plain
_____ dots
_____ stripes

## Write About It

Write whether the outcome is certain, cannot happen or is likely to happen.

4. land on stripes ______________________

5. land on plain ______________________

6. land on dots ______________________



**Notes for Home** Your child practiced making predictions. *Home Activity:* Ask your child to predict what time the sun will go down tonight.

Name ____________________



# Mixed Practice: Lessons 8–15

How many equal parts in each shape?

1. 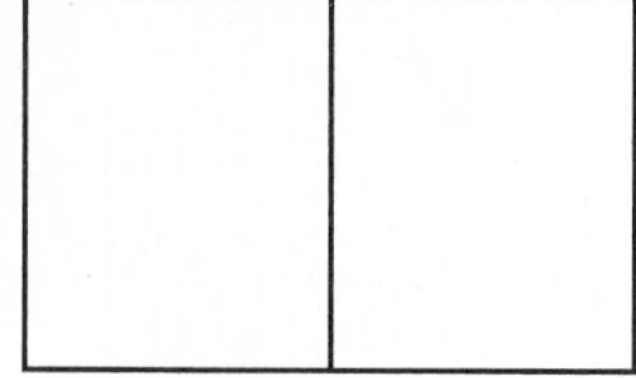 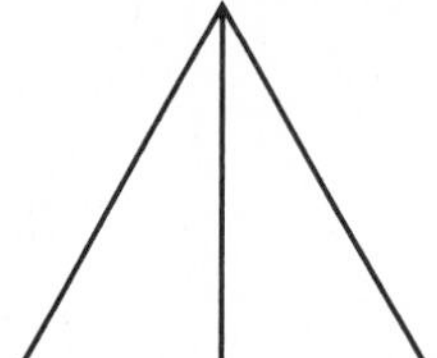 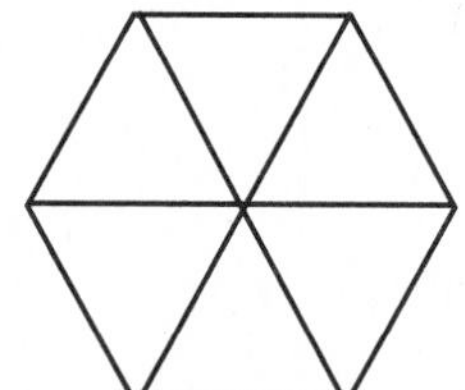

_____ equal parts _____ equal parts _____ equal parts

Write the fraction for the shaded part.

2. 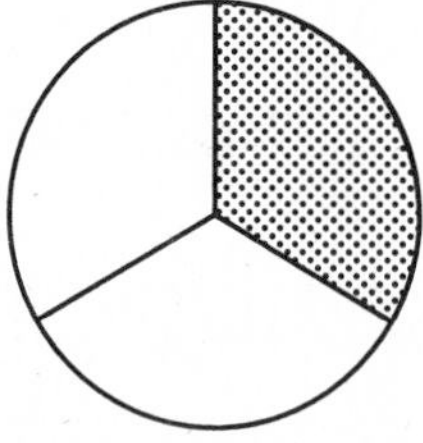

3. 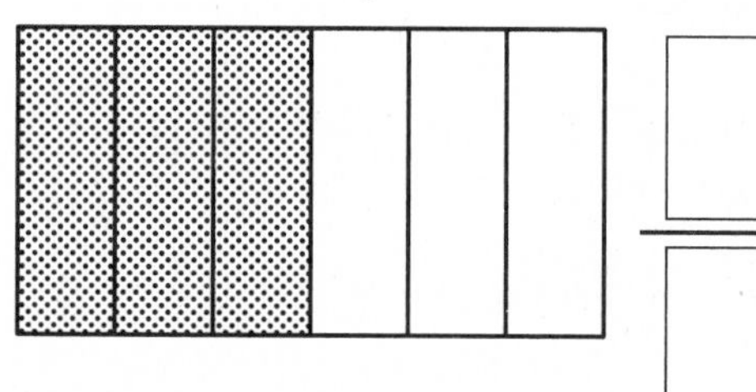

How much is left?
Circle the best estimate.

4. 

about $\frac{1}{3}$

about $\frac{1}{2}$

Draw a group of marbles.
Color $\frac{3}{5}$ yellow. Color $\frac{2}{5}$ blue.

5. 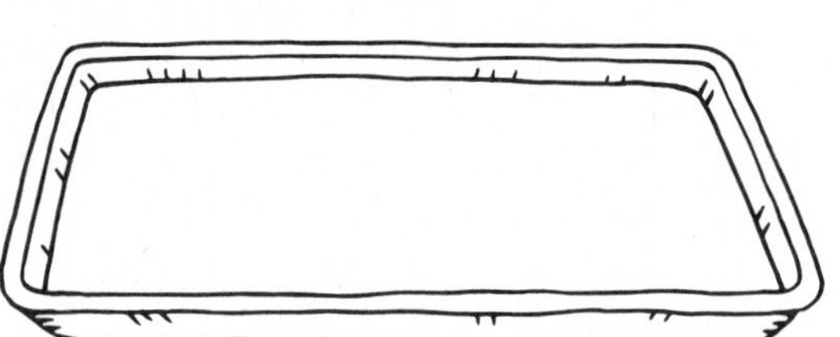

## Problem Solving

6. Predict. If you were to spin this spinner once, would it be more likely to land on plain, dots, or stripes? ____________

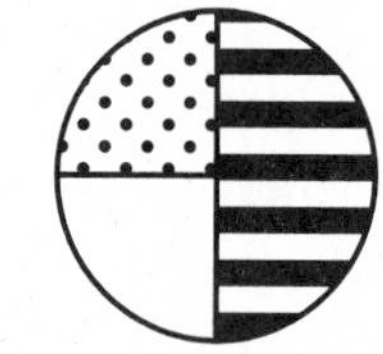

## Journal

7. How does knowing about equal parts help you if you want to share a pizza with friends? Explain.

**Notes for Home** Your child practiced identifying fractions. *Home Activity:* Ask your child to show you a way to cut a sandwich or piece of toast into 4 equal parts.

Name ______________________________

Practice Chapters 1–12 B

# Cumulative Review

Add or subtract.

1.

| 38 | 65 | 57 | 60 | 42 | 83 |
|---|---|---|---|---|---|
| − 9 | − 24 | − 13 | + 20 | − 8 | − 45 |

2.

| 29 | 74 | 31 | 50 | 76 | 47 |
|---|---|---|---|---|---|
| + 46 | − 20 | − 18 | + 17 | − 26 | − 19 |

## Problem Solving

3. Jason made 15 jelly sandwiches. He made 23 tuna sandwiches. How many sandwiches did he make in all?

   ______ sandwiches

4. Mee has 45 oranges to sell. She sells 26 oranges to Jason's class. How many does she have left to sell?

   ______ oranges

## Test Prep

Fill in the ○ for the correct answer.

5. Choose the correct symbol to compare the numbers.

   45  36

   ○ $<$  $=$ ○ $>$

6. Which numbers are in order from greatest to least?

   ○ 7, 42, 103, 324, 15

   ○ 324, 103, 42, 15, 7

   ○ 7, 15, 42, 103, 324



**Notes for Home** Your child reviewed adding and subtracting two-digit numbers, comparing numbers, and ordering numbers. *Home Activity:* Ask your child to subtract 37–18. (19)

Name ______________________________

# Explore Joining Equal Groups

Practice 13-1

You can add to find how many oranges in all.

$4 + 4 + 4 + 4 = 16$

Use counters to show the oranges.
Find how many oranges in all.

| | | Draw the oranges. | How many oranges in all? |
|---|---|---|---|
| 1. | 1 bag | | 4 |
| 2. | 2 bags | | 4 + 4 = ____ |
| 3. | 3 bags | | 4 + 4 + 4 = ____ |
| 4. | 4 bags | | 4 + 4 + 4 + 4 = ____ |

**Talk About It** How could you find out how many oranges would be in 5 bags?

______________________________

**Notes for Home** Your child made equal groups and added to find how many in all. *Home Activity:* Ask your child to use objects such as spoons to make 4 groups of 3 objects each. Ask your child to add to find how many objects in all. (12)

Name ______________________________

Practice 13-2

# Addition and Multiplication

Find how many in all. You can use cubes.

1. How many wheels?
   3 groups of 3

___ + ___ + ___ = ___

___ × ___ = ___

2. How many sails?
   3 groups of 2

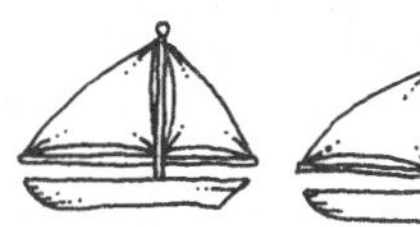

___ + ___ + ___ = ___

___ × ___ = ___

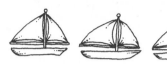

3. How many tennis balls?
   4 groups of 3

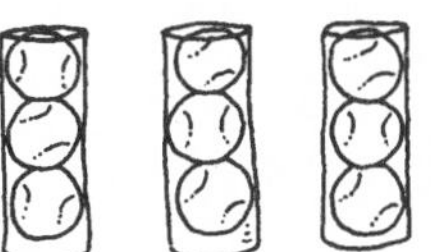

___ + ___ + ___ + ___ = ___

___ × ___ = ___

4. How many marbles?
   3 groups of 6

___ + ___ + ___ = ___

___ × ___ = ___

## Problem Solving Visual Thinking

Can you multiply to tell how many in all?
Tell why or why not.

5.

yes no

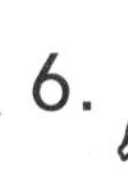

6.

yes no

7.

yes no



**Notes for Home** Your child added and multiplied to find the total number in several groups. *Home Activity:* Ask your child to find the total number of wheels for 5 bicycles with 2 wheels each. (5 x 2 = 10)

Name ______________________________

Practice 13-3

# Explore Building Arrays

2 rows of 6 bowling pins

$2 \times 6 = 12$

There are 12 bowling pins in all.

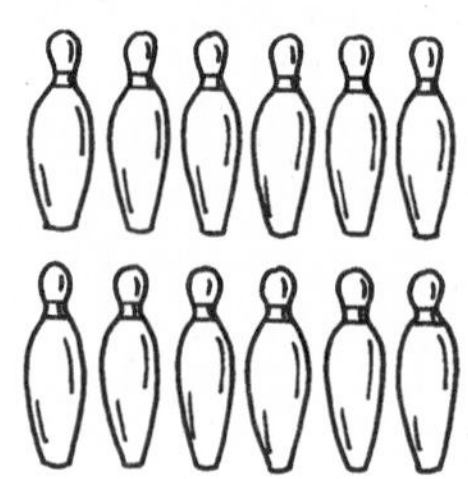

Color equal rows. Write how many. Find the product.

1. Show 5 rows of 3

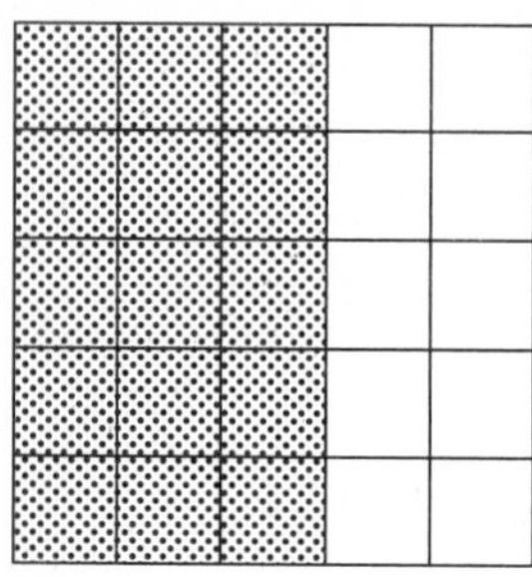

5 rows

3 in each row

$5 \times 3 = 15$

2. Show 4 rows of 4

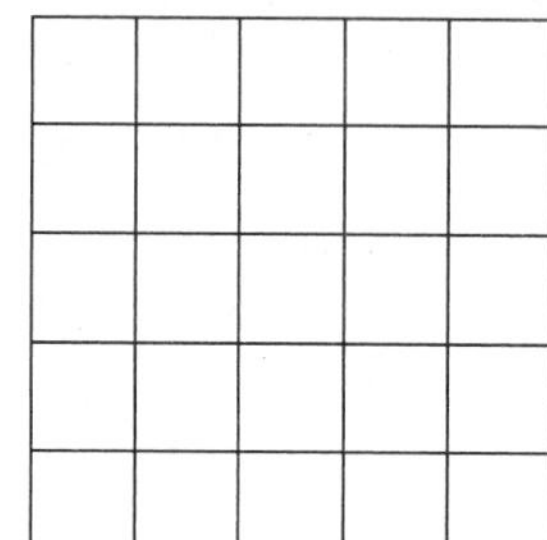

_____ rows

_____ in each row

$4 \times 4 =$ ____

3. Show 2 rows of 5

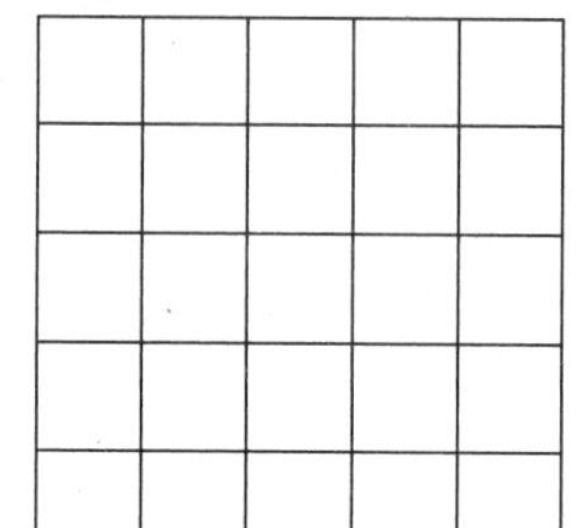

_____ rows

_____ in each row

$2 \times 5 =$ ____

## Problem Solving

4. Draw groups to show 3 x 4.

How many in all? _____

5. Draw groups to show 4 x 6.

How many in all? _____



**Notes for Home** Your child colored equal rows on a grid and completed a multiplication number sentence. *Home Activity:* Draw a picture which shows 3 groups of 7 objects and ask your child to write the multiplication sentence. (3 x 7 = 21)

Name ______________________

Practice 13-4

# Multiplication in Any Order

Find the product. You can use cubes.

1. 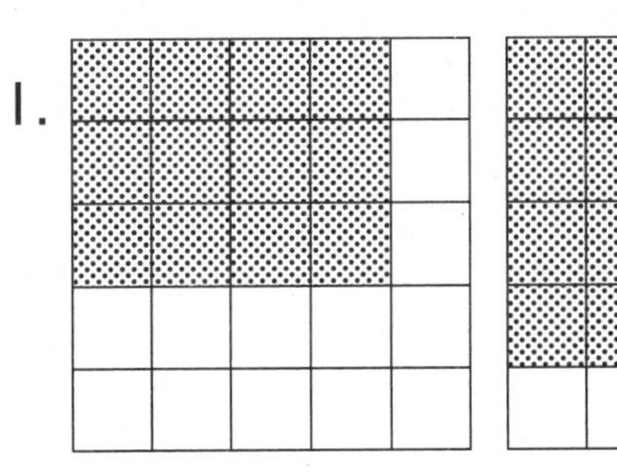

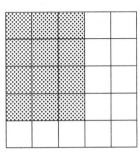

$3 \times 4 =$ ____ $4 \times 3 =$ ____

2. 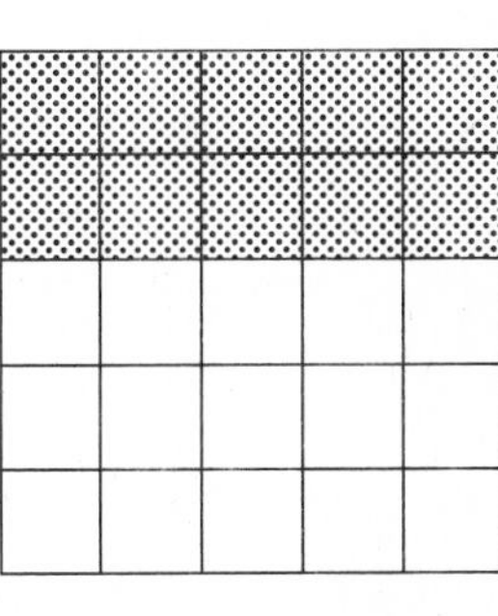

$5 \times 2 =$ ____ $2 \times 5 =$ ____

**Write your own**. Use the same numbers. Color different rows. Write different multiplication sentences.

3. 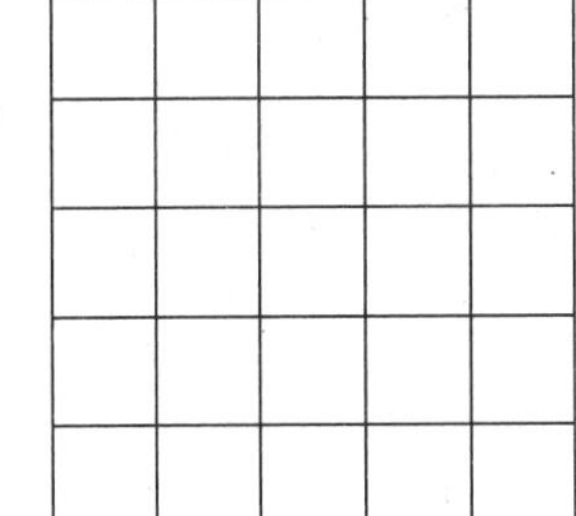

____ $\times$ ____ $=$ ____

4. 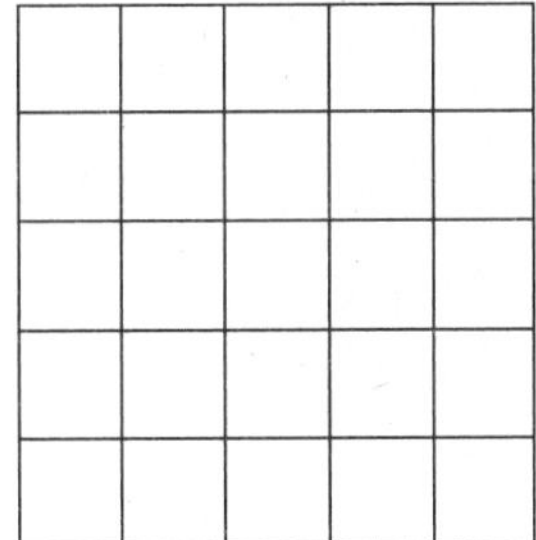

____ $\times$ ____ $=$ ____

5. $7 \times 2 =$ ____

$2 \times 7 =$ ____

6. $6 \times 3 =$ ____

$3 \times 6 =$ ____

7. $3 \times 5 =$ ____

$5 \times 3 =$ ____

## Problem Solving Patterns

8. Find the products. What pattern do you see?

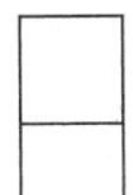

$2 \times 1 =$ ____

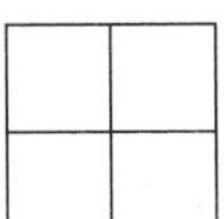

$2 \times 2 =$ ____

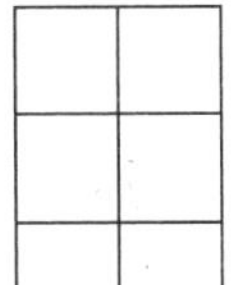

$2 \times 3 =$ ____

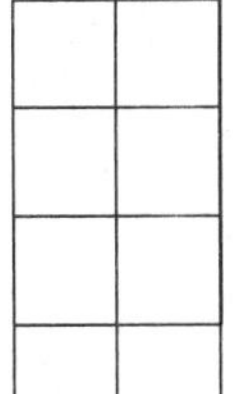

$2 \times 4 =$ ____



**Notes for Home** Your child found answers to related multiplication facts. *Home Activity:* Ask your child to arrange rows of pennies to show related multiplication facts such as 3 x 2 and 2 x 3.

Name ______________________

Practice 13-5

# Multiplication in Vertical Form

Write the multiplication fact in two ways.

1. 3 rows of 6

3 × 6 = 18

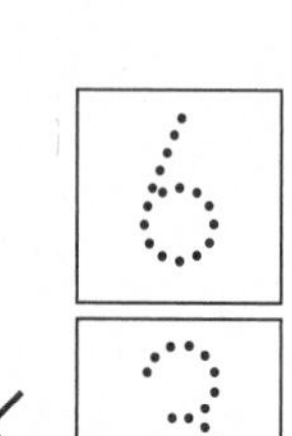

$$\begin{array}{r} 6 \\ \times\ 3 \\ \hline 18 \end{array}$$

2. 2 groups of 7

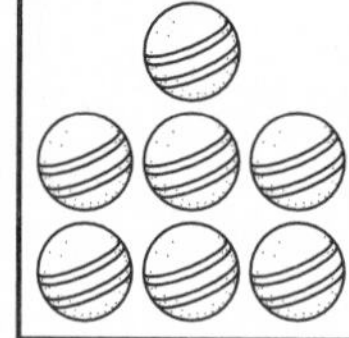

___ × ___ = ___

×

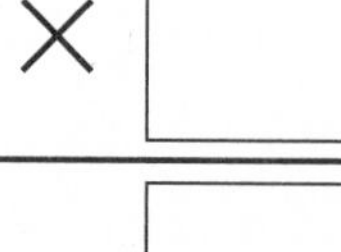

3. 4 rows of 3

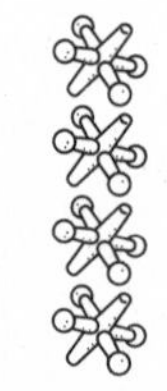

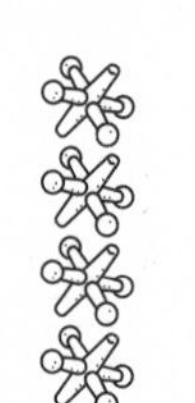

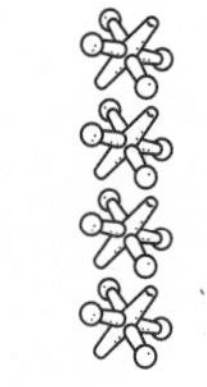

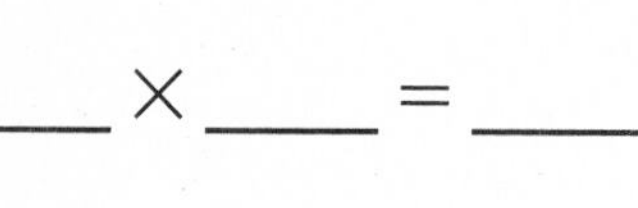

___ × ___ = ___

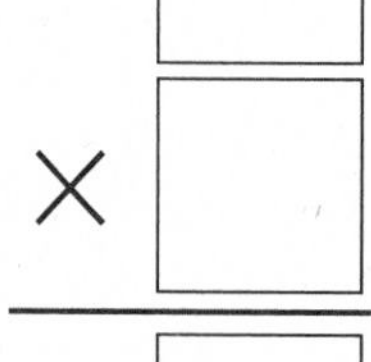

×

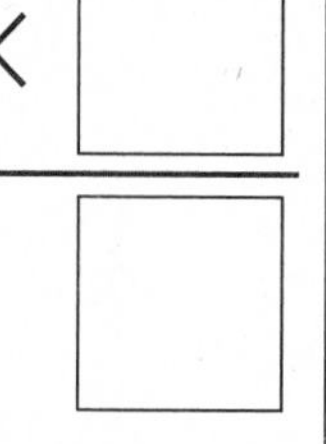

4. 5 rows of 4

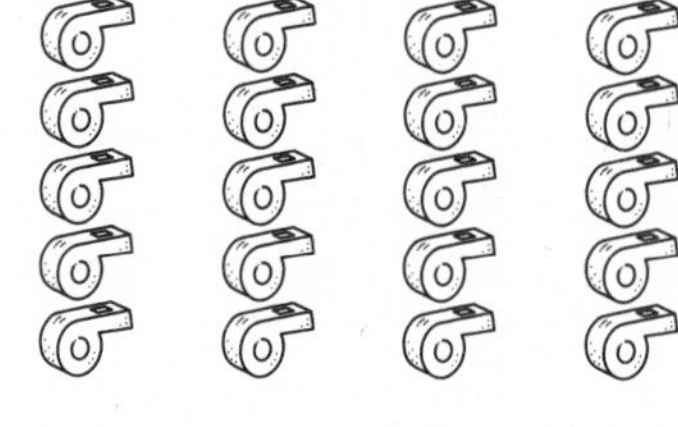

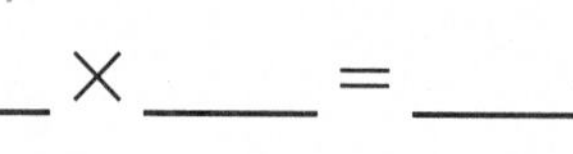

___ × ___ = ___

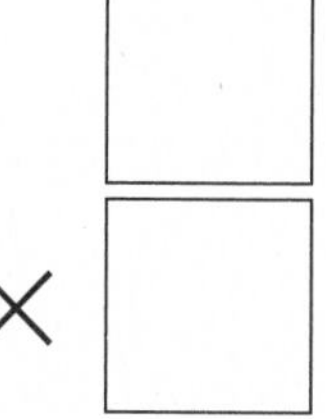

×

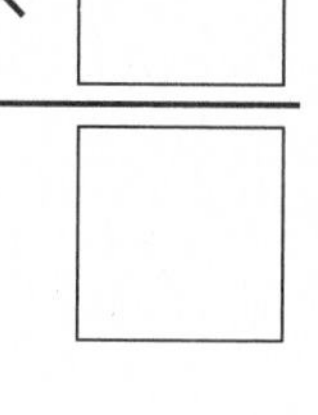

## Problem Solving Patterns

5. Find the number pattern. Write the missing numbers.

$$\begin{array}{r} 2 \\ \times\ 1 \\ \hline \end{array} \quad \begin{array}{r} 2 \\ \times\ 2 \\ \hline \end{array} \quad \begin{array}{r} 2 \\ \times\ 3 \\ \hline \end{array} \quad \begin{array}{r} 2 \\ \times\ \square \\ \hline \end{array} \quad \begin{array}{r} 2 \\ \times\ \square \\ \hline \end{array} \quad \begin{array}{r} 2 \\ \times\ \square \\ \hline \end{array}$$



**Notes for Home** Your child wrote multiplication facts in two different ways. *Home Activity:* Have your child write the multiplication fact for 3 groups of 4 two different ways.

Name ______________________________

Practice 13-6

# **Problem Solving:** Choose a Strategy

Choose a way to solve each problem.
Show what you did.

1. Jamal packed 5 bananas in each of 4 bags. How many bananas did he pack?

2. Kendra and Miguel each packed 8 baskets with fruit. How many baskets did they pack in all?

3. Erin made 6 gift baskets. Julie made 6 gift baskets. Andy made 6 gift baskets. How many gift baskets did the children make in all?

## Problem Solving Estimation

4. About how many mangos are ready to be packed?

   Circle the best estimate.

about 20 about 40 about 60

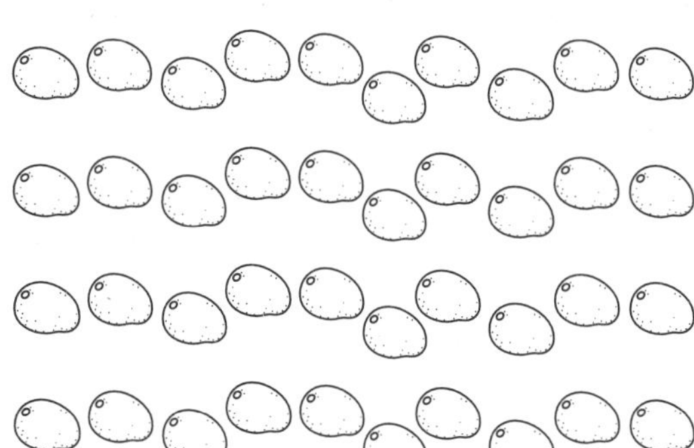



**Notes for Home** Your child chose strategies to solve problems involving multiplication. *Home Activity:* Ask your child to solve this problem: *6 children packed 2 gift baskets each. How many baskets did they pack?* (6 x 2 = 12)

Name ______________________________

Practice
Chapter 13
A

# Mixed Practice: Lessons 1–6

Find how many in all. You can use snap cubes.

1. How many grapes?
   4 groups of 4 grapes

  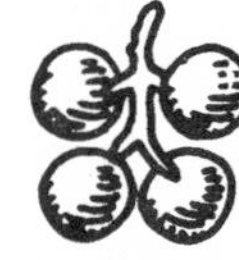 

_____ + _____ + _____ + _____ = _____ grapes

_____ × _____ = _____ grapes

---

Color equal rows. Find the product.

2. 4 rows of 3    3 rows of 4

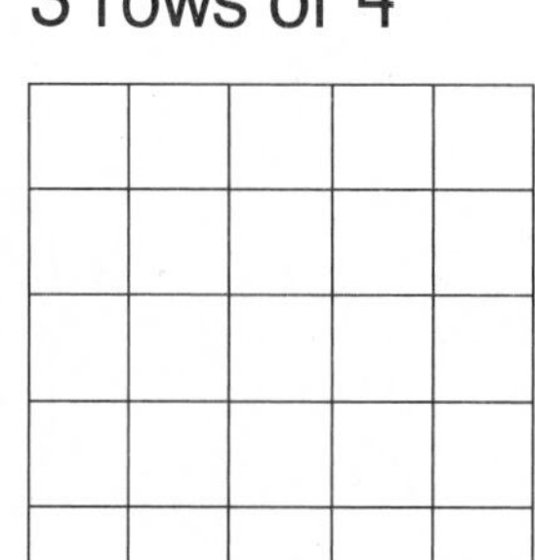

$4 \times 3 =$ _____    $3 \times 4 =$ _____

3. 5 rows of 2    2 rows of 5

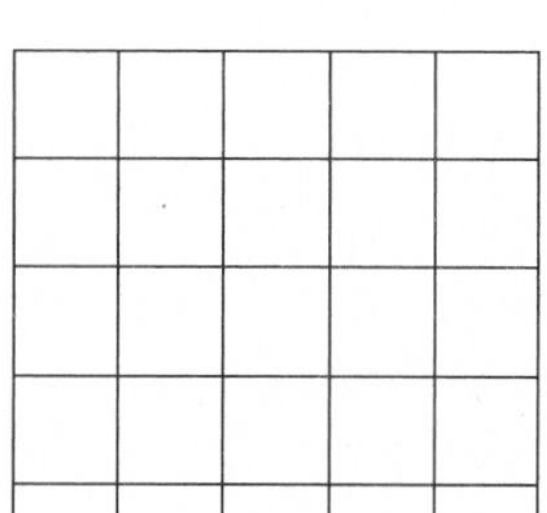

$5 \times 2 =$ _____    $2 \times 5 =$ _____

## Problem Solving

Draw a picture to solve the problem.

4. There are 3 plants on a shelf.
   Each plant has 5 flowers.
   How many flowers are there in all?

   _____ × _____ = _____ flowers

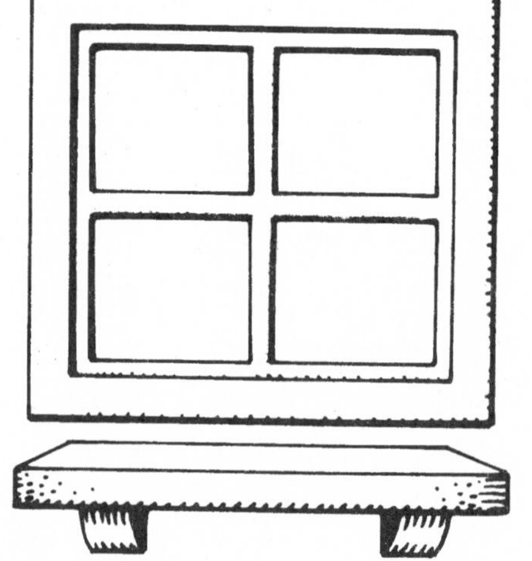

## Journal

5. Tell two ways you can find the total number of 3 + 3 + 3 + 3.

**Notes for Home** Your child practiced using pictures and drawing pictures to solve multiplication problems.
*Home Activity:* Ask your child to explain how he or she responded to the Journal question.



 Use with page 507.

Name ____________________

Practice
Chapters 1–13
A

# Cumulative Review

Shade some of the equal parts.

Write the fraction for the parts that are shaded.

1. Shade 5 equal parts.

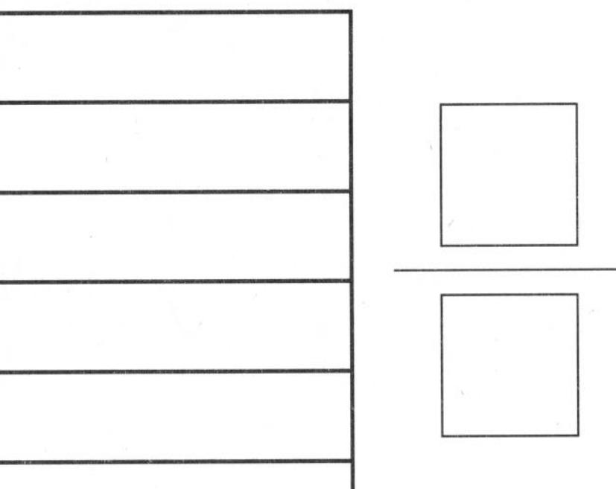

2. Shade 3 equal parts.

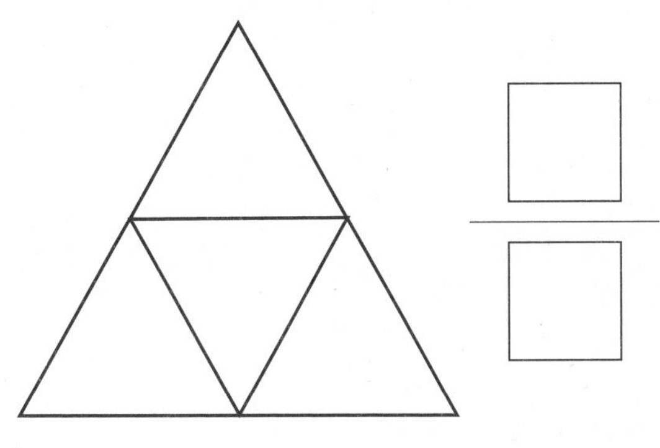

## Getting Ready for Next Year

Copy each problem on a separate piece of paper. Add or subtract.

3.

| | | | | | |
|---|---|---|---|---|---|
| 346 | 493 | 851 | 172 | 685 | 574 |
| + 125 | − 268 | − 419 | + 634 | − 372 | + 185 |

## Test Prep

Fill in the ○ for the correct answer.

Which shape would you make if you traced a face of each object?

4. 5. 6.

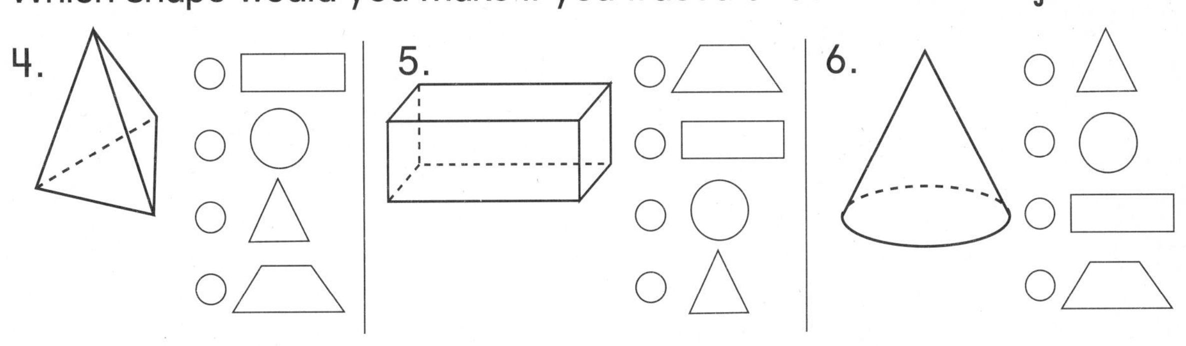



**Notes for Home** Your child reviewed fractions, solids, and addition and subtraction. *Home Activity:* Provide your child with an unopened can and ask him or her to show you one of the faces that is a circle.

Name ______________________

Practice 13-7

# Explore Making Equal Groups

At camp, 4 children share 12 plums equally. How many plums does each child get?

Each child gets 3 plums.

Use counters to make equal groups. Draw a picture to show your work.

1. 5 children share 10 flippers. How many flippers for each child?

   2 flippers

2. 6 children share 2 canoes. How many children in each canoe?

   ______ children

3. 3 children share 15 beads. How many beads for each child?

   ______ beads

4. 12 children share 2 tents. How many children in each tent?

   ______ children

**Talk About It** Could 3 children share 7 ears of corn equally? How do you know?

**Notes for Home** Your child drew pictures to share amounts equally. *Home Activity:* Give your child 8 pennies or other small objects and ask him or her to show you how to share them equally with you.



 Use with pages 509–510.

Name ______________________________



# Share and Divide

You can use counters. Draw a picture to show equal groups. Write the number sentence.

1. 12 balls in 3 boxes.

12 ÷ 3 = 4 balls

2. 16 pencils in 2 boxes.

____ ÷ ____ = ____ pencils

3. 18 beads in 3 bags.

____ ÷ ____ = ____ beads

4. 8 oranges in 4 bags.

____ ÷ ____ = ____ oranges

5. 20 peanuts in 5 bags.

____ ÷ ____ = ____ peanuts

6. 6 apples shared by 2 children.

____ ÷ ____ = ____ apples

## Problem Solving

Solve. You can use counters.

7. Suli has 12 hula hoops to pass out in the playground. If she gives 2 hula hoops to each child, how many children will get hula hoops?

_____ children

**Notes for Home** Your child drew pictures and completed number sentences. *Home Activity:* Ask your child to draw a picture and write a division sentence to show 14 hula hoops shared by 7 children. (14 ÷ 7 = 2)

Name ______________________________

Practice 13-9

# Problem Solving: Choose an Operation

Circle the number sentence that helps you solve the problem.

1. 7 children were hiking. Each child found 3 acorns. How many acorns did the children find?

$7 - 3 = 4$  $21 \div 7 = 3$  $7 \times 3 = 21$

2. 15 children take swim class. The coaches separate them into 3 equal groups. How many children are in each group?

$5 \times 3 = 15$  $15 \div 3 = 5$  $15 + 3 = 18$

3. 9 children enter a running race. 6 children finish the race. How many children didn't finish?

$9 \div 3 = 6$  $9 - 6 = 3$  $3 + 6 = 9$

## Tell a Math Story

Tell a story for each number sentence.

4. $15 - 5 = 10$ 5. $10 \div 2 = 5$ 6. $8 \times 2 = 16$



**Notes for Home** Your child identified a number sentence that could be used to solve a word problem. *Home Activity:* Ask your child to tell you a word problem for Exercise 5. (Possible answer: 10 children play a game. They play in 2 equal teams. How many children are on each team? 5)

Name ______________________________

Practice
Chapter 13
B

# Mixed Practice: Lessons 7–9

You can use counters to make equal groups.
Draw a picture to show your work.
Write the number sentence.

1. 9 children share 3 benches equally. How many children at each bench?

_____ ÷ _____ = _____ children

2. 14 balls go in 2 boxes equally. How many balls in each box?

_____ ÷ _____ = _____ balls

## Problem Solving

Circle the number sentence that solves the problem.

3. At a picnic, 4 people share 12 ears of corn equally. How many ears of corn did each person get?

$4 \times 3 = 12$  $12 \div 4 = 3$  $12 - 4 = 8$

4. There are 5 children playing with hula hoops. Each child has 2 hula hoops. How many hula hoops are there?

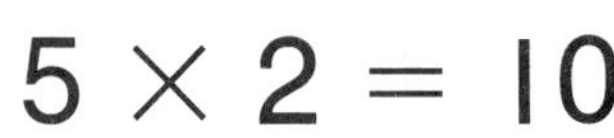

$5 \times 2 = 10$  $5 + 2 = 7$  $10 \div 5 = 2$

## Journal

5. Write a story for this number sentence. **8 ÷ 4 = 2**

**Notes for Home** Your child practiced multiplying and dividing. *Home Activity:* Ask your child to draw to find how many balls there are if 5 children each have 3 balls. (5 x 3 = 15)

Name ______________________________

Practice
Chapters 1–13
B

# Cumulative Review

Draw a shape that is congruent to each shape.

1. 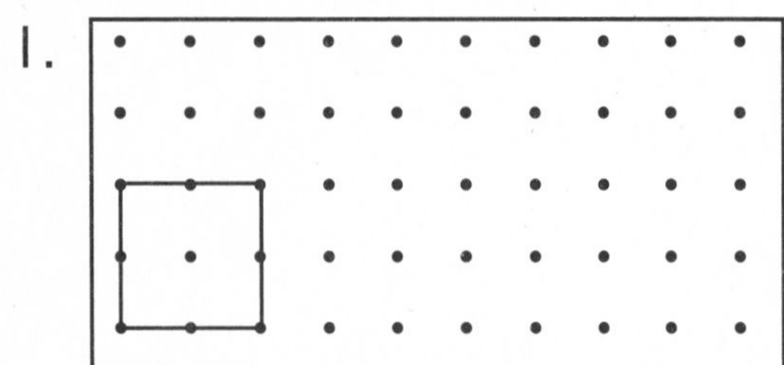

2. 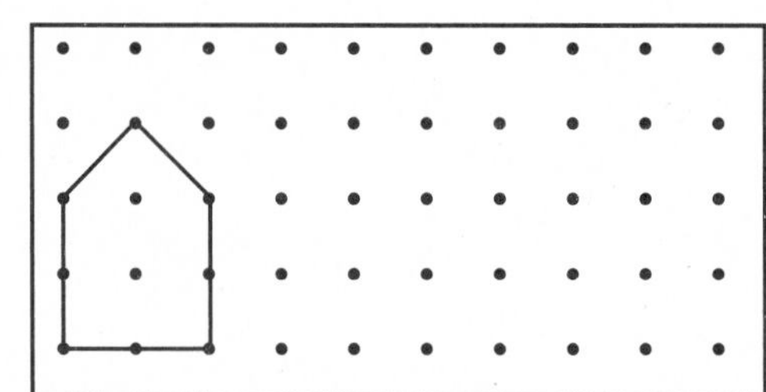

## Problem Solving

3. Tasha cooked 30 hot dogs and 18 hamburgers at the picnic. How many lunches did she cook in all?

   ______ lunches

4. At the picnic, there were 45 adults and 29 children. How many more adults were there than children?

   ______ adults

## Getting Ready for Next Year

Copy each problem on a seperate piece of paper. Add.

5.

| 11 | 25 | 33 | 24 | 46 | 18 |
|---|---|---|---|---|---|
| 12 | 14 | 10 | 15 | 21 | 19 |
| + 13 | + 3 | + 29 | + 17 | + 16 | + 20 |

## Test Prep

Fill in the ○ for the correct answer.

6. 218 + 535
   ○ 853
   ○ 643
   ○ 753
   ○ 743

7. 841 − 436
   ○ 415
   ○ 315
   ○ 406
   ○ 405

8. 327 + 234
   ○ 560
   ○ 561
   ○ 651
   ○ 156



**Notes for Home** Your child reviewed congruence, addition, subtraction, and word problems.
*Home Activity:* Draw a shape. Ask your child to draw a shape that is congruent, or has the same shape and size.

Name ______________________

Practice 1-1

## Explore Counting and Comparing

How many children in your class are wearing sneakers?
How many are wearing shoes?
Use ⬭ ⬬ to show how many.

| Wearing Shoes | Wearing Sneakers |
|---|---|
| | |

1. How many children are wearing sneakers? _____
2. How many children are wearing shoes? _____
3. Which group has more? ______________

Answers will vary.

4. Which group has fewer? ______________

### Journal

5. Tell how you know which group has more.

Sample answer: Match the counters one to one and see if any are left over.

**Notes for Home** Your child counted and compared numbers using *more*, *fewer*, and *equal*. *Home Activity:* Ask your child to use *more*, *fewer*, and *equal* to describe groups of things on the dinner table, such as cups, saucers, plates, forks, knives, and spoons.

Use with pages 3–4. **1**

Name ______________________

Practice 1-2

## More or Fewer

Jose // Victor
// Marlena / Frank /
Teresita Pam

1. How many letters are in each name? Put the names in order from the fewest to the most number of letters.

| Names | Number of Letters |
|---|---|
| P a m | 3 |
| J o s e | 4 |
| F r a n k | 5 |
| V i c t o r | 6 |
| M a r l e n a | 7 |
| T e r e s i t a | 8 |

### Problem Solving

Solve.

2. Marlena has 9 pens.
Pam has 3 pens.
How many more pens does Marlena have than Pam?
6 more pens

3. Frank has 7 books.
Jose has 5 books.
How many fewer books does Jose have than Frank?
2 fewer books

**Notes for Home** Your child compared sets. *Home Activity:* Arrange 3 sets of pens so that each set has a different number of pens. Ask your child to use *most* and *fewest* to compare the number of pens in each set.

**2** Use with pages 5–6.

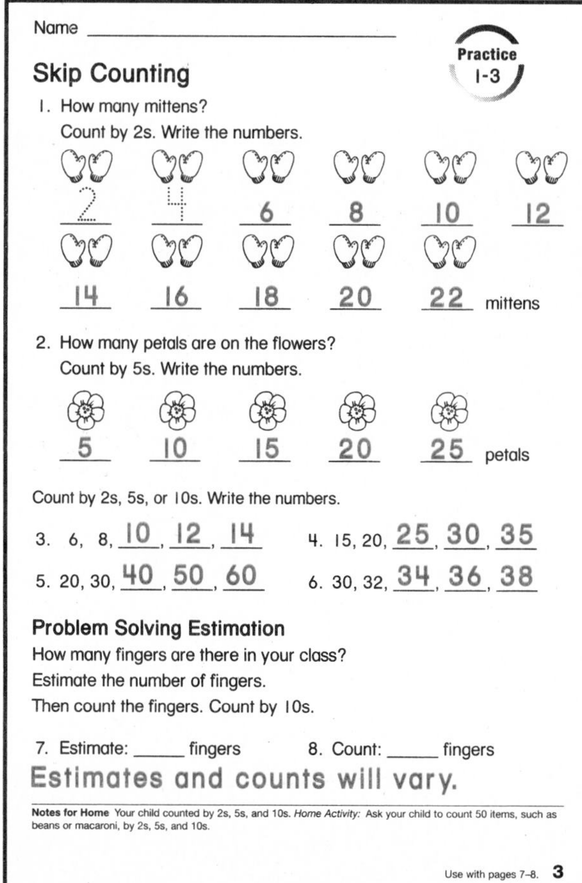

Name ______________________

Practice 1-3

## Skip Counting

1. How many mittens?
Count by 2s. Write the numbers.

2, 4, 6, 8, 10, 12
14, 16, 18, 20, 22 mittens

2. How many petals are on the flowers?
Count by 5s. Write the numbers.

5, 10, 15, 20, 25 petals

Count by 2s, 5s, or 10s. Write the numbers.

3. 6, 8, 10, 12, 14
4. 15, 20, 25, 30, 35
5. 20, 30, 40, 50, 60
6. 30, 32, 34, 36, 38

### Problem Solving Estimation

How many fingers are there in your class?
Estimate the number of fingers.
Then count the fingers. Count by 10s.

7. Estimate: _____ fingers
8. Count: _____ fingers

Estimates and counts will vary.

**Notes for Home** Your child counted by 2s, 5s, and 10s. *Home Activity:* Ask your child to count 50 items, such as beans or macaroni, by 2s, 5s, and 10s.

Use with pages 7–8. **3**

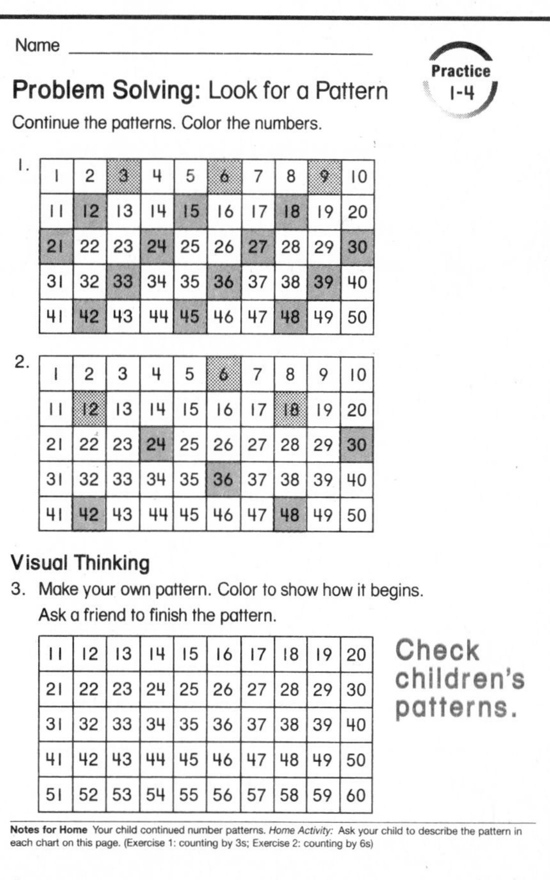

Name ______________________

Practice 1-4

## Problem Solving: Look for a Pattern

Continue the patterns. Color the numbers.

1.

| 1 | 2 | 3 | 4 | 5 | 6 | 7 | 8 | 9 | 10 |
|---|---|---|---|---|---|---|---|---|---|
| 11 | 12 | 13 | 14 | 15 | 16 | 17 | 18 | 19 | 20 |
| 21 | 22 | 23 | 24 | 25 | 26 | 27 | 28 | 29 | 30 |
| 31 | 32 | 33 | 34 | 35 | 36 | 37 | 38 | 39 | 40 |
| 41 | 42 | 43 | 44 | 45 | 46 | 47 | 48 | 49 | 50 |

2.

| 1 | 2 | 3 | 4 | 5 | 6 | 7 | 8 | 9 | 10 |
|---|---|---|---|---|---|---|---|---|---|
| 11 | 12 | 13 | 14 | 15 | 16 | 17 | 18 | 19 | 20 |
| 21 | 22 | 23 | 24 | 25 | 26 | 27 | 28 | 29 | 30 |
| 31 | 32 | 33 | 34 | 35 | 36 | 37 | 38 | 39 | 40 |
| 41 | 42 | 43 | 44 | 45 | 46 | 47 | 48 | 49 | 50 |

### Visual Thinking

3. Make your own pattern. Color to show how it begins.
Ask a friend to finish the pattern.

| 11 | 12 | 13 | 14 | 15 | 16 | 17 | 18 | 19 | 20 |
|---|---|---|---|---|---|---|---|---|---|
| 21 | 22 | 23 | 24 | 25 | 26 | 27 | 28 | 29 | 30 |
| 31 | 32 | 33 | 34 | 35 | 36 | 37 | 38 | 39 | 40 |
| 41 | 42 | 43 | 44 | 45 | 46 | 47 | 48 | 49 | 50 |
| 51 | 52 | 53 | 54 | 55 | 56 | 57 | 58 | 59 | 60 |

Check children's patterns.

**Notes for Home** Your child continued number patterns. *Home Activity:* Ask your child to describe the pattern in each chart on this page. (Exercise 1: counting by 3s; Exercise 2: counting by 6s)

**4** Use with pages 11–12.

Name ______________________

Practice Chapter 1 A

## Mixed Practice: Lessons 1–4

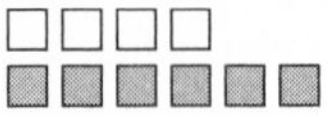

1. Circle the color that has more cubes.

white (gray)

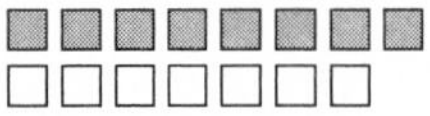

2. Circle the color that has fewer cubes.

(white) gray

Use the graph to answer the questions.

| Stars | Moons |
|---|---|
| ☆☆☆ ☆☆☆ ☆☆☆ ☆☆ | ☾☾☾ ☾☾☾ ☾☾ |

3. Are there more stars or moons?

stars

4. How many more? 3 more

Count by 2s or 5s. Write the numbers.

5. 15, 20, 25, 30, 35, 40, 45, 50, 55

6. 6, 8, 10, 12, 14, 16, 18, 20, 22

### Problem Solving

7. Continue the pattern. Color the numbers.

| 1 | 2 | 3 | 4 | 5 | 6 | 7 | 8 | 9 | 10 |
|---|---|---|---|---|---|---|---|---|---|
| 11 | 12 | 13 | 14 | 15 | 16 | 17 | 18 | 19 | 20 |
| 21 | 22 | 23 | 24 | 25 | 26 | 27 | 28 | 29 | 30 |

### Journal

8. Draw a picture of 2 groups. Circle the group that has fewer.

Sample drawing: (xxx) xxxx

**Notes for Home** Your child practiced comparing numbers and completing counting patterns. *Home Activity:* Ask your child to create a number pattern for you to continue. Then have him or her check your answers.

Use with page 13. 5

Name ______________________

Practice Chapter 1 A

## Cumulative Review

Count how many. Write the numbers.

1.  8

2.  6

3. Which group has more, the whales or the shells?

shells

4. How many more?

2 more

5. Which name has more letters?

| L | E | R | O | Y | | | |
|---|---|---|---|---|---|---|---|
| J | U | S | T | I | N | E | |

Justine

6. How many more? 2 more

### Test Prep

Fill in the ○ for the correct answer.

7. What number comes next?

46, 47, 48, 49, ____

○ 45 ○ 59 ● 50 ○ 60

8. What number comes next?

53, 54, 55, 56, ____

● 57 ○ 59 ○ 60 ○ 66

**Notes for Home** Your child reviewed number groups to 9, sorting and classifying, and counting patterns. *Home Activity:* Ask your child to say the next 5 numbers in Exercise 8. (58, 59, 60, 61, 62)

6 Use with page 14.

Name ______________________

Practice 1-5

## Graphs

Use the graphs to answer the questions.

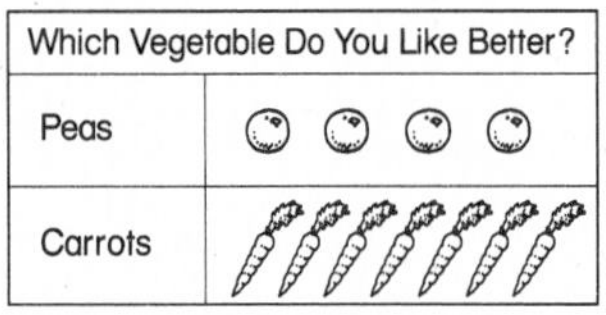

| Which Vegetable Do You Like Better? | |
|---|---|
| Peas | ●●●● |
| Carrots | 7 carrots |

1. How many children like peas?

4 children

2. How many more children like carrots than peas?

3 more

| What Is Your Favorite Sandwich? | | |
|---|---|---|
| 4 | 6 | 4 |
| Ham | Turkey | Cheese |

3. Which sandwiches do an equal number of children like best? Circle the foods.

(Ham) Turkey (Cheese)

4. Which sandwich was picked the greatest number of times?

Turkey

5. **Write your own** question about one of the graphs.

Questions will vary.

### Problem Solving Estimation

5. Do you think more children in your class like peanut butter and jelly sandwiches or tuna fish sandwiches? Circle your estimate.

peanut butter and jelly    tuna fish    Answers will vary.

You can make a graph to check your estimate.

**Notes for Home** Your child answered questions about graphs. *Home Activity:* Ask your child to make a graph like the one in Exercise 3 that shows family members' votes for favorite sandwiches.

Use with pages 15–16. 7

Name ______________________

Practice 1-6

## Pictographs

Use the graph. Give each answer.

| Favorite Fruit Juice | |
|---|---|
| Orange | ☺☺☺☺☺ |
| Apple | ☺☺☺☺☺☺☺ |
| Grape | ☺☺☺ |

Each ☺ means 1 child.

1. How many children like orange juice best?

5 children

2. Which fruit juice is the favorite of most of the children?

Apple

### Mixed Practice

Count by 2s to find each answer.

| Favorite Fruit Bread | |
|---|---|
| Apple | 5 figures |
| Banana | 4 figures |
| Apricot | 7 figures |

Each figure means 2 children.

3. How many children like apple bread best?

2, 4, 6, 8, 10

4. How many children like apricot bread best?

2, 4, 6, 8, 10, 12, 14

### Mental Math

5. How many more children picked apple juice than grape juice in the graph above? 4

**Notes for Home** Your child answered questions about pictographs. *Home Activity:* Ask your child to think of a question that compares two items in one of the graphs. (Possible question: How many more children like banana bread than apple bread? (3))

8 Use with pages 17–18.

Name ______________________

Practice 1-7

## Experiment and Tally

Karen tossed a 2-colored counter. Then she tallied her results. Count how many red, how many blue, and how many in all.

| Red | Blue |
|---|---|
| ||| | 卌 卌 || |

| Red | Blue |
|---|---|
| 卌 || | 卌 ||| |

1. How many red? 3
2. How many blue? 12
3. How many in all? 15

4. How many red? 7
5. How many blue? 8
6. How many in all? 15

Show the tallies for each chart.

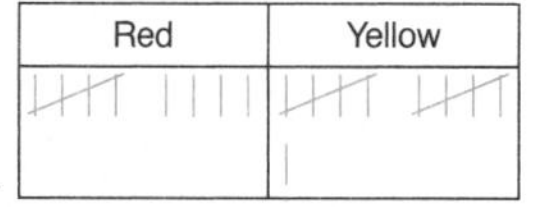

| Red | Yellow |
|---|---|
| 卌 |||| | 卌 卌 | |

| Red | Yellow |
|---|---|
| 卌 卌 | | 卌 卌 卌 ||| |

7. Show 9 red.
8. Show 11 yellow
9. How many in all? 20

10. Show 11 red.
11. Show 18 yellow.
12. How many in all? 29

### Problem Solving Critical Thinking

13. If you toss a number cube 20 times, could it land on six 20 times? Why or why not?
Sample answer: Yes, but it is highly unlikely.

**Notes for Home** Your child read and made tally charts. *Home Activity:* Ask your child to tell you which tally chart shows the most yellow tosses and the fewest yellow tosses. (Most: lower right chart with 18 tosses. Fewest: lower left chart with 11 tosses.)



Name ______________________

Practice 1-8

## Bar Graphs

1. Do you live on a street, avenue or road? Ask 10 classmates. How many letters are there in each street name? Make tally marks. Answers will vary.

| Number of Letters in Our Street Names | | | | | | | |
|---|---|---|---|---|---|---|---|
| 1 | 2 | 3 | 4 | 5 | 6 | 7 | 8 |
| | | | | | | | |
| 9 | 10 | 11 | 12 | 13 | 14 | 15 | 16 |
| | | | | | | | |

2. Make a bar graph. Color 1 space for each tally mark.

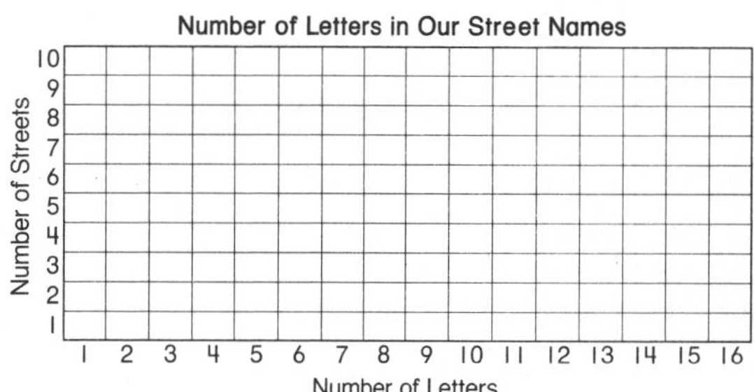


### Problem Solving Critical Thinking

3. Suppose 8 children have 9 letters in their street names. Explain how you would show this on a bar graph. Possible answer: By coloring 8 blocks above the number 9.

**Notes for Home** Your child has gathered and shown data using tally marks and a bar graph. *Home Activity:* Ask your child to add the street names of family members including cousins, uncles, aunts, and grandparents.



Name ______________________

Practice 1-9

## Problem Solving: Collect and Use Data

1. Show data for 8 classmates using a diagram.

Do You Like Roller Coasters or Water Slides?

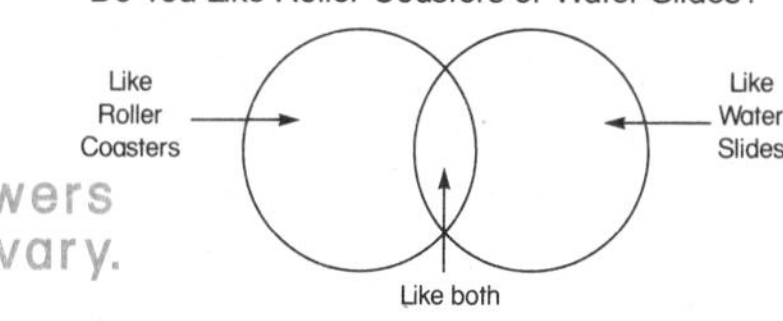


Answers will vary.

Use your diagram to answer the questions.

2. How many children like both roller coasters and water slides? ____
3. How many children like roller coasters? ____
4. How many children like roller coasters but not water slides? ____
5. How many children like water slides? ____
6. How many children like water slides but not roller coasters? ____

### Tell a Math Story

7. Tell a short story about 7 friends. Ask a friend to draw a diagram for your story.

**Notes for Home** Your child collected, organized, and used data to solve problems. *Home Activity:* Work with your child to create a diagram like the one on this page that shows how many family members like bananas, grapes, or both.



Name ______________________

Practice Chapter 1 B

## Mixed Practice: Lessons 5–9

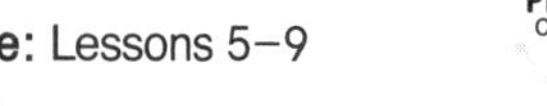

Use the graph. Solve.

1. How many children like strawberry best? 4
2. Do more children like chocolate or vanilla? Chocolate

| Favorite Milk Flavor | |
|---|---|
| Plain | 🥛🥛🥛🥛🥛 |
| Vanilla | 🥛🥛 |
| Chocolate | 🥛🥛🥛🥛🥛🥛🥛 |
| Strawberry | 🥛🥛🥛🥛 |

Each 🥛 means 1 child.

Use the graph to answer the questions.

3. Which soup was picked most often? Noodle
4. Which soup was picked least often? Bean

Favorite Soup
Tomato
Noodle
Bean
Vegetable
1 2 3 4 5 6 7 8 9 10

### Problem Solving

Look at the diagram. Answer the questions.

5. How many children like apples but not pears? 4
6. How many children like both apples and pears? 1

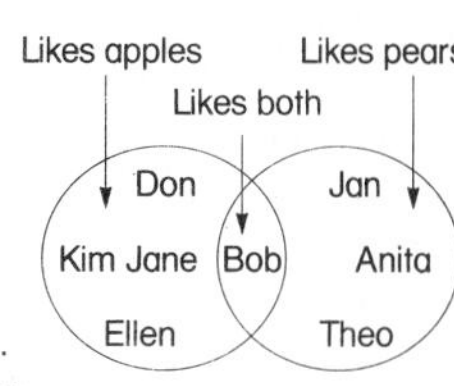


### Journal

7. Write a question about the diagram. Ask a friend to answer your question.

**Notes for Home** Your child practiced using graphs to compare information. *Home Activity:* Have your child add his or her vote to the graph about a favorite soup. Ask: *Does this change the answers to Exercises 3 and 4?* (No, 1 vote for any soup would not change the answers.)

Name ______________________

## Cumulative Review

Circle the number that is greater.

1. (7) 5
2. 10 (16)

Circle the number that is less.

3. 14 (11)
4. 8 (6)

### Problem Solving

Solve.

5. There are 7 frogs.
There are 5 toads.
Which group has more?
frogs

6. There are 6 wasps.
There are 9 hornets.
Which group has fewer?
wasps

### Test Prep

Fill in the ○ for the correct answer.

7. Count by 2s.
Mark the number that comes next.
2, 4, 6, 8, ____
9 ○ 10 ● 11 ○ 12 ○

8. Count by 5s.
Mark the number that comes next.
10, 15, 20, 25, ____
26 ○ 28 ○ 30 ● 35 ○

**Notes for Home** Your child reviewed number combinations, comparing sets, and skip counting. *Home Activity:* Ask your child to assemble 2 groups of objects at home that are equal in number, and then create a third group with fewer objects.



Name ______________________

## Explore Addition Stories

8 spoons.

Lea brings 2 more spoons.

How many spoons in all?

8 and 2 is 10.

Solve each problem. You can use ○ ●.

1. 7 beans on a plate.
3 more beans are added.
How many beans in all?
7 and 3 is 10.

2. 5 apples on Tim's plate.
4 apples on Kim's plate.
How many apples in all?
5 and 4 is 9.

3. 6 cups on the table.
2 more cups are added.
How many cups in all?
6 and 2 is 8.

4. 3 plates on the table.
5 plates are added.
How many plates in all?
3 and 5 is 8.

**Talk About It** Tell a classmate a number story about this picture.

Answers will vary.

**Notes for Home** Your child solved addition stories. *Home Activity:* Ask your child to tell you an addition story about 3 honey bees flying around and 4 honey bees on flowers.



Name ______________________

## Join Groups to Add

Practice 2-2

You can use ○ ● and a □□.

Write the number sentence. Solve.

1. 5 bees are in a hive.
4 more bees join them.
How many bees are there now?
5 and 4 is 9

2. 4 cats sit in the sun.
3 cats join them.
How many cats in all?
4 and 3 is 7

3. 3 dogs are playing.
5 more dogs also play.
How many dogs in all?
3 and 5 is 8

4. 7 butterflies on the flowers.
2 more butterflies come.
How many butterflies are on the flowers now?
7 and 2 is 9

### Problem Solving Critical Thinking

5. Solve. You can use ○ ●.
There are 9 cats in all.
How many cats are hiding under the blanket?
6

**Notes for Home** Your child wrote number sentences for addition stories. *Home Activity:* Ask you child to tell you an addition story and then explain how he or she would find the answer.



Name ______________________

## Count On and Add Zero

Practice 2-3

0 1 2 3 4 5 6 7 8 9 10 11 12

Use the number line. Write the sum.

1. $3 + 1 = 4$ $\quad 5 + 3 = 8$
2. $8 + 0 = 8$ $\quad 9 + 2 = 11$
3. $6 + 3 = 9$ $\quad 2 + 1 = 3$
4. $1 + 2 = 3$ $\quad 2 + 0 = 2$
5. $7 + 4 = 11$ $\quad 4 + 2 = 6$

Add.

6. $8 + 1 = 9$, $1 + 2 = 3$, $6 + 3 = 9$, $5 + 0 = 5$, $3 + 3 = 6$, $9 + 2 = 11$

7. $7 + 3 = 10$, $4 + 0 = 4$, $2 + 1 = 3$, $1 + 0 = 1$, $8 + 3 = 11$, $3 + 2 = 5$

### Problem Solving Critical Thinking

8. Start with 6. Add a number so that the sum is 6. What number did you add? 0

**Notes for Home** Your child added 0, 1, 2, or 3 to numbers. *Home Activity:* Show your child from 1 to 9 buttons or beans. Have your child use them to show you how many is 0, 1, 2, and 3 more.

Name ______________________

## Turnaround Facts

Write the number sentence for each train.

1. 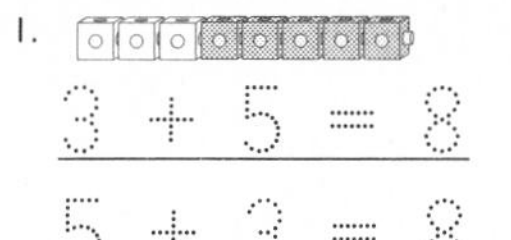


2. 7 + 3 = 10
3 + 7 = 10

3. 6 + 4 = 10
4 + 6 = 10

4. 7 + 5 = 12
5 + 7 = 12

Write the turnaround fact for each number sentence.

5. 4 + 7 = 11
7 + 4 = 11

6. 6 + 5 = 11
5 + 6 = 11

### Problem Solving

Write the number sentence. Solve.

7. 4 fly in the cave.
3 join them.
How many in all?
7

8. 3 are in a tree.
4 are in another tree.
Now how many are in trees?
7

**Notes for Home** Your child used turnaround facts to find sums to 12. *Home Activity:* Ask your child to tell you a set of turnaround facts with a sum of 8. (Possible answer: 5 + 3 = 7 and 3 + 5 = 8)



---

Name ______________________

Practice 2-5

## Ways to Make Numbers

Use . Show different ways to make 9.
Write the number sentences.

1.

| Ways to Make 9 | |
|---|---|
| 0 + 9 = 9 | 5 + 4 = 9 |
| 1 + 8 = 9 | 6 + 3 = 9 |
| 2 + 7 = 9 | 7 + 2 = 9 |
| 3 + 6 = 9 | 8 + 1 = 9 |
| 4 + 5 = 9 | 9 + 0 = 9 |

### Problem Solving Patterns

2. How many ways are there to make 7? 8
3. How many ways are there to make 8? 9
4. How many ways are there to make 9? 10
5. How many ways do you think there are to make 10? 11
6. How many ways do you think there are to make 11? 12
7. Why do you think so?

Possible answer: The number of ways is one more than the number.

**Notes for Home** Your child found all the ways to make 9. *Home Activity:* Ask your child what pattern he or she can use to tell the number of ways to make 7, 6 or 5. (Possible answer: There is 1 more way than the sum; 8 ways to make 7, 7 ways to make 6, and 6 ways to make 5.)



---

Name ______________________

Practice 2-6

## Problem Solving: Write a Number Sentence

Write a number sentence. Solve.

1. Dan sees 8 .
Ann sees 3 more .
How many do Dan and Ann see in all?
8 + 3 = 11

2. 4 are in the tree.
4 are on the ground.
How many in all?
4 + 4 = 8

3. Rita eats 5 .
Juan eats 7 .
How many do they eat in all?
5 + 7 = 12

4. Theo sees 4 on a bush and 2 near the bush.
How many did he see?
4 + 2 = 6

### Tell a Math Story

Use the picture.
Tell a word problem to a friend.
Ask your friend to solve by writing a number sentence.

____ + ____ = ____

Possible answer: The boy caught 3 fish. The girl caught 4 fish. How many fish did they catch in all? 7 fish

**Notes for Home** Your child wrote number sentences to solve story problems. *Home Activity:* Ask your child to tell you a word problem about members of your family. Have your child write the number sentence that he or she would use to solve the problem.



---

Name ______________________

Practice Chapter 2 A

## Mixed Practice: Lessons 1 – 6

Add.

1. 9 + 3 = 12; 4 + 0 = 4; 3 + 8 = 11; 5 + 2 = 7; 4 + 1 = 5; 7 + 2 = 9

These pictures show turnaround facts.
Write the number sentence for each picture.

2. 4 + 6 = 10
6 + 4 = 10

3. 8 + 3 = 11
3 + 8 = 11

### Problem Solving

Write a number sentence. Solve. You can use .

4. Gloria saw 7 in the pond
She saw 2 on the shore.
How many did she see?
7 + 2 = 9

5. 6 were playing ball.
5 joined them.
Now how many are playing ball in all?
6 + 5 = 11

### Journal

6. How do you find the turnaround fact for 5 + 3 = 8? Write about it.

**Notes for Home** Your child practiced addition and problem-solving skills. *Home Activity:* Ask you child how he or she decided what number sentence to write for Exercise 4. (Possible answer: When you join groups, you add. A group of 7 and a group of 2 is 7 + 2, or 9.)

Name ______________________

## Cumulative Review

Count by ones. Write the numbers.

1. 43, 44, 45, 46, 47, 48, 49, 50, 51

Count back by ones. Write the numbers.

2. 18, 17, 16, 15, 14, 13, 12, 11, 10

### Problem Solving

3. Use the tally marks to make a bar graph.

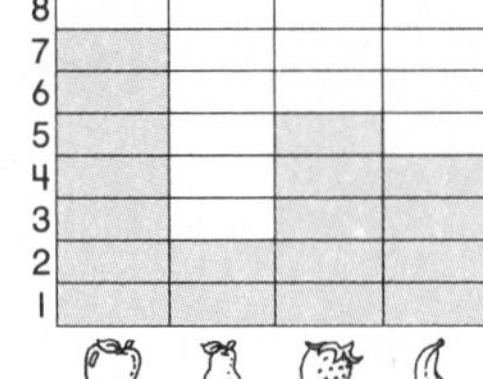


4. How many people chose ? 5 people

5. Which fruit was chosen the most often? Circle the picture.

 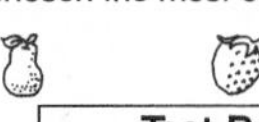 

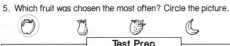

**Test Prep**

Fill in the ○ for the correct answer.

Mark the missing number in the pattern.

6. 10, 15, 20, ______, 30, 35

○ 22
● 25
○ 27
○ 30

**Notes for Home** Your child reviewed counting, using tally marks and graphs, and finding number patterns. *Home Activity:* Ask your child to tell which fruit was chosen least often in Exercise 3. (pear)



Name ______________________

## Separate Groups to Subtract

Use ⬭ ◉ to subtract.
Write the number sentence.

1. 7 are in a tree.
3 fly away.
How many are left?
7 − 3 = 4

2. 5 are playing.
2 run away.
How many are left?
5 − 2 = 3

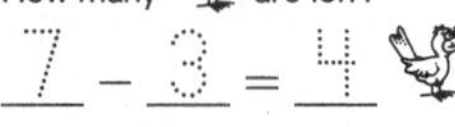

3. 8 are at the lake.
5 fly away.
How many are left?
8 − 5 = 3

4. 4 watch the birds.
2 walk away.
How many are left?
4 − 2 = 2

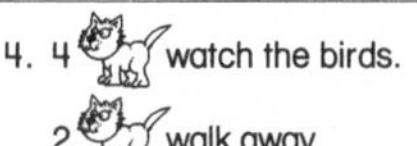

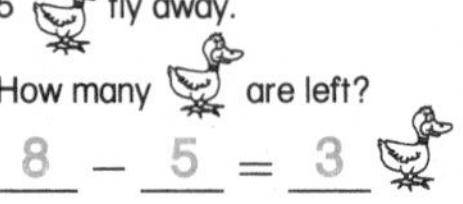

### Problem Solving Visual Thinking

Draw a picture to solve.
Write the number sentence.

5. There are 6 on the ground.
A horse eats 2 .
How many are left?
6 − 2 = 4

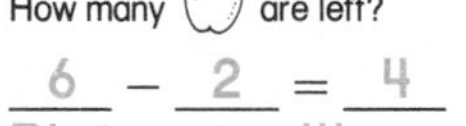

Pictures will vary.

**Notes for Home** Your child used counters to subtract and wrote number sentences. *Home Activity:* Ask your child to use dry beans or macaroni to show you how to subtract 8 − 4 = (4).



Name ______________________

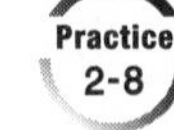


## Count Back and Subtract Zero

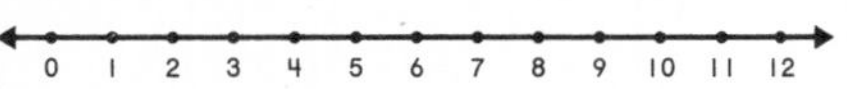


Use the number line. Write the difference.

1. 7 − 1 = 6; 3 − 2 = 1; 9 − 0 = 9; 3 − 1 = 2; 5 − 1 = 4; 12 − 2 = 10

2. 3 − 0 = 3; 11 − 2 = 9; 6 − 1 = 5; 2 − 2 = 0; 1 − 0 = 1; 9 − 1 = 8

3. 6 − 2 = 4; 7 − 0 = 7; 8 − 2 = 6; 11 − 3 = 8; 5 − 2 = 3; 10 − 1 = 9

### Mixed Practice

Add or subtract.

4. 9 − 2 = 7; 8 + 2 = 10; 5 − 0 = 5; 7 − 2 = 5; 1 + 8 = 9; 4 + 2 = 6

### Problem Solving Critical Thinking

Start with 8. Subtract a number.
The answer is 8. What did you subtract? 0

**Notes for Home** Your child added and subtracted using a number line. *Home Activity:* Ask your child to use the number line to find 8 + 3 = 11 and 9 - 2 = 7.



Name ______________________

Practice 2-9

## Explore How Many More

Use ⬭ ◉ to solve.

1. There are 12 .
There are 8 .
How many more are there?
4 more

2. There are 10 .
There are 8 .
How many more are there?
2 more

3. There are 9 .
There are 5 .
How many more are there?
4 more

4. There are 12 .
There are 5 .
How many more are there?
7 more

### Problem Solving Visual Thinking

5. How many more than ?

2 more

6. How many more than ?

2 more

**Notes for Home** Your child used counters to compare groups. *Home Activity:* Ask your child to take 3 cups and 5 saucers and compare the two groups. (There are 2 more saucers.)

Name ____________________

Practice 2-10

## Find How Many More

Write the number sentence. Solve.

You can use ▢▢.

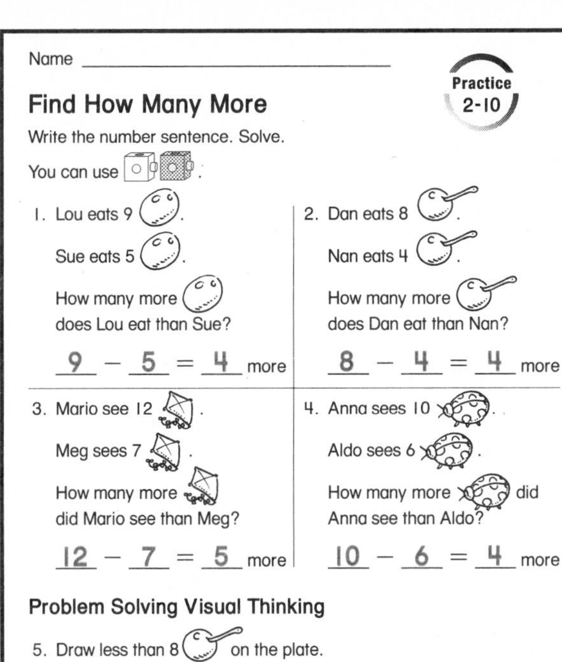

1. Lou eats 9 ○. Sue eats 5 ○. How many more ○ does Lou eat than Sue?
   9 − 5 = 4 more

2. Dan eats 8 ○. Nan eats 4 ○. How many more ○ does Dan eat than Nan?
   8 − 4 = 4 more

3. Mario see 12 ◇. Meg sees 7 ◇. How many more ◇ did Mario see than Meg?
   12 − 7 = 5 more

4. Anna sees 10 ○. Aldo sees 6 ○. How many more ○ did Anna see than Aldo?
   10 − 6 = 4 more

### Problem Solving Visual Thinking

5. Draw less than 8 ○ on the plate.
   How many more ○ are there than ○?
   11 − ___ = ___ more

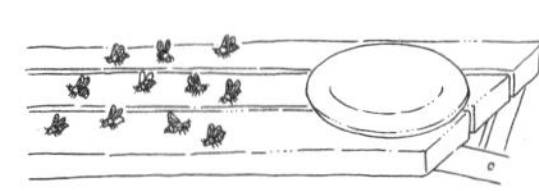

**Notes for Home** Your child used subtraction to compare groups. *Home Activity:* Show your child two groups of objects, such as 5 cups and 3 saucers. Have your child write a number sentence that tells how many more are in the larger group. (Possible answer: 5 − 3 = 2; there are 2 more cups.)



Name ____________________

Practice 2-11

## Relate Addition and Subtraction

Add or subtract.

Write the number sentence. Solve.

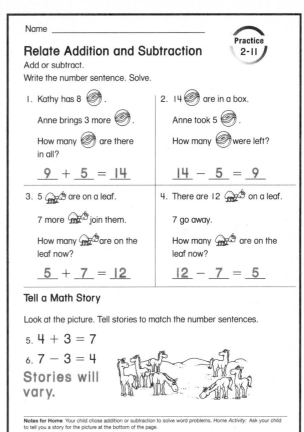

1. Kathy has 8 ○. Anne brings 3 more ○. How many ○ are there in all?
   9 + 5 = 14

2. 14 ○ are in a box. Anne took 5 ○. How many ○ were left?
   14 − 5 = 9

3. 5 ○ are on a leaf. 7 more ○ join them. How many ○ are on the leaf now?
   5 + 7 = 12

4. There are 12 ○ on a leaf. 7 go away. How many ○ are on the leaf now?
   12 − 7 = 5

### Tell a Math Story

Look at the picture. Tell stories to match the number sentences.

5. 4 + 3 = 7

6. 7 − 3 = 4

Stories will vary.

**Notes for Home** Your child chose addition or subtraction to solve word problems. *Home Activity:* Ask your child to tell you a story for the picture at the bottom of the page.



Name ____________________

Practice 2-12

## Problem Solving: Choose an Operation

Circle **add** or **subtract**.

Write the number sentence. Solve.

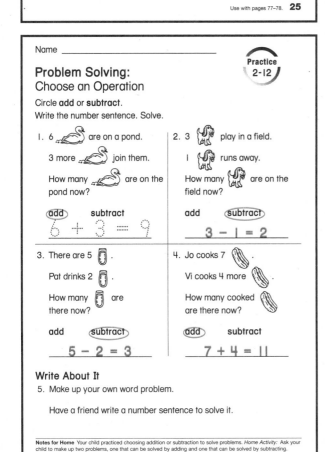

1. 6 ○ are on a pond. 3 more ○ join them. How many ○ are on the pond now?
   (add) subtract
   6 + 3 = 9

2. 3 ○ play in a field. 1 ○ runs away. How many ○ are on the field now?
   add (subtract)
   3 − 1 = 2

3. There are 5 ○. Pat drinks 2 ○. How many ○ are there now?
   add (subtract)

   5 − 2 = 3
   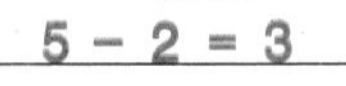

4. Jo cooks 7 ○. Vi cooks 4 more ○. How many cooked are there now?
   (add) subtract
   7 + 4 = 11

### Write About It

5. Make up your own word problem.
   Have a friend write a number sentence to solve it.

**Notes for Home** Your child practiced choosing addition or subtraction to solve problems. *Home Activity:* Ask your child to make up two problems, one that can be solved by adding and one that can be solved by subtracting.



Name ____________________

Practice Chapter 2 B

## Mixed Practice: Lessons 7–12

Subtract. You can use ○ ○.

1.

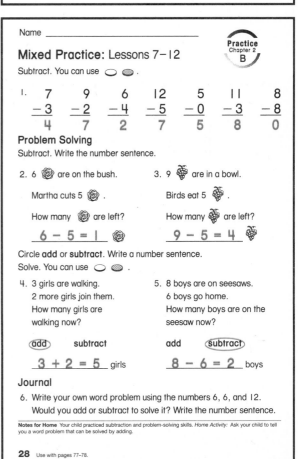

| 7 | 9 | 6 | 12 | 5 | 11 | 8 |
|---|---|---|---|---|---|---|
| −3 | −2 | −4 | −5 | −0 | −3 | −8 |
| 4 | 7 | 2 | 7 | 5 | 8 | 0 |

### Problem Solving

Subtract. Write the number sentence.

2. 6 ○ are on the bush. Martha cuts 5 ○. How many ○ are left?
   6 − 5 = 1 ○

3. 9 ○ are in a bowl. Birds eat 5 ○. How many ○ are left?
   9 − 5 = 4 ○

Circle **add** or **subtract**. Write a number sentence.

Solve. You can use ○ ○.

4. 3 girls are walking. 2 more girls join them. How many girls are walking now?
   (add) subtract
   3 + 2 = 5 girls

5. 8 boys are on seesaws. 6 boys go home. How many boys are on the seesaw now?
   add (subtract)
   8 − 6 = 2 boys

### Journal

6. Write your own word problem using the numbers 6, 6, and 12. Would you add or subtract to solve it? Write the number sentence.

**Notes for Home** Your child practiced subtraction and problem-solving skills. *Home Activity:* Ask your child to tell you a word problem that can be solved by adding.

Name ______________________

Practice Chapters 1–2 B

## Cumulative Review

Write the number sentence. Solve.

1. 8  are playing.
3  run away.
How many  are still playing?
8 − 3 = 5

2. 7  are in a box.
3 are outside.
How many  are there in all?
7 + 3 = 10

Count back by ones. Write the numbers.

3. 36, 35, 34, 33, 32, 31, 30, 29, 28

Count by ones. Write the numbers.

4. 73, 74, 75, 76, 77, 78, 79, 80, 81

### Test Prep

Fill in the ○ for the correct answer.

5. Which train and number sentence show the turnaround fact for this train and number sentence?

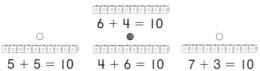

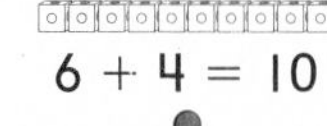
6 + 4 = 10

○ 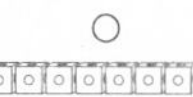 5 + 5 = 10
● 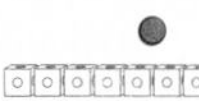 4 + 6 = 10
○ 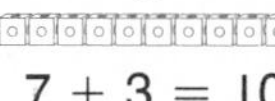 7 + 3 = 10

**Notes for Home** Your child reviewed addition and subtraction skills. *Home Activity:* Ask your child to tell what the turnaround fact for 7 + 3 = 10 would be. (3 + 7 = 10)



Name ______________________

Practice 3-1

## Explore Doubles

5 + 5 = 10

Add. Write the sums. You can use cubes.

1. 3 + 3 = 6 6 + 6 = 12 8 + 8 = 16
2. 7 + 7 = 14 1 + 1 = 2 4 + 4 = 8
3. 2 + 2 = 4 9 + 9 = 18 5 + 5 = 10

4.

| 7 | 6 | 5 | 4 | 3 | 2 | 1 |
|---|---|---|---|---|---|---|
| +7 | +6 | +5 | +4 | +3 | +2 | +1 |
| 14 | 12 | 10 | 8 | 6 | 4 | 2 |

5.

| 3 | 7 | 6 | 4 | 9 | 4 | 8 |
|---|---|---|---|---|---|---|
| +3 | +7 | +6 | +4 | +9 | +4 | +8 |
| 6 | 14 | 12 | 8 | 18 | 8 | 16 |

**Talk About It**
Look at Exercise 4. What pattern do you see in the sums?
The sums decrease by 2.

**Notes for Home** Your child found the sums for doubles facts (such as 4 + 4 = 8). *Home Activity:* Ask your child to give one example of a doubles fact (3 + 3 = 6) and one example of an addition sentence that is not a doubles fact (3 + 5 = 8).



Name ______________________

Practice 3-2

## Use Doubles Plus One

Add.

1. 5 + 5 = 10 5 + 6 = 11 6 + 5 = 11
2. 8 + 8 = 16 8 + 9 = 17 9 + 8 = 17

3.

| 6 | 6 | 7 |
|---|---|---|
| +6 | +7 | +6 |
| 12 | 13 | 13 |

4.

| 7 | 7 | 8 |
|---|---|---|
| +7 | +8 | +7 |
| 14 | 15 | 15 |

5.

| 2 | 5 | 1 | 9 | 6 | 7 | 4 |
|---|---|---|---|---|---|---|
| +2 | +5 | +1 | +9 | +6 | +7 | +4 |
| 4 | 10 | 2 | 18 | 12 | 14 | 8 |

6.

| 5 | 2 | 6 | 5 | 8 | 2 | 4 |
|---|---|---|---|---|---|---|
| +6 | +1 | +7 | +4 | +7 | +3 | +3 |
| 11 | 3 | 13 | 9 | 15 | 5 | 7 |

**Mixed Practice** Add.

7.

| 7 | 4 | 9 | 6 | 7 | 6 | 8 |
|---|---|---|---|---|---|---|
| +0 | +4 | +5 | +7 | +3 | +6 | +9 |
| 7 | 8 | 14 | 13 | 10 | 12 | 17 |

**Problem Solving Critical Thinking**

8. A ladybug has landed on a mirror. How many legs can you see? Explain your answer. 12

**Notes for Home** Your child solved addition facts with sums through 18. *Home Activity:* Ask your child how to solve 6 + 7. (6 + 6 = 12 plus 1 = 13)



Name ______________________

Practice 3-3

## Explore Making 10

Put a picture in each empty box.
Complete the number sentence.

1. 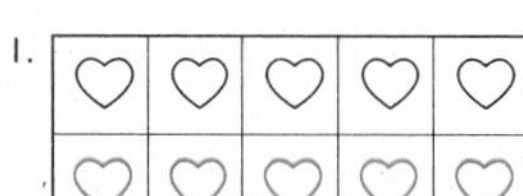 5 + 5 = 10

2.  3 + 7 = 10

3. 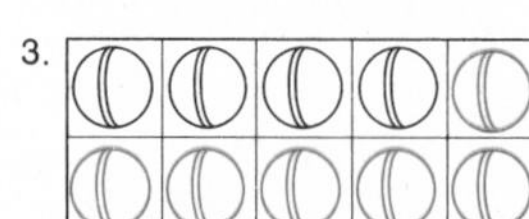 4 + 6 = 10

4. 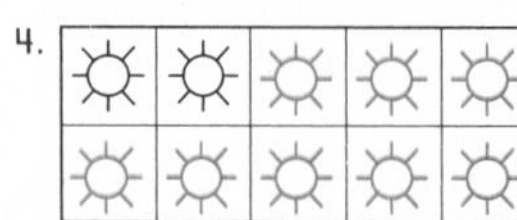 2 + 8 = 10

**Talk About It** What number would you add to 10 to make the sum of 10? 0

**Notes for Home** Your child drew pictures and wrote number sentences with the sum of 10. *Home Activity:* Ask your child to use objects to show 5 + 5 = 10 and to write the number sentence.

Name ______________________

## Make 10 When Adding 9

Practice 3-4

Add. Write the addition sentence.

1. 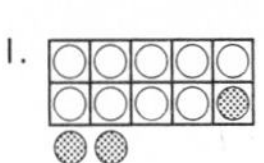
9 + 3 = 12

2. 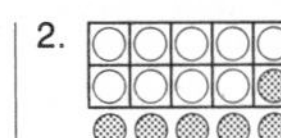
9 + 6 = 15

3. 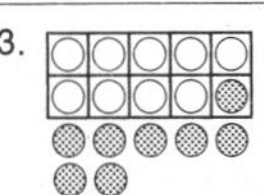
9 + 8 = 17

4. 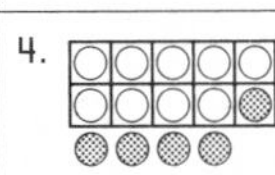
9 + 5 = 14

Add.

5.

| 9 | 9 | 9 | 9 | 9 | 9 | 9 |
|---|---|---|---|---|---|---|
| +5 | +8 | +2 | +7 | +3 | +6 | +4 |
| 14 | 17 | 11 | 16 | 12 | 15 | 13 |

**Mixed Practice** Add.

6. 5 + 4 = 9   7 + 7 = 14   9 + 8 = 17

### Problem Solving Visual Thinking

Frank has 9 stamps on his card.
He gets 8 more stamps.
How many stamps does he have in all? 17 stamps

How many stamps will he carry over to a new card? 7 stamps

**Notes for Home** Your child practiced adding 9 to another number by first making a ten. *Home Activity:* Ask your child to explain how he or she solved Exercise 3.



Name ______________________

## Make 10 When Adding 6, 7, or 8

Practice 3-5

Add. Write the addition sentence.

1. 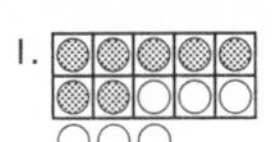
7 + 6 = 13

2. 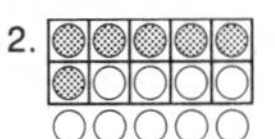
6 + 9 = 15

3. 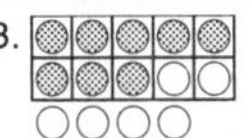
8 + 6 = 14

4. 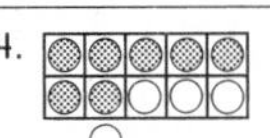
7 + 4 = 11

Add.

5.

| 6 | 4 | 7 | 8 | 9 | 8 | 5 |
|---|---|---|---|---|---|---|
| +7 | +7 | +5 | +5 | +6 | +8 | +6 |
| 13 | 11 | 12 | 13 | 15 | 16 | 11 |

### Problem Solving Critical Thinking

6. Maria tossed these numbers.

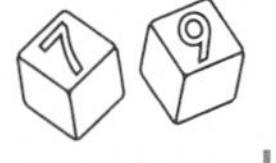

What is the sum? 16

7. Roberto tossed a sum of 13. Circle the cubes that he might have rolled.

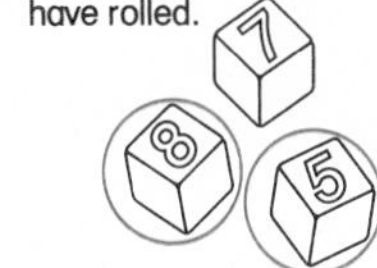

**Notes for Home** Your child practiced adding 6, 7, or 8 to another number by first making a ten. *Home Activity:* Ask your child to explain how he or she would find 7 + 5. (7 + 3 = 10 plus 2 = 12)



Name ______________________

## Problem Solving: Make a List

Practice 3-6

Martha has 15 special marbles.
Her father built 2 boxes for Martha to keep them.

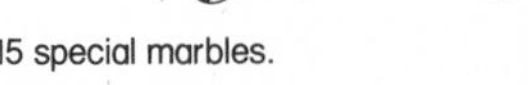

Find all the ways Martha can put 15 marbles in 2 boxes.
You can use 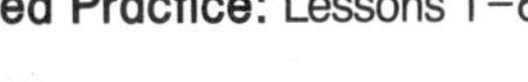.
Write your numbers in the list.

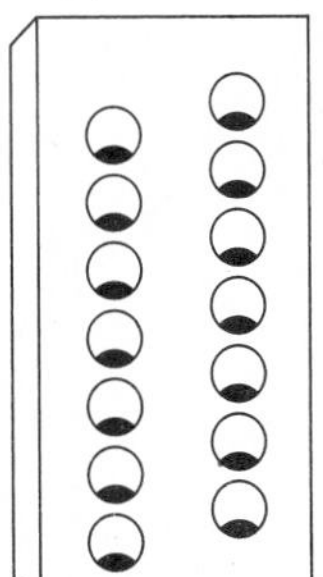
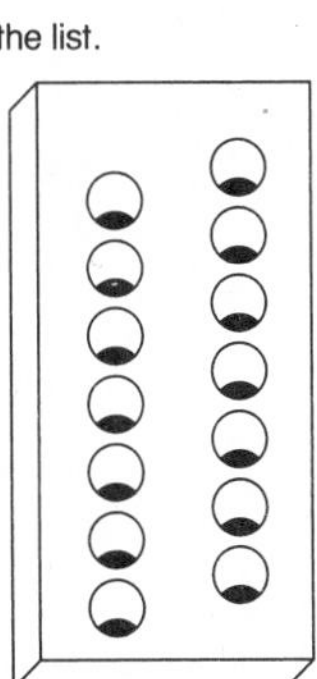

| Left Box | Right Box |
|---|---|
| 14 | 1 |
| 13 | 2 |
| 12 | 3 |
| 11 | 4 |
| 10 | 5 |
| 9 | 6 |
| 8 | 7 |
| 7 | 8 |
| 6 | 9 |
| 5 | 10 |
| 4 | 11 |
| 3 | 12 |
| 2 | 13 |
| 1 | 14 |

### Patterns

What patterns do you see in your list?
Numbers decreased in the left column and increased in the right column.

**Notes for Home** Your child practiced making a list to solve a problem. *Home Activity:* Ask your child to make a list to show all the ways that 6 bananas can be put in 2 baskets. (1 and 5, 2 and 4, 3 and 3, 4 and 2, 5 and 1)



Name ______________________

## Mixed Practice: Lessons 1–6

Practice Chapter 3 A

Add.

1. 6 + 6 = 12   5 + 5 = 10   4 + 4 = 8

Complete the number sentences.

2. 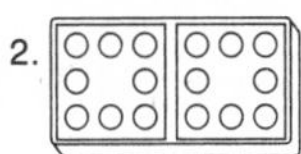
8 + 8 = 16

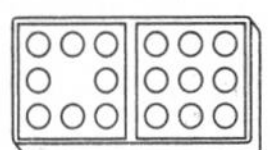
8 + 9 = 17

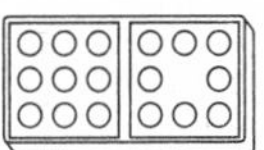
9 + 8 = 17

Add. Write the number sentences.

3. 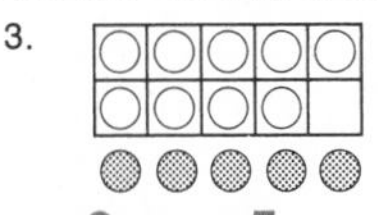
9 + 5 = 14

4. 
7 + 7 = 14

### Problem Solving

Write a number sentence. Solve.

5. Mark's cat had 6 kittens. His dog had 5 puppies. How many puppies and kittens are there in all?
6 + 5 = 11

6. Amir has 8 red cars and 7 blue cars. How many cars does he have in all?
8 + 7 = 15

### Journal

Draw a picture to show doubles plus one.

**Notes for Home** Your child practiced concepts, skills, and problem solving from Lessons 1 through 6. *Home Activity:* Ask your child to use a 10-frame to show you how he or she would find the sum of 8 + 6. (14)

Name ______________________

## Cumulative Review

Continue the pattern.
Write the missing numbers.

1. 2, 4, 6, 8, 10, 12
2. 4, 8, 12, 16, 20, 24

Add.

3. $6 + 8 = 14$   $9 + 3 = 12$   $4 + 7 = 11$

### Problem Solving

Solve. Write a number sentence.

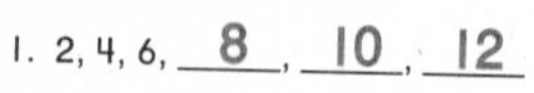

4. Stephanie had 6 stickers.
   Suli gave her 7 more.
   How many stickers does she have in all?

   6 + 7 = 13 stickers

### Test Prep

Fill in the ○ to show the correct answer.

5. Which color do most children like best?
   Brown ○ Yellow ● Blue ○ Red ○

6. How many more children like blue than brown?
   5 ○ 3 ○ 4 ● 6 ○

| Favorite Colors | |
|---|---|
| Brown | ☺☺☺ |
| Yellow | ☺☺☺☺☺☺☺☺☺☺ |
| Blue | ☺☺☺☺☺☺☺ |
| Red | ☺☺☺☺☺ |

**Notes for Home** Your child reviewed number patterns, addition and subtraction facts to 12, and pictographs. *Home Activity:* Ask your child explain how he or she determined the pattern in Exercise 2.



Name ______________________

## Use Doubles to Subtract

Add or subtract.
Match each doubles fact with a subtraction fact.

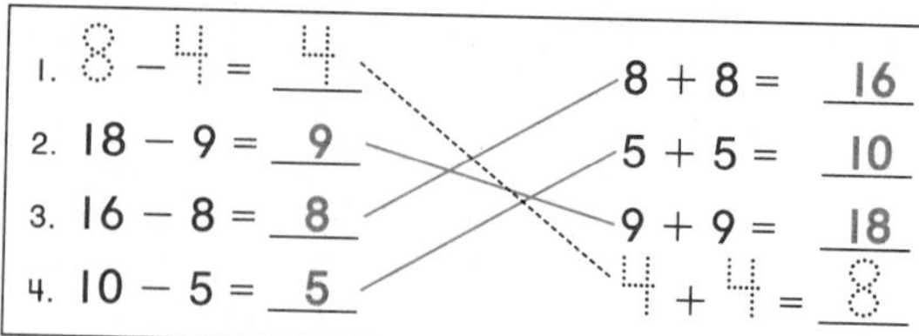

1. 8 − 4 = 4
2. 18 − 9 = 9
3. 16 − 8 = 8
4. 10 − 5 = 5

8 + 8 = 16
5 + 5 = 10
9 + 9 = 18
4 + 4 = 8

Subtract. Write the double that helps.

5. 12 − 6 = 6   6 + 6 = 12
6. 6 − 3 = 3   3 + 3 = 6
7. 14 − 7 = 7   7 + 7 = 14

### Mental Math

Felix and Dina have shell collections. Both collections have two kinds of shells which are equal in number. Write the number of shells each child has.

8. Felix has 16 shells.
   8 are pink shells.
   8 are white shells.

9. Dina has 14 shells.
   7 are conch shells.
   7 are snail shells.

**Notes for Home** Your child matched addition and subtraction facts. *Home Activity:* Ask your child what doubles fact helps to find 12 − 6. (6 + 6 = 12)



Name ______________________

## Use Addition Facts to Subtract

Add or subtract. Color each addition fact to match the related subtraction fact. Use a different color for each set of facts.

1.

| | | | |
|---|---|---|---|
| $11 - 5 = 6$ | $16 - 8 = 8$ | $13 - 9 = 4$ | $9 - 6 = 3$ |
| $18 - 9 = 9$ | $12 - 7 = 5$ | $14 - 6 = 8$ | $15 - 8 = 7$ |

2.

| | | | |
|---|---|---|---|
| $8 + 8 = 16$ | $3 + 6 = 9$ | $9 + 9 = 18$ | $5 + 7 = 12$ |
| $4 + 9 = 13$ | $7 + 8 = 15$ | $6 + 5 = 11$ | $8 + 6 = 14$ |

### Tell a Math Story

Answers will vary.

3. Tell an addition story and a related subtraction story for the picture.

**Notes for Home** Your child used addition facts to subtract. *Home Activity:* Ask your child to explain how 4 + 8 = 12 helps to find 12 − 8 = 4.



Name ______________________

## Relate Addition and Subtraction

Write a number sentence. Solve.

1. Stacy had 5 celery sticks on her plate. She gave 3 to her brother. How many were left?

   5 − 3 = 2

2. There were 2 carrot sticks on Stacy's plate. Her brother gave her 3 of his carrot sticks. How many carrot sticks does Stacy have?

   2 + 3 = 5

### Write About It

Answers will vary.

3. Use the numbers 8, 9, and 17.
   Write an addition story and a related subtraction story.

Write number sentences for your stories.

______________ ______________

**Notes for Home** Your child practiced writing and solving story problems with related facts. *Home Activity:* Ask your child to write related addition and subtraction facts using these numbers: 9, 4, 13. (9 + 4 = 13 or 4 + 9 = 13 and 13 − 4 = 9 or 13 − 9 = 4)

Name ______________________

Practice 3-10

## Problem Solving: Group Decision Making

Work with a group to make a bar graph.

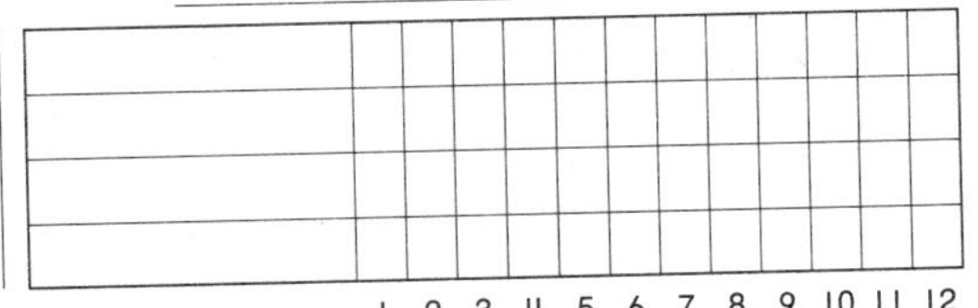

1 2 3 4 5 6 7 8 9 10 11 12

1. Write the title of your graph at the top.
2. Put a choice at the start of each row.
3. Label the side and bottom of your graph.
4. Color to show how many votes for each choice.

**Write your own.** With your group, decide on 2 questions that can be answered by your graph. Write your questions.

5. Questions and answers will vary.
6. ______________________

### Journal

7. What did you learn about working in a group? What will you do the same way the next time? What might you change? Why?

**Notes for Home** Your child made a bar graph. *Home Activity:* Ask your child to describe how he or she worked with a group to collect the information and to create the graph.



Name ______________________

Practice Chapter 3 B

## Mixed Practice: Lessons 7–10

Add or subtract.

1. $8 + 8 = 16$, $16 - 8 = 8$
2. $9 + 8 = 17$, $17 - 8 = 9$
3. $8 + 6 = 14$, $14 - 6 = 8$
4. $18 - 9 = 9$, $8 + 5 = 13$, $6 + 5 = 11$, $15 - 7 = 8$, $9 + 6 = 15$, $11 - 4 = 7$, $12 - 8 = 4$

### Problem Solving

Write a number sentence. Solve.

5. Steven had 8 pennies. He found 7 more. How many does he have now?
$8 + 7 = 15$ pennies

6. Steven had 15 pennies. He gave 7 to his sister. How many does he have left?
$15 - 7 = 8$ pennies

Use the graph to answer the questions.

Our Favorite Fruits

7. Which fruit got the most votes? Peaches
8. How many more votes did Apples get than Grapes? 2 more votes

### Journal

9. Draw a picture to show these related facts:
$8 + 6 = 14$ $14 - 6 = 8$

**Notes for Home** Your child practiced adding and subtracting related facts, reading a graph, and solving problems. *Home Activity:* Ask your child to tell you a related subtraction fact for 8 + 4 = 12 (12 – 4 = 8 or 12 – 8 = 4).



Name ______________________

Practice Chapters 1–3 B

## Cumulative Review

Write the number sentence. Then write the turnaround fact.

1. $6 + 3 = 9$
$3 + 6 = 9$

2. $5 + 8 = 13$
$8 + 5 = 13$

### Problem Solving

Write a number sentence. Solve.

3. Markus has 6 toy trucks. Marcy brings 6 more. How many do they have in all?
$6 + 6 = 12$ toy trucks

4. Marcy brings 7 toy trucks. Markus still has 6. How many do they have now?
$6 + 7 = 13$ toy trucks

### Test Prep

Fill in the ○ for the correct answer.
What fact matches each picture?

5.  
○ 12 – 4 ○ 7 + 4 ● 7 + 5 ○ 7 – 5

6. 
● 13 – 9 ○ 9 + 4 ○ 13 + 4 ○ 9 – 4

**Notes for Home** Your child reviewed addition and subtraction facts to 12. *Home Activity:* Ask your child to tell you the turnaround fact for 2 + 9. (9 + 2 = 11)



Name ______________________

Practice 4-1

## Explore Fact Families

$5 + 9 = 14$ $14 - 5 = 9$

$9 + 5 = 14$ $14 - 9 = 5$

Complete each fact family.
Add or subtract.

1.
$7 + 5 = 12$ $12 - 7 = 5$
$5 + 7 = 12$ $12 - 5 = 7$

2.
$8 + 5 = 13$ $13 - 5 = 8$
$5 + 8 = 13$ $13 - 8 = 5$

### Talk About It

Tell the fact family for the numbers 8, 6, and 14.
$8 + 6 = 14$, $6 + 8 = 14$, $14 - 8 = 6$, $14 - 6 = 8$

**Notes for Home** Your child added and subtracted using fact families. *Home Activity:* Ask your child to write the fact family for the numbers 6, 6, and 12. (6 + 6 = 12; 12 - 6 = 6)

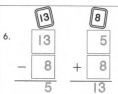

Name ______________________

Practice 4-2

## Fact Families

Complete each fact family. Add or subtract

1. 4 + 9 = 13
   9 + 4 = 13
   13 − 9 = 4
   13 − 4 = 9

2. 7 + 9 = 16
   9 + 7 = 16
   16 − 9 = 7
   16 − 7 = 9

3. 8 + 9 = 17
   9 + 8 = 17
   17 − 9 = 8
   17 − 8 = 9

4. 9 + 6 = 15
   6 + 9 = 15
   15 − 6 = 9
   15 − 9 = 6

5. 8 + 8 = 16; 16 − 8 = 8

6. 6 + 6 = 12; 12 − 6 = 6

**Problem Solving Critical Thinking**

Write two different fact families using the number 11.

Answers may include: 7 + 4, 4 + 7, 11 − 4, 11 − 7; 8 + 3, 3 + 8, 11 − 3, 11 − 8; 9 + 2, 2 + 9, 11 − 2, 11 − 9.

**Notes for Home** Your child added and subtracted using fact families. *Home Activity:* Ask your child to explain why he or she can write only two number facts using 6 and 12. (Possible answer: A fact family with doubles has only 2 facts; others have four.)



Name ______________________

Practice 4-3

## Use Addition to Check Subtraction

Use these numbers. Write a subtraction fact.
Write an addition fact to check.

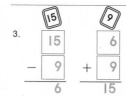

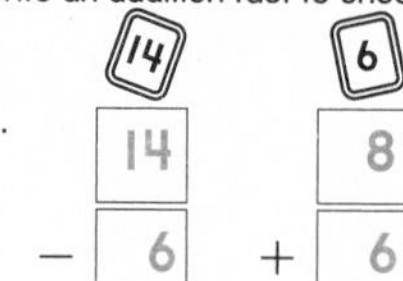

1. (14) (6): 14 − 6 = 8; 8 + 6 = 14

2. (17) (8): 17 − 8 = 9; 9 + 8 = 17

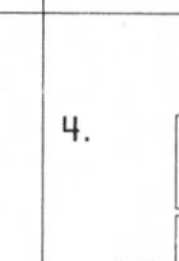

3. (15) (9): 15 − 9 = 6; 6 + 9 = 15

4. (13) (6): 13 − 6 = 7; 7 + 6 = 13

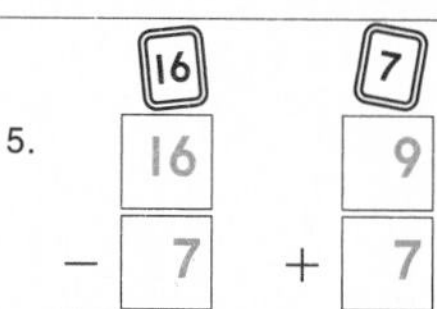

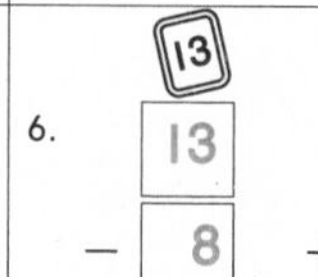

5. (16) (7): 16 − 7 = 9; 9 + 7 = 16

6. (13) (8): 13 − 8 = 5; 5 + 8 = 13

**Problem Solving**

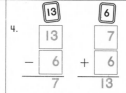

Complete the number sentence. 15 − 7 = 8

Write two related addition facts that you can use to check your answer.

**Notes for Home** Your child checked subtraction problems using addition. *Home Activity:* Ask your child to subtract 14 − 8 and to check the answer by adding. (14 − 8 = 6; 8 + 6 = 14)



Name ______________________

Practice 4-4

## Problem Solving: Draw a Picture

Draw a picture to solve the problem.

1. Tia made 8 muffins. She eats 1 muffin and Sara eats 2 muffins. They each eat 1 muffin later. How many muffins are left?

   3 muffins

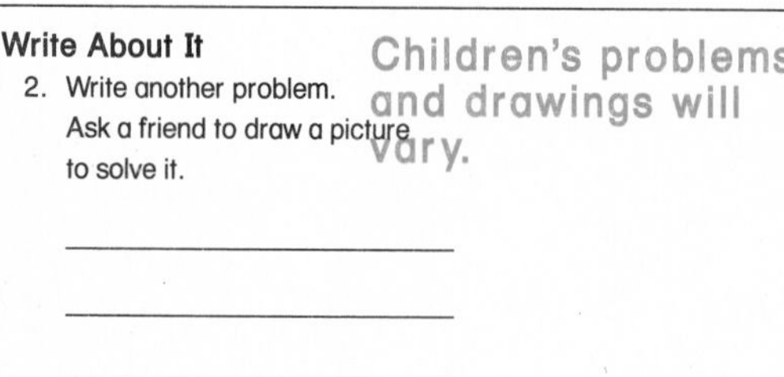

**Write About It**

2. Write another problem. Ask a friend to draw a picture to solve it.

Children's problems and drawings will vary.

**Notes for Home** Your child drew pictures to solve problems. *Home Activity:* Have your child draw pictures to solve this word problem: There were four apples in the bowl. Jim took one to school for lunch. His mother had one. His brother ate two more. How many apples were left? (No apples were left.)



Name ______________________

Practice Chapter 4 A

## Mixed Practice: Lessons 1–4

Write the number sentences to make a fact family.

1.    8 + 6 = 14    14 − 6 = 8
   6 + 8 = 14    14 − 8 = 6

Subtract. Then write a related addition fact.

2. 14 − 9 = 5    9 + 5 = 14

3. 13 − 5 = 8    8 + 5 = 13

**Problem Solving**

Draw a picture to solve the problem.

4. Kim blew 16 bubbles. His brother broke 5. 3 more flew away. How many were left?

   8 bubbles

Drawings will vary, but should start with 16.

**Journal**

5. Write a problem about a picnic. Draw a picture. Write the fact family that your picture shows.

**Notes for Home** Your child practiced addition and subtraction facts and solving problems. *Home Activity:* Ask your child to write a related addition fact for 16 − 8 = 8. (8 + 8 = 16)

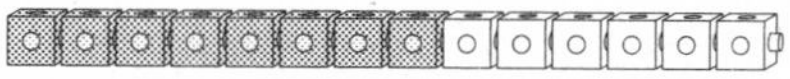

Name ______________________

Practice Chapters 1–4 A

## Cumulative Review

Add.

1. 8 + 5 = 13; 7 + 6 = 14; 6 + 9 = 15; 9 + 7 = 16; 8 + 7 = 15; 9 + 9 = 18; 7 + 5 = 12

### Problem Solving

Use the graph to answer the questions.

2. How many children like plain popcorn?
   5 children

3. How many more children like plain popcorn than butter popcorn?
   2 more children

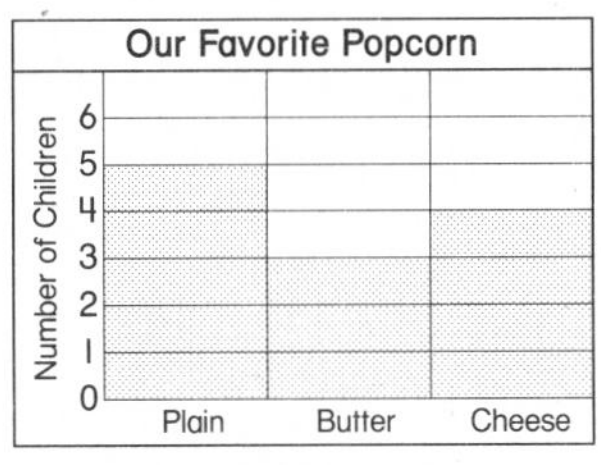



### Test Prep

Fill in the ○ for the correct answer.

Solve each problem.

4. Roy has 8 green balls and 9 red balls. How many balls does he have?
   ○ 16 ○ 5 ○ 18 ● 17

5. Mr. Brown's class has 18 books. 9 are math books. How many are science books?
   ○ 6 ● 9 ○ 8 ○ 7

**Notes for Home** Your child reviewed addition facts, reading a graph, and solving word problems. *Home Activity:* Ask your child how many fewer children like butter popcorn than cheese popcorn on the graph? (1)



Name ______________________

Practice 4-5

## Missing Addends

Find the missing number.

Use the fact family to help you.

1.

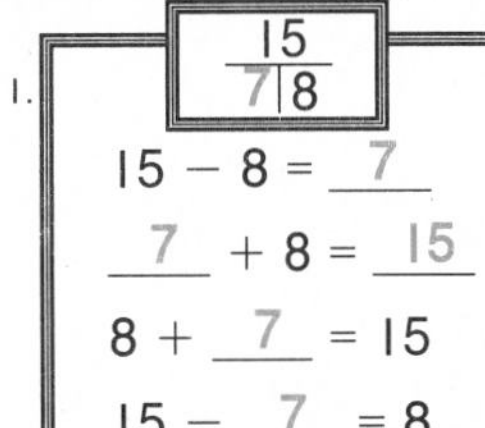



15 − 8 = 7
7 + 8 = 15
8 + 7 = 15
15 − 7 = 8

2.

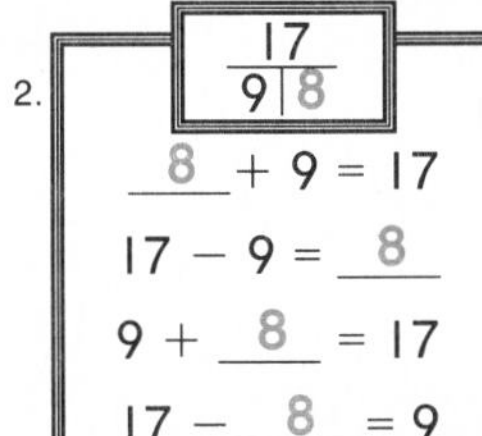



8 + 9 = 17
17 − 9 = 8
9 + 8 = 17
17 − 8 = 9

3. There were 13 children in line for lemonade. There were 8 children in the first line. How many were in the second line?
   5 children

4. Ben had 5 kiddie car rides the first day. He rode 9 times the second day. How many rides did he have in all?
   14 rides

### Problem Solving Patterns

5. Find the missing numbers. Find the pattern. Write the next fact.

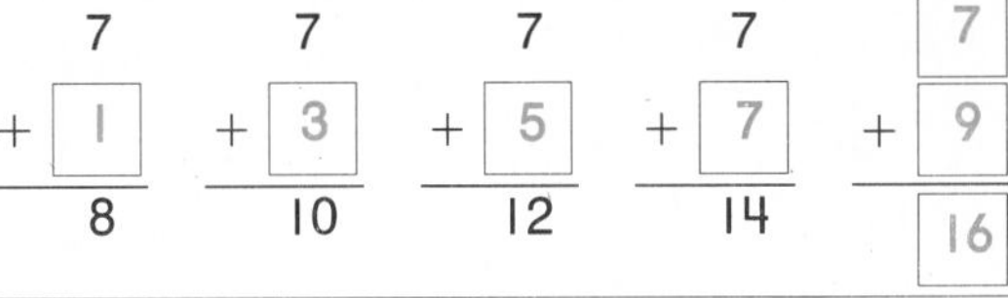



**Notes for Home** Your child used fact families to find missing numbers. *Home Activity:* Ask your child to solve 9 + __ = 15. (6)



Name ______________________

Practice 4-6

## Three Addends

Add across.

5 + 4 + 6 = 15

Add down.

4 + 7 + 2 = 13

1.

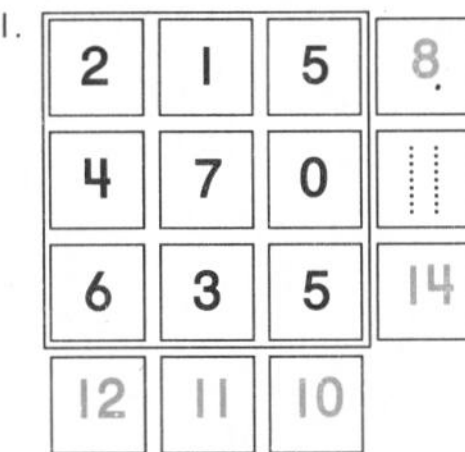

| 2 | 1 | 5 | 8 |
|---|---|---|---|
| 4 | 7 | 0 | 11 |
| 6 | 3 | 5 | 14 |
| 12 | 11 | 10 | |

2.

| 4 | 4 | 5 | 13 |
|---|---|---|---|
| 7 | 2 | 7 | 16 |
| 5 | 4 | 3 | 12 |
| 16 | 10 | 15 | |

### Problem Solving

3. A team needs 10 points to win a prize. Find each team's total score. Circle the names of the winning teams.

| Team | First Race | Second Race | Third Race | Total Score |
|---|---|---|---|---|
| Cats | 8 | 0 | 1 | 9 points |
| (Stars) | 6 | 2 | 4 | 12 points |
| (Foxes) | 7 | 4 | 3 | 14 points |
| (Bears) | 1 | 5 | 5 | 11 points |

**Notes for Home** Your child added three numbers. *Home Activity:* Ask your child which team in the Problem Solving chart won the most points. (Foxes)



Name ______________________

Practice 4-7

## Use Addition and Subtraction Rules

Follow the rule. Add or subtract.

1.

| Add 7 | |
|---|---|
| 7 | 14 |
| 6 | 13 |
| 9 | 16 |

2.

| Subtract 4 | |
|---|---|
| 12 | 8 |
| 17 | 13 |
| 13 | 9 |

3.

| Subtract 6 | |
|---|---|
| 14 | 8 |
| 11 | 5 |
| 15 | 9 |

Add the numbers in the first column.

Then follow the rule.

4.

| | Add 4 |
|---|---|
| 5 + 6 | 15 |
| 3 + 7 | 14 |
| 2 + 6 | 12 |

5.

| | Add 6 |
|---|---|
| 4 + 5 | 15 |
| 6 + 5 | 17 |
| 3 + 1 | 10 |

### Problem Solving

Write your own rule for each chart. Then follow the rule. Add or subtract. **Answers will vary.**

6.

| Add ____ | |
|---|---|
| 5 | |
| 7 | |
| 8 | |

7.

| Subtract ____ | |
|---|---|
| 18 | |
| 11 | |
| 13 | |

8.

| Subtract ____ | |
|---|---|
| 14 | |
| 12 | |
| 15 | |

**Notes for Home** Your child added and subtracted. *Home Activity:* Ask your child to choose three numbers less than 10 and add 3 to each of them.

Name ______________________

## What's My Rule?

Practice 4-8

Find the rule. Then write the missing number.

1.

| Subtract 3 | |
|---|---|
| 10 | 7 |
| 5 | 2 |
| 7 | 4 |
| 4 | 1 |

2.

| Add 5 | |
|---|---|
| 2 + 5 | 12 |
| 3 + 5 | 13 |
| 4 + 6 | 15 |
| 7 + 5 | 17 |

Write you own tables.
Fill in the numbers.
Ask a friend to find the rule.

Answers will vary.

3.

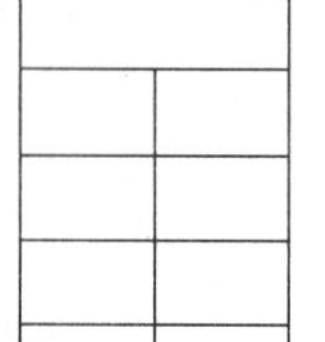

4.

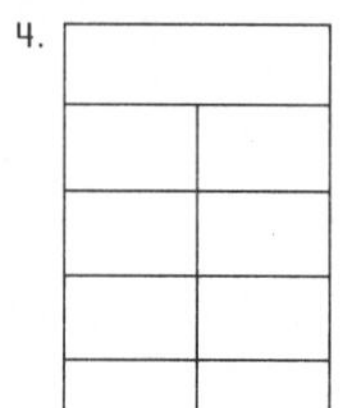

### Problem Solving

5. Shane made 6 key chains. Luis make 3 key chains. Rona made 5 key chains. They each sold 1 key chain at the class fair. How many key chains does each have now?

Shane: 5 key chains

Luis: 2 key chains

Rona: 4 key chains

**Notes for Home** Your child found the rule (such as add 3 or subtract 5) for addition and subtraction tables. *Home Activity:* Ask your child to explain his or her reasoning for solving the Problem Solving exercises.



Name ______________________

## Problem Solving: Multiple-Step Problems

Practice 4-9

Use .
Write each number sentence. Solve.

1. At the beach, Sam found 12 seashells. He lost 7.  12 − 7 = 5 seashells

   Later, he found 6 more shells. How many does he have now?  5 + 6 = 11 seashells

2. Jamal bought 15 stickers. He used 7.  15 − 7 = 8 stickers

   He used 5 more. How many stickers does Jamal have now?  8 − 5 = 3 stickers

3. On the beach, Ali found 10 pennies. He spent 5.  10 − 5 = 5 pennies

   He spent 5 more. How many pennies does he have now?  5 − 5 = 0 pennies

### Tell a Math Story

4. Tell a story problem about balloons. Include addition and subtraction in your story.
   Ask a friend to solve your problem.

**Notes for Home** Your child practiced solving word problems. *Home Activity:* Ask your child to tell you the word problem he or she made up for *Tell a Math Story*.



Name ______________________

## Mixed Practice: Lessons 5–9

Practice Chapter 4 B

Find the missing number in the facts family.

1. 8 + 7 = 15
   7 + 8 = 15
   15 − 8 = 7
   15 − 7 = 8

Add.

2.

| 8 | 6 | 7 |
|---|---|---|
| 1 | 3 | 3 |
| + 2 | + 6 | + 5 |
| 11 | 15 | 15 |

Follow the rule.
Write the missing numbers.

3.

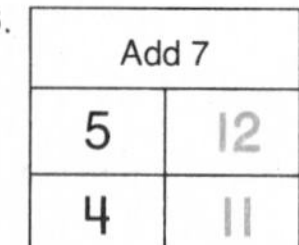

| Add 7 | |
|---|---|
| 5 | 12 |
| 4 | 11 |

Find the rule.
Write the rule.

4.

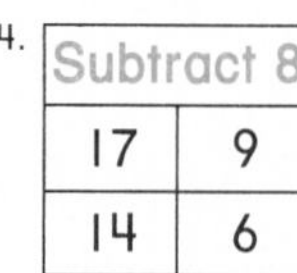

| Subtract 8 | |
|---|---|
| 17 | 9 |
| 14 | 6 |

### Problem Solving

Write each number sentence. Solve.

5. Bob bought 9 plums.
   He gave 2 to Sally.  7 plums

   He bought 3 more plums.
   How many plums does Bob have now?  10 plums

### Journal

6. Write all the ways you can solve 6 + 4 + 5.

**Notes for Home** Children practiced finding missing numbers, adding three numbers, and solving problems. *Home Activity:* Ask your child to tell you how to find the missing numbers in Exercise 5.



Name ______________________

## Cumulative Review

Practice Chapter 1-4 B

Add.
Write the number sentence.

1. 7 + 6 = 13

2. 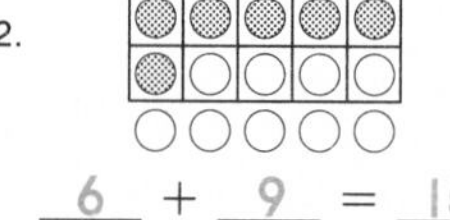

   6 + 9 = 15

### Problem Solving

Use the graph to answer the questions.

3. How many children had pony rides on Friday?
   40 children

4. On which day did the most children take pony rides?
   Saturday

| Number of Children on Pony Rides | |
|---|---|
| Friday | 🯅🯅🯅🯅 |
| Saturday | 🯅🯅🯅🯅🯅🯅🯅 |
| Sunday | 🯅🯅🯅🯅🯅🯅 |

Each 🯅 stands for 10 children.

### Test Prep

Fill in the ○ for the correct answer.

5. Which fact is shown in the picture?

   ○ 3 + 5  ● 4 + 4  ○ 5 + 4  ○ 5 + 5

6. Add 7 more.
   How many in all?

   ○ 13  ● 14  ○ 15

**Notes for Home** Your child reviewed numbers, used graphs to solve problems, and practiced addition facts. *Home Activity:* Ask your child to use the graph on this page to find how many children had pony rides on Sunday.

Name ______________________________

## Explore Estimation

Practice 5-1

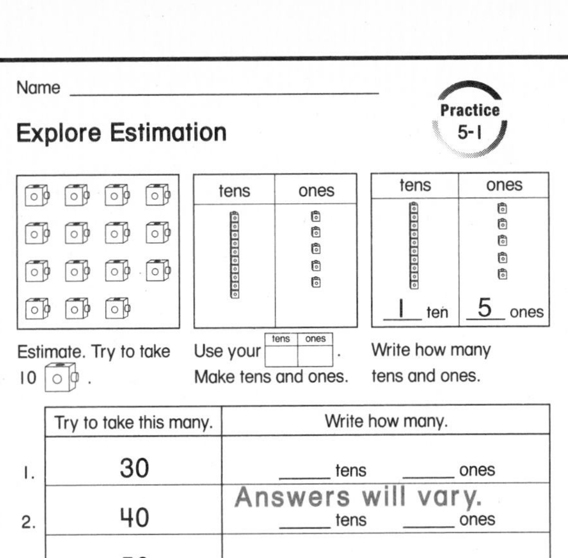


Estimate. Try to take 10 [cube].

Use your [tens | ones] mat. Make tens and ones.

Write how many tens and ones.

| | Try to take this many. | Write how many. |
|---|---|---|
| 1. | 30 | ____ tens ____ ones |
| 2. | 40 | Answers will vary. ____ tens ____ ones |
| 3. | 50 | ____ tens ____ ones |
| 4. | 60 | ____ tens ____ ones |
| 5. | 70 | ____ tens ____ ones |
| 6. | 80 | ____ tens ____ ones |
| 7. | 90 | ____ tens ____ ones |

**Talk About It** Which time did you get the closest to your estimate? How close did you get? Tell a classmate.

**Notes for Home** Your child used grouping by tens to estimate and count. *Home Activity:* Put some macaroni or dried beans in 3 piles. Ask your child to divided each pile into groups of tens and ones, and to count how many there are in each pile.



Name ______________________________

## Record Numbers

Practice 5-2

Write how many tens and ones. Write the number.

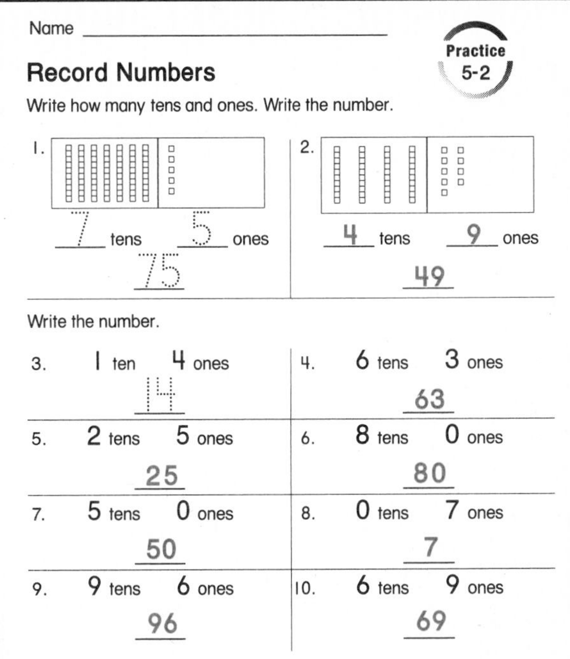


Write the number.

3. 1 ten 4 ones **14**

4. 6 tens 3 ones **63**

5. 2 tens 5 ones **25**

6. 8 tens 0 ones **80**

7. 5 tens 0 ones **50**

8. 0 tens 7 ones **7**

9. 9 tens 6 ones **96**

10. 6 tens 9 ones **69**

**Problem Solving Critical Thinking**

11. Look at the numbers you wrote for Exercises 9 and 10. How are the numbers alike? How are they different?

Sample answer: Both numbers have the same digits. The digits are in a different order.

**Notes for Home** Your child wrote numbers as tens and ones and as 2-digit numbers. *Home Activity:* Tell your child a number such as 4 tens and 6 ones and ask him or her to tell you the 2-digit number. (46.)



Name ______________________________

## Number Words

Practice 5-3

Write the number.

1. thirty-seven **37**
2. fifty-six **56**
3. eighty **80**
4. seventy-one **71**

5. Use the clues to write each word. Fill in the puzzle.

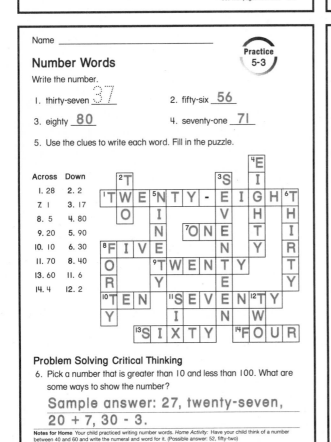

| Across | Down |
|---|---|
| 1. 28 | 2. 2 |
| 7. 1 | 3. 17 |
| 8. 5 | 4. 80 |
| 9. 20 | 5. 90 |
| 10. 10 | 6. 30 |
| 11. 70 | 8. 40 |
| 13. 60 | 11. 6 |
| 14. 4 | 12. 2 |

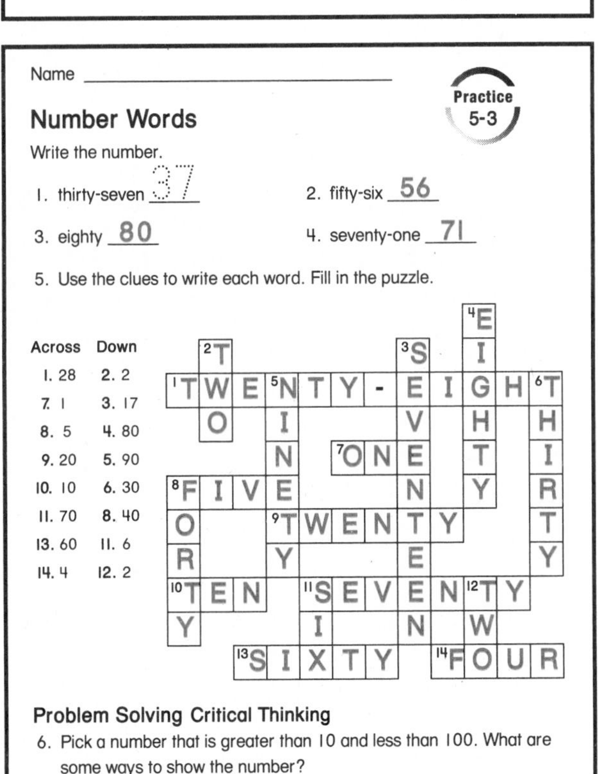


**Problem Solving Critical Thinking**

6. Pick a number that is greater than 10 and less than 100. What are some ways to show the number?

Sample answer: 27, twenty-seven, 20 + 7, 30 - 3.

**Notes for Home** Your child practiced writing number words. *Home Activity:* Have your child think of a number between 40 and 60 and write the numeral and word for it. (Possible answer: 52, fifty-two)



Name ______________________________

## Tell About 100

Practice 5-4

These show 100.

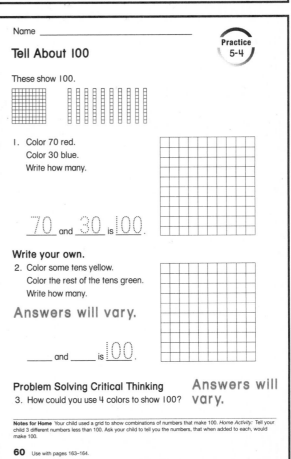

1. Color 70 red.
   Color 30 blue.
   Write how many.

   **70** and **30** is **100**.

**Write your own.**

2. Color some tens yellow.
   Color the rest of the tens green.
   Write how many.

   Answers will vary.

   ____ and ____ is **100**.

**Problem Solving Critical Thinking**

3. How could you use 4 colors to show 100? Answers will vary.

**Notes for Home** Your child used a grid to show combinations of numbers that make 100. *Home Activity:* Tell your child 3 different numbers less than 100. Ask your child to tell you the numbers, that when added to each, would make 100.

Name ______________________________

Practice 5-5

## Problem Solving: Use Data from a Graph

| Coin Collections | |
|---|---|
| Abe | ○○○○○○ |
| Beth | ○○○○ |
| Carlos | ○○ |
| Dory | ○○○○○○○ |

Each ○ means 2 coins.

Use the graph to solve.

1. How many coins did Abe collect? 12 coins
2. How man coins did Carlos collect? 4 coins
3. How many coins did Beth and Dory collect? 22 coins
4. How many more coins did Dory collect than Abe? 2 more

### Visual Thinking

5. Carlos adds 14 more coins to his collection. What would you add to the graph? Explain.

7 circles; since each circle means 2 coins, 7 circles would be 14 coins.

**Notes for Home** Your child used a graph to answer questions. *Home Activity:* Ask your child to show you how to use the graph to count the coins in Dory's collection. (Possible answer: Each picture stands for 2. Count by 2s: 2, 4, 6, 8, 10, 12, 14.)



Name ______________________________

Practice Chapter 5 A

## Mixed Practice: Lessons 1–5

Write how many tens and ones.
Write the number.

1. 

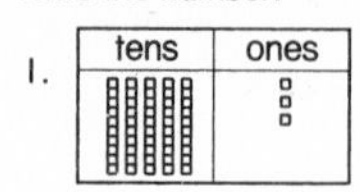

| tens | ones |
|---|---|
| | |

5 tens 3 ones

53

Write the number.

2. twenty-seven 27
3. seventy-three 73
4. sixty-nine 69
5. forty-two 42

### Problem Solving

Use the graph to answer the questions.

6. How many more books does Larry have than Leon? 5 more
7. How many books do Leon and Lacy have together? 55 books

| Book Collections | |
|---|---|
| Larry | 📖📖📖📖 |
| Leon | 📖📖📖 |
| Lacy | 📖📖📖📖📖📖📖📖 |

Each 📖 means 5 books

### Journal

8. Pick an even and an odd number between 10 and 100. Draw pictures of tens and ones to show your numbers.

Answers and drawings will vary.

**Notes for Home** Your child counted by tens and ones, wrote numbers, and read graphs. *Home Activity:* Write the words for 3 numbers below 100. Ask your child to read the words aloud and to write the numbers. (Sample: twenty-two: 22; fifteen: 15; ninety-seven: 97)



Name ______________________________

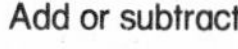

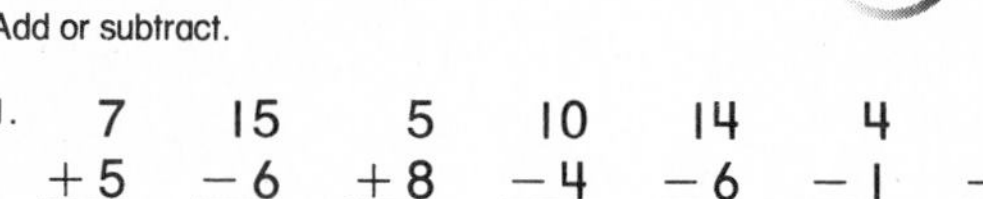

Practice Chapters 1–5 A

## Cumulative Review

Add or subtract.

1. $7 + 5 = 12$ | $15 - 6 = 9$ | $5 + 8 = 13$ | $10 - 4 = 6$ | $14 - 6 = 8$ | $4 - 1 = 3$ | $13 - 6 = 7$

2. $6 + 7 = 13$ | $15 - 8 = 7$ | $9 + 9 = 18$ | $11 - 3 = 8$ | $8 + 0 = 8$ | $5 + 6 = 11$ | $10 - 2 = 8$

### Problem Solving

Solve.

3. Tia has 6 seashells. Then she finds 4 more. How many seashells does Tia have now? 10 seashells
4. Tom has 9 seashells. He gives 3 to Tia. How many seashells does Tom have now? 6 seashells

**Test Prep**

Fill in the ○ for the correct answer.

5. $7 + 2 + 6 =$ ____ ○ 10 ○ 9 ● 15 ○ 8

6. $4 + 3 + 7 =$ ____ ○ 16 ○ 7 ○ 10 ● 14

**Notes for Home** Your child reviewed addition and subtraction facts and problem solving. *Home Activity:* Ask your child how many tens and ones are in the number 85. (8 tens and 5 ones)



Name ______________________________

Practice 5-6

## Hundred Chart and Skip Counting Patterns

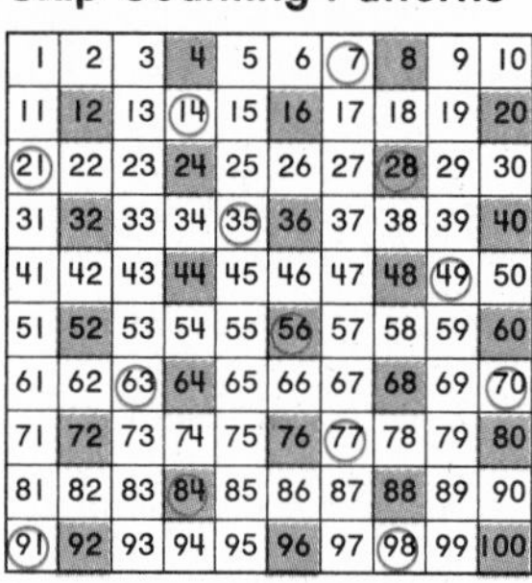

| 1 | 2 | 3 | 4 | 5 | 6 | 7 | 8 | 9 | 10 |
|---|---|---|---|---|---|---|---|---|---|
| 11 | 12 | 13 | 14 | 15 | 16 | 17 | 18 | 19 | 20 |
| 21 | 22 | 23 | 24 | 25 | 26 | 27 | 28 | 29 | 30 |
| 31 | 32 | 33 | 34 | 35 | 36 | 37 | 38 | 39 | 40 |
| 41 | 42 | 43 | 44 | 45 | 46 | 47 | 48 | 49 | 50 |
| 51 | 52 | 53 | 54 | 55 | 56 | 57 | 58 | 59 | 60 |
| 61 | 62 | 63 | 64 | 65 | 66 | 67 | 68 | 69 | 70 |
| 71 | 72 | 73 | 74 | 75 | 76 | 77 | 78 | 79 | 80 |
| 81 | 82 | 83 | 84 | 85 | 86 | 87 | 88 | 89 | 90 |
| 91 | 92 | 93 | 94 | 95 | 96 | 97 | 98 | 99 | 100 |

1. Count by 4s on the chart. Shade each number.
2. Count by 7s on the chart. Circle each number.
3. Which numbers were both shaded and circled? 28, 56, 84
4. What patterns do you see in the chart when you count by 4s?

2 numbers are shaded in the first row, 3 in the next. The pattern repeats.

5. What patterns do you see when you count by 7s?

The third, seventh, and tenth rows have 2 numbers circles, the other rows have 1 number circled.

### Mental Math

3. Ellen has 4 robot models. Each model has 5 arms. How many arms are there? 20 arms

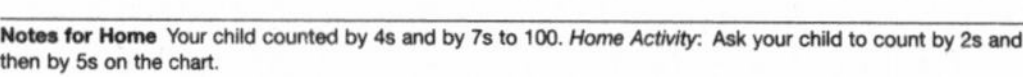

**Notes for Home** Your child counted by 4s and by 7s to 100. *Home Activity:* Ask your child to count by 2s and then by 5s on the chart.

Name ______________________

## Before, After, Between

Use the number line. Answer each question.

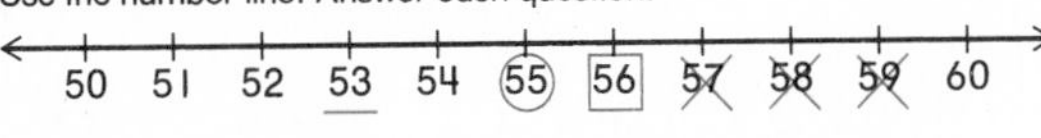


| | |
|---|---|
| 1. Draw a box around the number that is one before 57. | 2. Put a line under the number that comes after 52. |
| 3. Circle the number that is between 54 and 56. | 4. Put an X on all the numbers that are between 56 and 60. |

Answer each question.

| | |
|---|---|
| 5. What number is one before 73? 72 | 6. What number is one after 27? 28 |
| 7. What number is between 93 and 95? 94 | 8. What number before is one 90? 89 |

### Problem Solving Critical Thinking

9. Solve the riddle.
   I am between 37 and 41.
   I have 4 tens.

   What number am I? 40

   Make up your own riddles for a classmate to solve.

**Notes for Home** Your child answered questions about numbers. *Home Activity:* Pick a number from the number line on this page. Ask your child to describe it using before, between, and after. (Possible answer: 53 is before 54, 53 is between 52 and 54, and 53 is after 52.)



Name ______________________

Practice
5-8

## Find the Nearest Ten

**Write your own.**

Pick a number on the number line. Put a dot above that number.

Write your answer. Answers will vary.

1. 20 21 22 23 24 25 26 27 28 29 30

   Is your number closer to 20 or 30? ______

2. 40 41 42 43 44 45 46 47 48 49 50

   Is your number closer to 40 or 50? ______

3. 10 11 12 13 14 15 16 17 18 19 20

   Is your number closer to 10 or 20? ______

For each number, write the nearest ten.

| | |
|---|---|
| 4. 57 60 | 5. 32 30 |
| 6. 71 70 | 7. 24 20 |
| 8. 46 50 | 9. 18 20 |
| 10. 93 90 | 11. 79 80 |

### Problem Solving Estimation

12. About how many pencils in all?
    Circle you estimate.

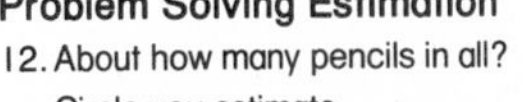

About 20    About 50

**Notes for Home** Your child found the nearest ten. (For example, 40 is the nearest ten for 36.) *Home Activity:* Tell your child a number less than 100. Ask him or her to tell you the nearest ten for that number.



Name ______________________

Practice
5-9

## Compare Numbers

Circle the number that is least.

| | | | |
|---|---|---|---|
| 1. | 38 | 52 | 19 |
| 2. | 27 | 96 | 43 |
| 3. | 61 | 47 | 72 |
| 4. | 81 | 18 | 55 |

Circle the number that is greatest.

| | | | |
|---|---|---|---|
| 5. | 76 | 68 | 81 |
| 6. | 91 | 96 | 99 |
| 7. | 45 | 61 | 38 |
| 8. | 51 | 29 | 35 |

Write the numbers in order from least to greatest.

| | | | | | | |
|---|---|---|---|---|---|---|
| 9. | 46 | 18 | 37 | 18 | 37 | 46 |
| 10. | 89 | 56 | 72 | 56 | 72 | 89 |
| 11. | 19 | 65 | 38 | 19 | 38 | 65 |
| 12. | 93 | 48 | 89 | 48 | 89 | 93 |

### Problem Solving

Three friends sold calendars for their club.
Josh sold 76 calendars.
Jane sold 58 calendars.
June sold the least number of calendars.
How many calendars could June have sold?

______ calendars 57 or fewer

**Notes for Home** Your child compared numbers using *least* and *greatest* and put numbers in order. *Home Activity:* Tell your child 3 numbers less than 100. Ask him or her to put them in order from least to greatest and from greatest to least.



Name ______________________

Practice
5-10

## Ordinal Numbers

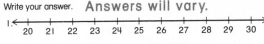

B R Y O P B

| | |
|---|---|
| 1. Color the 1st car blue. | 2. Color the 10th car brown. |
| 3. Color the second car red. | 4. Color the 7th car orange. |
| 5. Color the 4th car yellow. | 6. Color the eighth car purple. |

Answer each question.

| | |
|---|---|
| 7. How many cars are behind the 8th car? 2 | 8. How many cars are behind the 4th car? 6 |
| 9. How many cars are in front of the 6th car? 5 | 10. How many cars are in front of the 10th car? 9 |

### Problem Solving

11. Solve.
    6 children are in front of you.
    7 children are behind you.
    What number are you? 8th

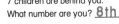

**Notes for Home** Your child used ordinal numbers from 1st through 20th. *Home Activity:* Ask your child to use ordinal numbers to describe the order of something in your home.

Name ____________________

Practice 5-11

## Odd and Even Numbers

Write how many in all. Then write **even** or **odd**.

1. ✎✎✎✎✎✎✎✎✎✎✎✎✎✎ ✎✎✎✎✎✎✎✎✎✎✎✎✎

27 odd

2. ★★★★★★★★★★★★★★★★★★★★★★ ★★★★★★★★★★★★★★★★★★★★★★

44 even

Write **even** or **odd**.

3. 36 even
4. 47 odd
5. 53 odd
6. 78 even

**Write your own.** Write two odd numbers. Then write two even numbers. Answers will vary.

7. Odd numbers: _____ _____
8. Even numbers: _____ _____

**Problem Solving Patterns** Algebra Readiness

9. Is the number 4,625 odd or even? How do you know?
Odd. Answers will vary.

**Notes for Home** Your child worked with odd and even numbers. *Home Activity: Ask your child: I am thinking of an odd number between 56 and 59. What number is it?* (57)



Name ____________________

Practice 5-12

## Problem Solving: Group Decision Making

1. Work with your group. Collect some items.
As a group, sort your items the way you like best.
Decide as a group how to show your sorted items.
Draw how you sorted them.

Drawings and labels for groups will vary.

**Journal**

2. Why did you choose this way to sort your items?

**Notes for Home** Your child made decisions with a group about how to sort items. *Home Activity:* With your child, list 10 items that you see around you. Discuss with your child ways you could sort the items.



Name ____________________

Practice Chapter 5 B

## Mixed Practice: Lessons 6–12

Count by 3s. Write the numbers.

1. 3, 6, 9, 12, 15, 18, 21, 24

Write the missing numbers.

2. 45 46 47 48 49 50 51 52 53

For each number, write the nearest ten.

3. 47 50
4. 82 80
5. 64 60

Write these numbers in order from least to greatest.

6. 76 39 82 — 39 76 82

**Problem Solving**

Use the picture to answer the questions.

7. What is the shirt number of the third soccer player? 40
8. What is the shirt number of the fifth soccer player? 19

**Journal**

9. Are these numbers even or odd? 14 8 26 4
How do you know? Even. Answers will vary.

**Notes for Home** Your child practiced number skills from this chapter. *Home Activity:* Ask your child to think of 2 odd numbers less than 100 and tell you how he or she knows they are odd.



Name ____________________

Practice Chapters 1–5 B

## Cumulative Review

Add or subtract.

1. 9 + 7 = 16; 16 − 8 = 8; 15 − 7 = 8; 8 + 6 = 14; 11 − 4 = 7; 9 + 9 = 18; 12 + 6 = 18

**Problem Solving**

Write the number sentences. Solve.

2. Marsha has 17 books. Rob has 8 books. How many more books does Marsha have than Rob?
17 − 8 = 9 more books

3. Eric has 13 marbles. Kate has 7 marbles. How many more marbles does Eric have than Kate?
13 − 7 = 6 more marbles

**Test Prep**

Fill in the ○ for the correct answer.

4. Debbie has 11 stickers. She gave 7 stickers to Joan. How many stickers does she have now?
○ 11 − 0 = 11
○ 11 + 7 = 18
● 11 − 7 = 4
○ 7 + 7 = 14

5. Rachel has 7 hair ribbons. Janet gives her 8 more. How many hair ribbons does Rachel have now?
○ 7 + 7 = 14
○ 8 − 7 = 1
○ 8 + 8 = 16
● 8 + 7 = 15

**Notes for Home** Your child reviewed addition and subtraction facts and problem solving. *Home Activity:* Ask your child to tell you a subtraction fact with a difference of 7. (Possible answers: 12 − 5 = 7; 10 − 3 = 7)

Name

Practice 6-1

# Explore Counting Dimes, Nickels, and Pennies

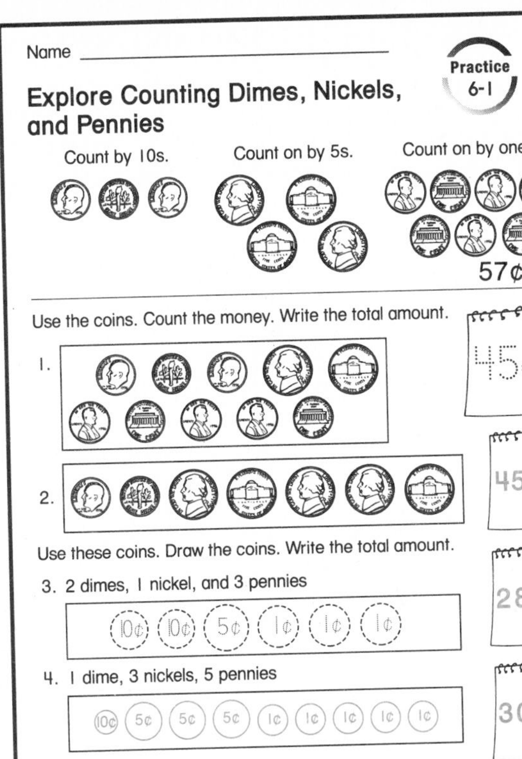
Count by 10s.
Count on by 5s.
Count on by ones.
57¢ in all
Use the coins. Count the money. Write the total amount.
45¢
45¢
Use these coins. Draw the coins. Write the total amount.
28¢
10¢ 10¢ 5¢ 1¢ 1¢ 1¢

1. 45¢
2. 45¢

3. 2 dimes, 1 nickel, and 3 pennies — 28¢

4. 1 dime, 3 nickels, 5 pennies — 10¢ 5¢ 5¢ 5¢ 1¢ 1¢ 1¢ 1¢ 1¢ — 30¢

**Talk About It** Is it easier for you to count coins from greatest value to least, or least to greatest value? Why?

**Notes for Home** Your child counted groups of dimes, nickels, and pennies. *Home Activity:* Ask your child to draw dimes, nickels, and pennies to show 52¢.

Name

Practice 6-2

# Quarters

Use coins. Count the money. Write the total amount.

1. 98¢

2. 81¢

Use these coins. Draw the coins. Write how much in all.

3. 1 quarter, 4 dimes, 1 nickel, and 3 pennies — 73¢

4. You pick 5 coins.

Answers will vary.

## Problem Solving Visual Thinking

5. Would you like to have the stack of nickels or the stack of dimes to spend? Explain.

dimes;
nickels = 45¢
dimes = 50¢

**Notes for Home** Your child counted groups of coins that included quarters. *Home Activity:* Tell your child an amount less than a dollar. Have him or her show you this amount using any combinations of quarters, dimes, nickels, and pennies.

Name

Practice 6-3

# Half Dollars

Fill in the table to show some ways to make 50¢.
Write how many of each coin is used. Use coins to help.

| Half dollar | Quarters | Dimes | Nickels | Value of coins |
|---|---|---|---|---|
| 1 | 0 | 0 | 0 | 50¢ |
| 0 | 2 | 0 | 0 | 50¢ |
| 0 | 0 | 3 | 4 | 50¢ |
| 0 | 1 | 0 | 5 | 50¢ |
| 0 | 0 | 5 | 0 | 50¢ |
| 0 | 0 | 0 | 10 | 50¢ |
| 0 | 0 | 1 | 8 | 50¢ |

## Problem Solving

How much could one of these cost?
Choose a price between 50¢ and 79¢.
Draw coins. Write the price.

Answers will vary.

**Notes for Home** Your child used coins to show 50¢. *Home Activity:* Ask your child which coins have the greatest value: 10 dimes, 2 quarters, or 1 fifty-cent piece. (They all have the same value.)

Name

Practice 6-4

# Problem Solving: Make a List

1. Yoko needs 40¢ to buy juice from a vending machine. Use coins. Find all the ways to make 40¢ using quarters, dimes, and nickels.

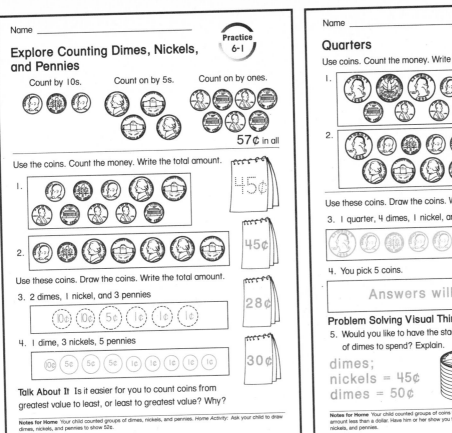

| Quarters | Dimes | Nickels |
|---|---|---|
| 1 | 1 | 1 |
| 1 | 0 | 3 |
| 0 | 4 | 0 |
| 0 | 3 | 2 |
| 0 | 2 | 4 |
| 0 | 1 | 6 |
| 0 | 0 | 8 |

Use 1 quarter.
Use 1 quarter again.

## Critical Thinking

Taro has these coins in his hand.
He has 50¢ in all.
What coins could he have in his pocket?

Show 2 ways. Draw the coins.

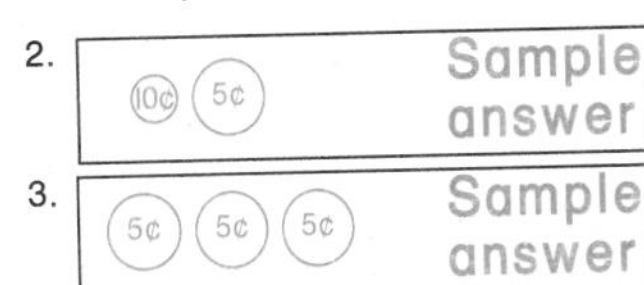

2. 10¢ 5¢ Sample answer

3. 5¢ 5¢ 5¢ Sample answer

**Notes for Home** Your child found ways to make 40¢ and put the information into an organized list. *Home Activity:* Use quarters, dimes, and nickels. Ask your child to show you all the ways to make 50¢. (There are 10 different ways. Possible answers: 2 quarters; 1 quarter and 2 dimes and 1 nickel; 5 dimes; 10 nickels.)

Name ______________________

Practice Chapter 6 A

## Mixed Practice: Lessons 1–4

Use coins. Count the money. Write the total amount.

1. 

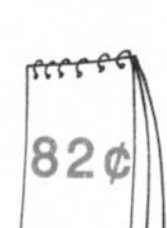


Use these coins. Draw the coins. Write the total amount.

2. 1 half dollar, 1 quarter, 1 dime, 2 nickels, 2 pennies

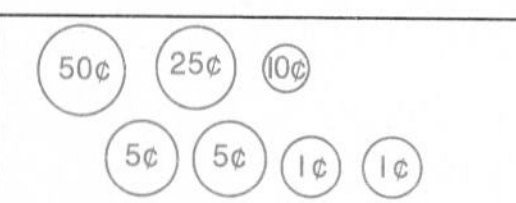

### Problem Solving

3. Randi needs 30¢ for a vending machine. Use coins. Find all the ways to make 30¢ using quarters, dimes, and nickels. Make a list.

| Quarter | Dime | Nickel |
|---|---|---|
| 1 | 0 | 1 |
| 0 | 3 | 0 |
| 0 | 2 | 2 |
| 0 | 1 | 4 |
| 0 | 0 | 6 |

### Journal

Choose an amount between 27¢ and 63¢. Write the amount.
Use coins. Show the amount in 2 different ways. Draw the coins.

**Notes for Home** Your child practiced making a list and counting half dollars, quarters, dimes, nickels, and pennies. *Home Activity:* Have your child use coins to show you different ways to make 40¢.



Name ______________________

Practice Chapters 1–6 A

## Cumulative Review

Count by ones, 5s, or 10s.
Write the numbers.

1. 55, 60, 65, 70, 75, 80
2. 40, 50, 60, 70, 80, 90
3. 14, 15, 16, 17, 18, 19
4. 0, 5, 10, 15, 20, 25

### Problem Solving

Use the graph to answer the questions.

| School Calendars Sold | |
|---|---|
| Gloria | XXXXX |
| Markus | XXXXXXX |
| Tony | XXX |
| Debbie | XXXXXX |

Each X stands for 5 calendars.

5. How many calendars did Debbie sell?

30 Calendars

6. How many more calendars did Markus sell than Tony?

20 more calendars

### Test Prep

Fill in the ○ for the correct answer.

3. Mark the word that names this number.

67

○ sixteen
○ twenty-seven
● sixty-seven
○ sixty

4. Mark the number for this word.

forty

○ 50 ○ 14 ○ 4 ● 40

**Notes for Home** Your child reviewed skip counting, picture graphs, and number words. *Home Activity:* Ask your child to read the graph and tell you who sold the most calendars (Markus) and who sold the next greatest number. (Debbie).



Name ______________________

Practice 6-5

## Coin Combinations

Use the fewest coins to show each amount.
Draw the coins.

1. 

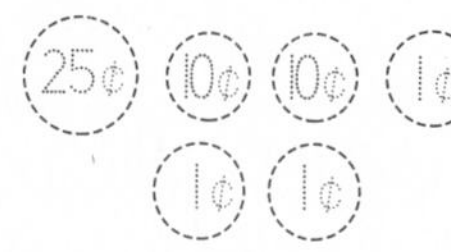


2. 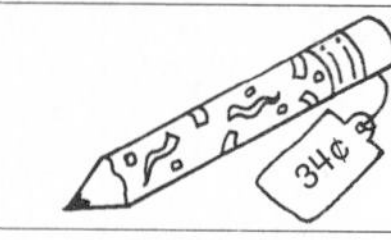


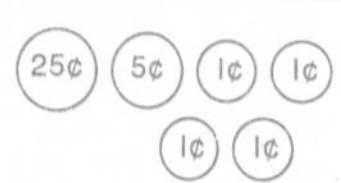


3. 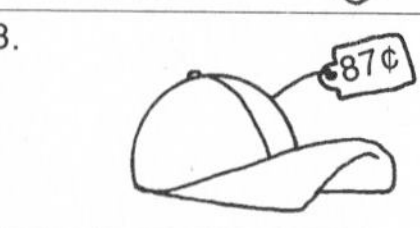


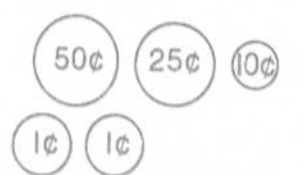


4. 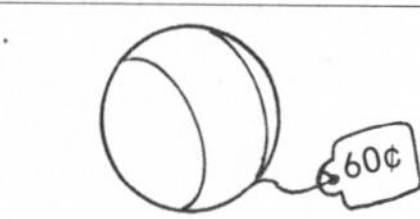

### Problem Solving

5. Draw the same amount of money using the least number of coins.

**Notes for Home** Your child practiced showing amounts of money using the fewest coins. *Home Activity:* Ask your child to think of an amount between 25¢ and 99¢, and to show the amount using the fewest number of coins.



Name ______________________

Practice 6-6

## Dollar Bill

Use some , , , and .

Fill in the table to show some ways to make $1.00.
Write how many of each coin is used. Use coins to help.

| Half dollar | Quarters | Dimes | Nickels | Value of coins |
|---|---|---|---|---|
| 2 | 0 | 0 | 0 | $1.00 |
| 0 | 4 | 0 | 0 | $1.00 |
| 0 | 0 | 10 | 0 | $1.00 |
| 0 | 0 | 0 | 20 | $1.00 |
| 1 | 2 | 0 | 0 | $1.00 |
| 1 | 0 | 5 | 0 | $1.00 |
| 0 | 3 | 2 | 1 | $1.00 |
| 0 | 2 | 3 | 4 | $1.00 |
| 0 | 3 | 0 | 5 | $1.00 |

### Journal

Pretend that you have $1.00 to spend.
What are some things you could buy that cost exactly $1.00? Answers will vary.

**Notes for Home** Your child made different coin combinations for $1.00. *Home Activity:* Ask your child how many of each coin it takes to make $1.00: pennies (100), nickels (20), dimes (10), quarters (4), and half-dollars (2).

Name ______________________

Practice 6-7

## Problem Solving: Act It Out

Take turns buying and selling. Use dimes to pay for items.
Use pennies to make change.

| | Cost | Amount Paid | Change |
|---|---|---|---|
| 1. | 35¢ | 4 dimes | 5¢ |
| 2. | | | |
| 3. | | | |
| 4. | | | |
| 5. | | | |

### Problem Solving Critical Thinking

6. Use the picture. Name 2 items you could buy with 8 dimes.
How much would you have left over?
Answers will vary.

**Notes for Home** Your child used coins to make change. *Home Activity:* Ask your child to point to the highest-priced item and the lowest-priced item, and tell how many dimes it would take to buy each. (95¢: 10 dimes; 18¢: 2 dimes)



Name ______________________

Practice Chapter 6 B

## Mixed Practice: Lessons 5–7

Use the fewest coins to show the amount.
Draw the coins.

1.

Use some [half dollar], [quarter], [dime], and [nickel].

Show 2 ways to make $1.00. Draw the coins.

2. Answers will vary.

3. Answers will vary.

### Problem Solving

Solve.

4. Leon has 5 dimes. He buys a model truck for 48¢. How much change should she get back?
2¢

### Journal

5. What coins could you use to pay for something that costs 63¢? What change would you get back?
Answers will vary.

**Notes for Home** Your child practiced choosing coins to show amounts of money and making change to solve problems. *Home Activity:* Ask your child to draw 2 other ways to show the amount in Exercise 1.



Name ______________________

Practice Chapters 1–6 B

## Cumulative Review

For each number, write the nearest ten.

1. Is 56 closer to 50 or 60?
56 is closer to 60.

2. Is 84 closer to 80 or 90?
84 is closer to 80.

Write the numbers in order from least to greatest.

3. 83 29 45 — 29 45 83

### Problem Solving

Solve the riddles.

4. I am between 27 and 37.
I have 5 ones.
What number am I? 35

5. I am less than 41.
I have 4 tens.
What number am I? 40

### Test Prep

Fill in the ○ for the correct answer.

6. Which sentence tells about the picture?

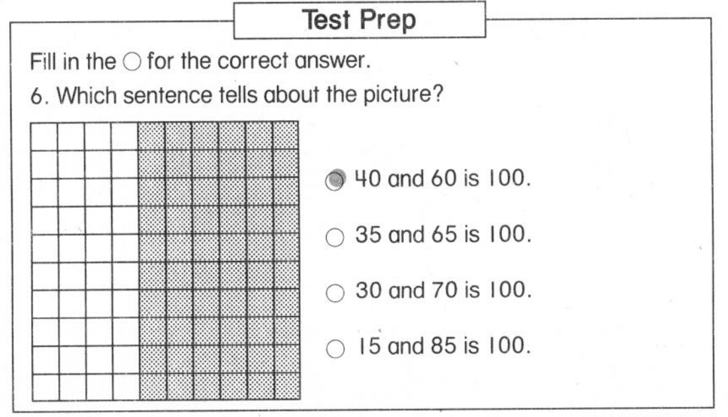

- ● 40 and 60 is 100.
- ○ 35 and 65 is 100.
- ○ 30 and 70 is 100.
- ○ 15 and 85 is 100.

**Notes for Home** Your child reviewed comparing numbers, finding the nearest ten for a number, and solving problems. *Home Activity:* Ask your child to put 48, 27, 51, and 39 in order from least to greatest. (27, 39, 48, 51)



Name ______________________

Practice 7-1

## Explore One Minute

How many times can you do each activity in one minute?
Estimate. Then do the activity. Write how many.

1. Write a five-letter word.
Estimate: _____ times
How many? _____ times

2. Draw a star.
Estimate: _____ times
How many? _____ times

3. Do jumping jacks.
Estimate: _____ times
How many? _____ times

4. Bounce a ball.
Estimate: _____ times
How many? _____ times

Answers will vary.

**Talk About It** Where your estimates accurate? Do you think you could make better estimates now? Why or why not? Compare your answers with a classmate.

**Notes for Home** Your child estimated how many times he or she could do an activity in one minute. Then he or she timed the activity to check. *Home Activity:* Ask your child to name two other activities that take one minute.

Name ______________________________

## Estimate Time

Practice 7-2

Draw an activity you can do in each amount of time.

1. More than one minute

Drawings will vary.

2. Less than one minute

3. About one minute

### Tell a Math Story

4. You have one minute to tell someone about school.
   What would you say?

**Notes for Home** Your child drew a picture of an activity that would take less than, more than, and about one minute. *Home Activity:* Ask your child to name one more activity for each amount of time.

Use with pages 235–236. 85

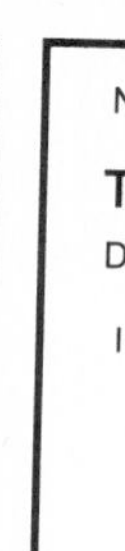

Name ______________________________

## Time to the Hour

Practice 7-3

Draw the clock hands to show each time.

1. 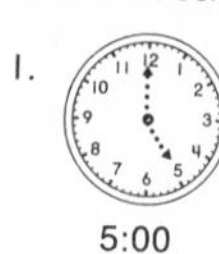 5:00
2.  12:00
3.  4:00

**Write your own.** Choose your own time.
Draw the clock hands. Write the time.

4.  ____ :00
5. ____ :00
6.  ____ :00

Answers will vary.

### Problem Solving Visual Thinking

Look at the picture. What time do you think it is?
Circle the time. How do you know?

7. 
(8:00) 3:00

8. 3:00 (12:00)

**Notes for Home** Your child showed time to the hour. *Home Activity:* Ask your child to tell where the hour hand and minute hand would be at 4:00. (The minute hand would be at 12, the hour hand at 4.)

86 Use with pages 237–238.

Name ______________________________

## Elapsed Time

Practice 7-4

Use your clock. Draw the clock hands.
Write the ending times.

1. Start 9:00 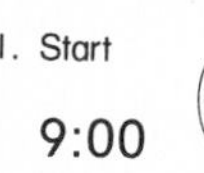  2 hours later  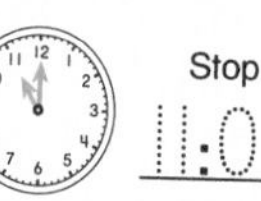 Stop 11:00
2. Start 5:00 — 3 hours later — Stop 8:00

Use your clock. When will each activity end?
Write the ending time.

3. Melvin goes to a friend's house at 3:00. He leaves in 1 hour. The time is 4:00.
4. Dena comes home from school at 3:00. Her mother comes home 2 hours later. They make dinner for 1 hour. The time is 6:00.

### Problem Solving Critical Thinking

Solve.

5. Tony stopped playing the flute at 7:00.
   He had played for 1 hour.

   What time did he start playing? 6:00

**Notes for Home** Your child solved problems involving the passing of time. *Home Activity:* Ask your child to tell you how many hours have gone by between 6:00 and 9:00 in the evening. (3 hours)

Use with pages 239–240. 87

Name ______________________________

## Problem Solving: Use Data from a Table

Practice 7-5

| School Play Rehearsals | | |
|---|---|---|
| Day | Start | End |
| Monday | 2:00 | 4:00 |
| Tuesday | 3:00 | 5:00 |
| Wednesday | 2:00 | 5:00 |
| Thursday | 2:00 | 6:00 |
| Friday | 3:00 | 6:00 |

Use the table. Solve the problems.
Write each answer.

1. This Monday, classes end 1 hour before rehearsal begins. What time do classes end?
   1:00
2. On what day is rehearsal the longest? How long is it?
   Thursday; 4 hours
3. How long is rehearsal on Wednesday?
   3 hours
4. Which days have rehearsals that last 2 hours?
   Monday, Tuesday

   Which days have rehearsals that last 3 hours?
   Wednesday, Friday

### Journal

5. Copy this table into your journal.
   Add another column at the right that tells how long rehearsal was each day. (2, 2, 3, 4, 3)

**Notes for Home** Your child used a table to solve problems. *Home Activity:* Ask your child to tell you how many hours children rehearsed in all. (2 + 2 + 3 + 4 + 3 = 14 hours in all)

88 Use with pages 243–244.

Name ______________________

## Mixed Practice: Lessons 1–5

1. Estimate how many times you can count to 20 in one minute. Then do the activity. Write how many.

Estimate: ______ times

How many? ______ times

Write the time.

2.  8:00

3. 5:00

Read both clocks.
How many hours have gone by?

4. 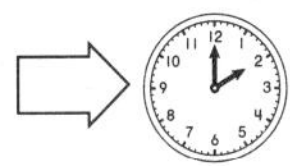 3 hours

### Problem Solving

Use the table.
Answer the question.

| Party Times | Start | End |
|---|---|---|
| Make crafts | 1:00 | 2:00 |
| Play "Treasure Hunt" | 2:00 | 3:00 |
| Eat a snack | 3:00 | 4:00 |

5. How long is the party?

3 hours

### Journal

6. Draw two clocks.
Show 8 o'clock on one.
Show 4 hours later on the other.

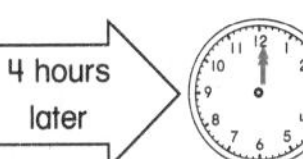


**Notes for Home** Your child practiced showing and telling time. *Home Activity:* Draw 3 clocks, each with a different time. Ask your child to tell you what time each clock would show 3 hours later.



---

Name ______________________

## Cumulative Review

Count by 2s. Write the numbers.

1. 12, 14, 16, 18, 20, 22, 24, 26, 28, 30

Count by 5s. Write the numbers.

2. 5, 10, 15, 20, 25, 30, 35, 40

Add or subtract.

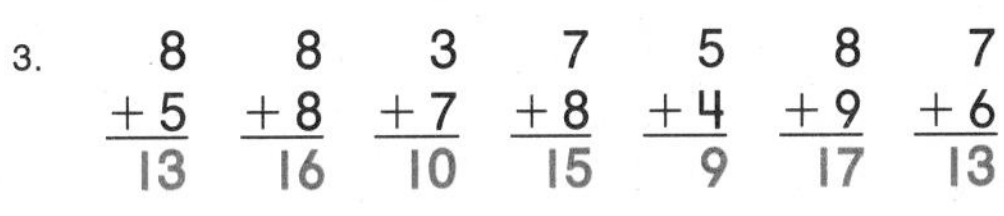

3. $8 + 5 = 13$ $8 + 8 = 16$ $3 + 7 = 10$ $7 + 8 = 15$ $5 + 4 = 9$ $8 + 9 = 17$ $7 + 6 = 13$

4. $13 - 8 = 5$ $14 - 6 = 8$ $15 - 7 = 8$ $12 - 9 = 3$ $13 - 7 = 6$ $17 - 8 = 9$ $12 - 7 = 5$

### Test Prep

Fill in the ○ for the correct answer.
Count the money. How much in all?

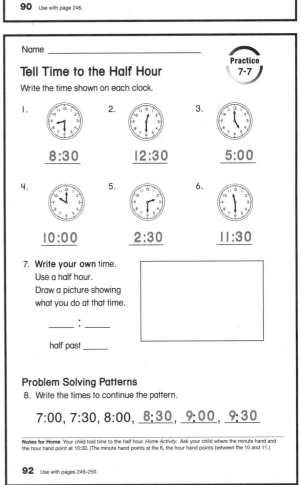

89¢ ○ 94¢ ● 96¢ ○ 66¢ ○

**Notes for Home** Your child reviewed concepts from earlier chapters. *Home Activity:* Ask your child to count by 10s to 100.



---

Name ______________________

Practice 7-6

## Tell Time to Five Minutes

Write the time for each clock.

1.  10:10

2.  2:35

3.  8:40

Draw the minute hand to show the time.

4.  4:05

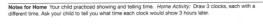

5.  8:50

6.  11:55

### Problem Solving

Solve. Write the time.

7. The muffins went into the oven at 10 minutes before 4. At what time did they go in the oven?

 3:50

8. Jon started his homework at 25 minutes before 8. At what time did he begin his homework?

 7:35

**Notes for Home** Your child told time to 5 minute intervals. *Home Activity:* Ask your child to tell where the minute hand would point at 2:40. (8)



---

Name ______________________

Practice 7-7

## Tell Time to the Half Hour

Write the time shown on each clock.

1.  8:30

2.  12:30

3.  5:00

4.  10:00

5.  2:30

6.  11:30

7. **Write your own** time.
Use a half hour.
Draw a picture showing what you do at that time.

_____ : _____

half past _____

### Problem Solving Patterns

8. Write the times to continue the pattern.

7:00, 7:30, 8:00, 8:30, 9:00, 9:30

**Notes for Home** Your child told time to the half hour. *Home Activity:* Ask your child where the minute hand and the hour hand point at 10:30. (The minute hand points at the 6, the hour hand points between the 10 and 11.)

Name ______________________

## Tell Time to the Quarter Hour

Practice 7-8

Write the time for each clock.

1. 

12:15

15 minutes after 12

2. 

4:45

45 minutes after 4

15 minutes before 5

3. 

1:30

half past 1

4. 11:45

45 minutes after 11

15 minutes before 12

### Problem Solving Visual Thinking

5. Some watches do not show all the numbers.
Write the time shown on this watch.

8:45

**Notes for Home** Your child learned how to tell time in 15 minute intervals. *Home Activity:* Ask your child to tell you the time for each 15-minute interval from 7:00 to 8:00. (7:00, 7:15, 7:30, 7:45, 8:00)



Name ______________________

## Problem Solving: Make a Table

1. The calendar shows all the months and days in a year.
Circle the first and last day of school. Answers will vary.
Circle a month in which a friend or relative has a birthday.

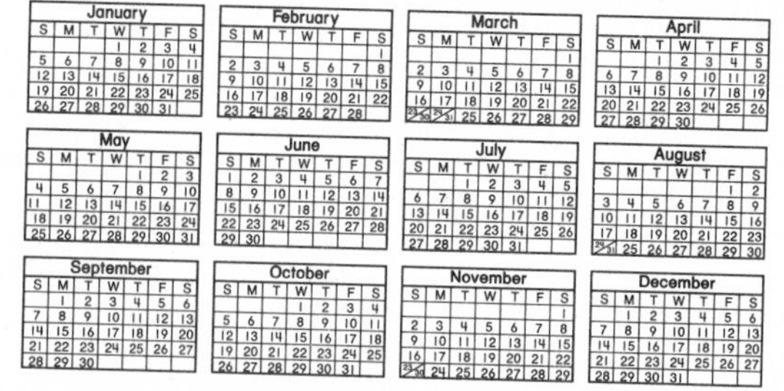

**January**

| S | M | T | W | T | F | S |
|---|---|---|---|---|---|---|
| | | | 1 | 2 | 3 | 4 |
| 5 | 6 | 7 | 8 | 9 | 10 | 11 |
| 12 | 13 | 14 | 15 | 16 | 17 | 18 |
| 19 | 20 | 21 | 22 | 23 | 24 | 25 |
| 26 | 27 | 28 | 29 | 30 | 31 | |

**February**

| S | M | T | W | T | F | S |
|---|---|---|---|---|---|---|
| | | | | | | 1 |
| 2 | 3 | 4 | 5 | 6 | 7 | 8 |
| 9 | 10 | 11 | 12 | 13 | 14 | 15 |
| 16 | 17 | 18 | 19 | 20 | 21 | 22 |
| 23 | 24 | 25 | 26 | 27 | 28 | |

**March**

| S | M | T | W | T | F | S |
|---|---|---|---|---|---|---|
| | | | | | | 1 |
| 2 | 3 | 4 | 5 | 6 | 7 | 8 |
| 9 | 10 | 11 | 12 | 13 | 14 | 15 |
| 16 | 17 | 18 | 19 | 20 | 21 | 22 |
| 23/30 | 24/31 | 25 | 26 | 27 | 28 | 29 |

**April**

| S | M | T | W | T | F | S |
|---|---|---|---|---|---|---|
| | | 1 | 2 | 3 | 4 | 5 |
| 6 | 7 | 8 | 9 | 10 | 11 | 12 |
| 13 | 14 | 15 | 16 | 17 | 18 | 19 |
| 20 | 21 | 22 | 23 | 24 | 25 | 26 |
| 27 | 28 | 29 | 30 | | | |

**May**

| S | M | T | W | T | F | S |
|---|---|---|---|---|---|---|
| | | | | 1 | 2 | 3 |
| 4 | 5 | 6 | 7 | 8 | 9 | 10 |
| 11 | 12 | 13 | 14 | 15 | 16 | 17 |
| 18 | 19 | 20 | 21 | 22 | 23 | 24 |
| 25 | 26 | 27 | 28 | 29 | 30 | 31 |

**June**

| S | M | T | W | T | F | S |
|---|---|---|---|---|---|---|
| 1 | 2 | 3 | 4 | 5 | 6 | 7 |
| 8 | 9 | 10 | 11 | 12 | 13 | 14 |
| 15 | 16 | 17 | 18 | 19 | 20 | 21 |
| 22 | 23 | 24 | 25 | 26 | 27 | 28 |
| 29 | 30 | | | | | |

**July**

| S | M | T | W | T | F | S |
|---|---|---|---|---|---|---|
| | | 1 | 2 | 3 | 4 | 5 |
| 6 | 7 | 8 | 9 | 10 | 11 | 12 |
| 13 | 14 | 15 | 16 | 17 | 18 | 19 |
| 20 | 21 | 22 | 23 | 24 | 25 | 26 |
| 27 | 28 | 29 | 30 | 31 | | |

**August**

| S | M | T | W | T | F | S |
|---|---|---|---|---|---|---|
| | | | | | 1 | 2 |
| 3 | 4 | 5 | 6 | 7 | 8 | 9 |
| 10 | 11 | 12 | 13 | 14 | 15 | 16 |
| 17 | 18 | 19 | 20 | 21 | 22 | 23 |
| 24/31 | 25 | 26 | 27 | 28 | 29 | 30 |

**September**

| S | M | T | W | T | F | S |
|---|---|---|---|---|---|---|
| | 1 | 2 | 3 | 4 | 5 | 6 |
| 7 | 8 | 9 | 10 | 11 | 12 | 13 |
| 14 | 15 | 16 | 17 | 18 | 19 | 20 |
| 21 | 22 | 23 | 24 | 25 | 26 | 27 |
| 28 | 29 | 30 | | | | |

**October**

| S | M | T | W | T | F | S |
|---|---|---|---|---|---|---|
| | | | 1 | 2 | 3 | 4 |
| 5 | 6 | 7 | 8 | 9 | 10 | 11 |
| 12 | 13 | 14 | 15 | 16 | 17 | 18 |
| 19 | 20 | 21 | 22 | 23 | 24 | 25 |
| 26 | 27 | 28 | 29 | 30 | 31 | |

**November**

| S | M | T | W | T | F | S |
|---|---|---|---|---|---|---|
| | | | | | | 1 |
| 2 | 3 | 4 | 5 | 6 | 7 | 8 |
| 9 | 10 | 11 | 12 | 13 | 14 | 15 |
| 16 | 17 | 18 | 19 | 20 | 21 | 22 |
| 23/30 | 24 | 25 | 26 | 27 | 28 | 29 |

**December**

| S | M | T | W | T | F | S |
|---|---|---|---|---|---|---|
| | 1 | 2 | 3 | 4 | 5 | 6 |
| 7 | 8 | 9 | 10 | 11 | 12 | 13 |
| 14 | 15 | 16 | 17 | 18 | 19 | 20 |
| 21 | 22 | 23 | 24 | 25 | 26 | 27 |
| 28 | 29 | 30 | 31 | | | |

2. Make a table using the calendar.
Use tallies to show how many months have 3 or 4 full weeks.

| Months with 3 full weeks | Months with 4 full weeks |
|---|---|
| ~~||||~~ || | ~~||||~~ |

### Journal

3. Look at this year's calendar. Make a table using tallies to show how many months have the last day on a weekend and how many have the last day on a weekday.

**Notes for Home** Your child made a table to solve problems. *Home Activity:* Ask your child to show you his or her journal entries and to explain the entries.



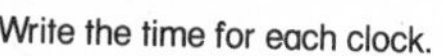

Name ______________________

## Mixed Practice: Lessons 6–9

Practice Chapter 7 B

Write the time for each clock.

1. 

2:15

15 minutes after 2

2. 7:30

half past 7

3. 4:45

45 minutes after 4

15 minutes before 5

Write the time for each clock.

4. 

8:35

5. 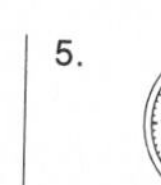

5:55

### Problem Solving

Use the calendar to answer the questions.

**March**

| S | M | T | W | T | F | S |
|---|---|---|---|---|---|---|
| | | | | | | 1 |
| 2 | 3 | 4 | 5 | 6 | 7 | 8 |
| 9 | 10 | 11 | 12 | 13 | 14 | 15 |
| 16 | 17 | 18 | 19 | 20 | 21 | 22 |
| 23/30 | 24/31 | 25 | 26 | 27 | 28 | 29 |

6. How many Saturdays are in this month? 5

7. On what day of the week is the last day of the month? Monday

### Journal

8. Draw two clocks. Show 6:15 on one clock.
Show 6:45 on the other clock.
Tell how much time has passed. What time will it be in 15 minutes?

**Notes for Home** Your child told time and used a calendar. *Home Activity:* Ask your child to tell you the time right now. What time will it be in 5 minutes? 15 minutes? 30 minutes? 1 hour?



Name ______________________

## Cumulative Review

Practice Chapters 1–7 B

Use the graph. Answer the questions.

**How I Spend My Time on a School Day**

Activity: School, Homework, Playing, Eating, Sleeping

Hours: 1 2 3 4 5 6 7 8 9 10

1. Which activity did this child spend the most time doing? Sleeping

2. What did the child spend about the same time doing? Playing and eating

Add or subtract.

3. $7 + 9 = 16$ $17 - 8 = 9$ $12 - 7 = 5$ $14 - 6 = 8$ $7 + 5 = 12$ $13 - 7 = 6$ $6 + 8 = 14$

### Test Prep

Fill in the ○ for the correct answer.

4. What number completes the table?

| Ways to Show 35¢ | |
|---|---|
| Nickels | Dimes |
| 7 | 0 |
| ? | 1 |
| 3 | 2 |
| 1 | 3 |

4 ○ 6 ○ 8 ○ 5 ●

**Notes for Home** Your child reviewed concepts from earlier chapters. *Home Activity:* Ask your child how many hours they spend each day doing the activities in the graph.

Name ______________________

## Explore Adding Tens

How many in all?

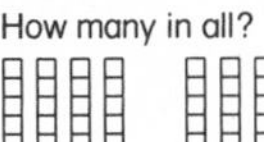
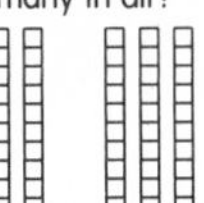

4 tens + 3 tens = 7 tens

40 + 30 = 70

Use ▭ to find how many in all.

1. 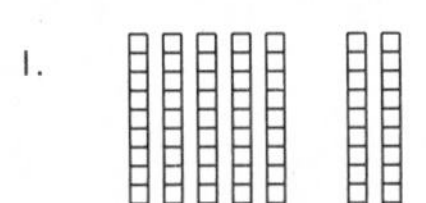

5 tens + 2 tens = 7 tens

50 + 20 = 70

2. 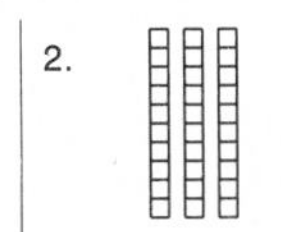

3 tens + 5 tens = 8 tens

30 + 50 = 80

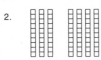

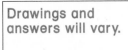

**Write your own** problems about adding tens.

3. Draw the ▭ you use.

Drawings and answers will vary.

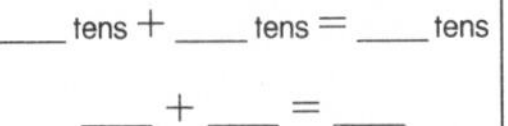

___ tens + ___ tens = ___ tens

___ + ___ = ___

4. Draw the ▭ you use.

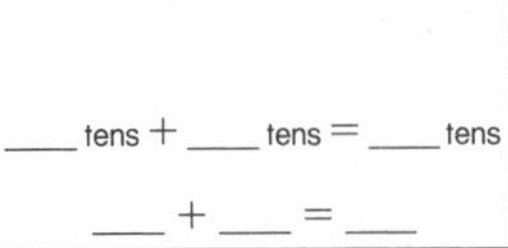

___ tens + ___ tens = ___ tens

___ + ___ = ___

**Talk About It** Tell a classmate how 4 + 2 and 40 + 20 are alike and how they are different.

**Notes for Home** Your child explored adding tens. *Home Activity:* Ask your child to tell you the sum of 3 and 3. (6) Then ask him or her to tell you the sum of 30 and 30. (60)



Name ______________________

## Add Tens with a Hundred Chart

1. 34 + 10 = 44; 25 + 40 = 65
2. 68 + 20 = 88; 86 + 10 = 96
3. 50 + 30 = 80; 73 + 10 = 83

Add. You can use the hundreds chart.

| 1 | 2 | 3 | 4 | 5 | 6 | 7 | 8 | 9 | 10 |
|---|---|---|---|---|---|---|---|---|---|
| 11 | 12 | 13 | 14 | 15 | 16 | 17 | 18 | 19 | 20 |
| 21 | 22 | 23 | 24 | 25 | 26 | 27 | 28 | 29 | 30 |
| 31 | 32 | 33 | 34 | 35 | 36 | 37 | 38 | 39 | 40 |
| 41 | 42 | 43 | 44 | 45 | 46 | 47 | 48 | 49 | 50 |
| 51 | 52 | 53 | 54 | 55 | 56 | 57 | 58 | 59 | 60 |
| 61 | 62 | 63 | 64 | 65 | 66 | 67 | 68 | 69 | 70 |
| 71 | 72 | 73 | 74 | 75 | 76 | 77 | 78 | 79 | 80 |
| 81 | 82 | 83 | 84 | 85 | 86 | 87 | 88 | 89 | 90 |
| 91 | 92 | 93 | 94 | 95 | 96 | 97 | 98 | 99 | 100 |

### Problem Solving Patterns

4. Add. What patterns do you see?

40 + 30 = 70
41 + 30 = 71
42 + 30 = 72
43 + 30 = 73
44 + 30 = 74

**Write your own** number sentences to make a pattern.

___ + ___ = ___
___ + ___ = ___
___ + ___ = ___
___ + ___ = ___
___ + ___ = ___

Answers will vary.

**Notes for Home** Your child practiced adding tens. *Home Activity:* Ask your child to show you a pattern that starts with the number sentence 20 + 20 = ___. (Possible answers: 21 + 20 = 41, 22 + 20 = 42, 23 + 20 = 43, and so on.)



Name ______________________

## Add Using Mental Math

Use mental math to add.

1. 14 + 30 = 44; 56 + 20 = 76
2. 37 + 40 = 77; 29 + 50 = 79
3. 63 + 20 = 83; 82 + 10 = 92
4. 55 + 30 = 85; 72 + 20 = 92
5. 75 + 10 = 85; 41 + 30 = 71

### Problem Solving Patterns

Add. Use mental math. Then write the number sentences to continue the patterns.

6. 22 + 20 = 42
22 + 30 = 52
22 + 40 = 62
22 + 50 = 72
22 + 60 = 82

7. 48 + 10 = 58
48 + 20 = 68
48 + 30 = 78
48 + 40 = 88
48 + 50 = 98

8. Describe the patterns you see. Answers will vary.

______________________

______________________

**Notes for Home** Your child practiced using mental math to add. *Home Activity:* Ask your child to tell you how old he or she will be 10 years from now, 20 years from now, and 30 years from now.



Name ______________________

Practice 8-4

## Estimate Two-Digit Sums

Find the nearest ten. Estimate the sum.

1. 21 + 48

Think: 20 + 50 = 70

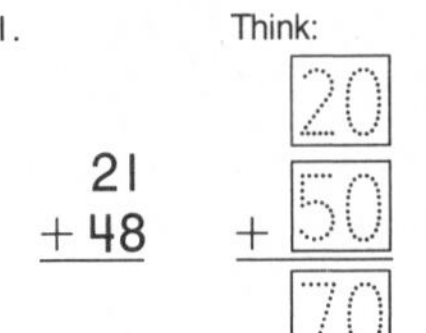

21 + 48 is about 70.

2. 58 + 17

Think: 60 + 20 = 80

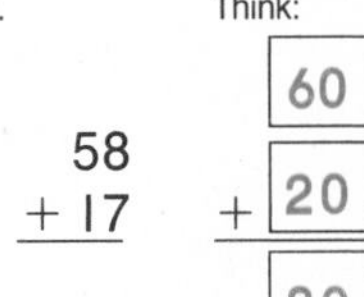

58 + 17 is about 80.

3. 33 + 22

Think: 30 + 20 = 50

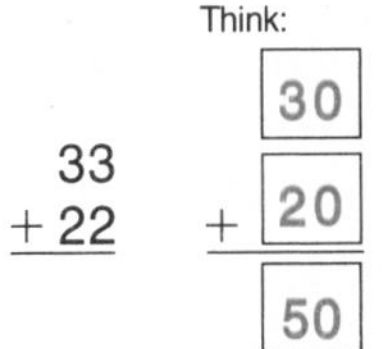

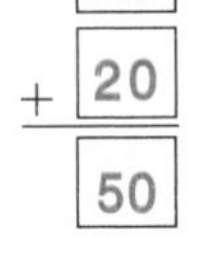

33 + 22 is about 50.

4. 48 + 41

Think: 50 + 40 = 90

48 + 41 is about 90.

### Problem Solving Estimation

5. This graph shows how many children chose sandwiches for lunch yesterday. About how many children chose sandwiches for lunch? 50

About how many chose turkey sandwiches? 30

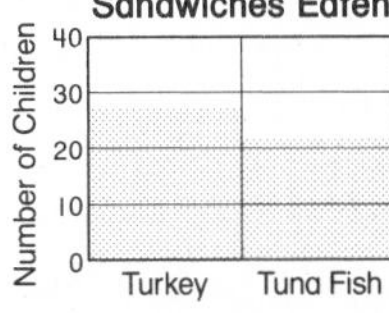


**Notes for Home** Your child used nearest tens to estimated sums. *Home Activity:* Ask your child to tell you how to estimate the sum of 32 and 18. (32 is about 30 and 18 is about 20. 30 plus 20 is 50.)

Name ______________________

Practice 8-5

## Problem Solving: Make Predictions

1. Predict. Which fruit do you think your classmates like best?

______________________

2. Why do you think so?

Answers will vary.

______________________

3. Ask your classmates. Record the results.

| Fruit | Tally | Total |
|---|---|---|
| | | |
| | | |
| | | |
| | | |
| | | |
| | | |

4. Was your prediction close? ______________

### Critical Thinking

5. What do you think you can do to make better predictions?

Answers will vary.

**Notes for Home** Your child made a prediction and then found information to test the prediction. *Home Activity:* Have your child make a prediction and then test it. Predict how many people or how many birds will you see in the next 15 minutes.



Name ______________________

Practice 8-6

## Explore Addition With or Without Regrouping

15 children ride bikes to school. 8 children walk.
How many children in all?

| Tens | Ones |
|---|---|
| 1 ten | 5 ones |

Start with 15.

| Tens | Ones |
|---|---|
| 1 ten | 13 ones |

Add 8.

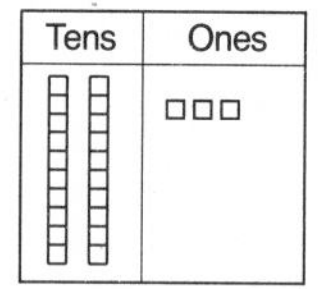

Regroup 10 ones as 1 ten.

Write how many in all. 2 tens 3 ones 23 in all

Use tens/ones mat, tens, and ones.

1. Show 26. Add 9. How many in all?
   3 tens 5 ones
   35 in all

2. Show 48. Add 5. How many in all?
   5 tens 3 ones
   53 in all

3. Show 12. Add 5. How many in all?
   1 ten 7 ones
   17 in all

4. Show 37. Add 8. How many in all?
   4 tens 5 ones
   45 in all

**Talk About It** Explain to a classmate when it is important to regroup.

**Notes for Home** Your child explored regrouping in addition. *Home Activity:* Have your child use dry beans or macaroni to show how to regroup when adding 16 and 7. (6 + 7 = 1 ten and 3 ones; 16 + 7 = 23)



Name ______________________

Practice 8-7

## Add With or Without Regrouping

Use tens/ones mat, tens, and ones.

| | Show this many. | Add this many. | Do you need to regroup? | Solve. |
|---|---|---|---|---|
| 1. | 27 | 5 | yes | 27 + 5 = 32 |
| 2. | 45 | 3 | no | 45 + 3 = 48 |
| 3. | 58 | 8 | yes | 58 + 8 = 66 |
| 4. | 34 | 7 | yes | 34 + 7 = 41 |
| 5. | 75 | 4 | no | 75 + 4 = 79 |
| 6. | 13 | 9 | yes | 13 + 9 = 22 |
| 7. | 66 | 6 | yes | 66 + 6 = 72 |

### Problem Solving Critical Thinking

8. Which one-digit numbers can you add to 15 without needing to regroup? How do you know?

0, 1, 2, 3, and 4. Each number added to 5 gives a sum less than 10.

**Notes for Home** Your child decided when to regroup to add numbers and then found the sums. *Home Activity:* Ask your child to show you two addition problems, one where you must regroup and one where you do not have to regroup. (Possible answer: you must regroup for 15 + 6; you do not regroup for 15 + 4.)



Name ______________________

Practice 8-8

## Record Addition

Add. Then circle the exercise if you regrouped.

Use tens/ones mat, tens, and ones.

1. 43 + 7 = 50 (tens | ones: 4 3 / + 7 / 5 0; regrouped 1)

2. 37 + 1 = 38 (tens | ones: 3 7 / + 1 / 3 8)

3. 53 + 8 = 61 (circled)   72 + 4 = 76   61 + 9 = 70 (circled)   45 + 7 = 52 (circled)

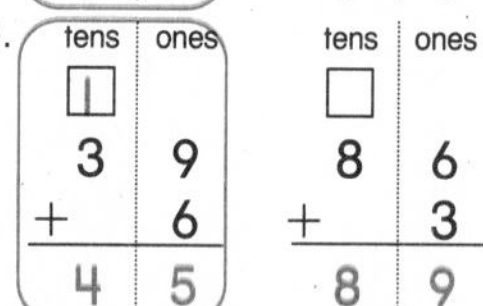

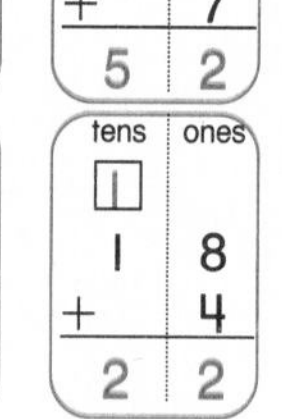

4. 39 + 6 = 45 (circled)   86 + 3 = 89   25 + 8 = 33 (circled)   18 + 4 = 22 (circled)

### Problem Solving Critical Thinking

5. Lenny dropped grape jam on his math paper. Now Lenny cannot read some of the numbers. What could the missing numbers be? How do you know?

38 + ? = 4?

2, 0; 3, 1; 4, 2; 5, 3; 6, 4; 7, 5; 8, 6; 9, 7.

**Notes for Home** Your child added tens and ones where regrouping was sometime required. *Home Activity:* Ask your child to write addition problems where regrouping is and is not required, and explain his or her reasoning.

Name ______________________

## Mixed Practice: Lessons 1–8

Estimate the sum.

1. 

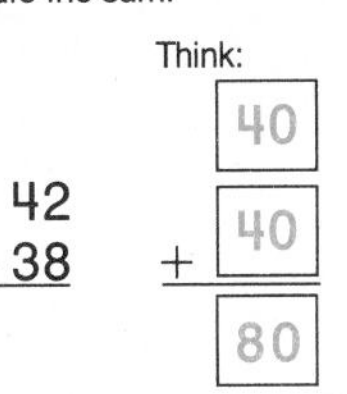

Think:

$$\begin{array}{r} 42 \\ +38 \\ \hline \end{array} \qquad \begin{array}{r} \boxed{40} \\ +\boxed{40} \\ \hline \boxed{80} \end{array}$$

42 + 38 is about 80.

Add. Use mental math.

2. 38 + 20 = 58

42 + 50 = 92

19 + 30 = 49

### Problem Solving

3. Complete the chart. Fill in the totals.

| Color of Shirts | Tally | Totals |
|---|---|---|
| yellow | ~~////~~ / | 6 |
| red | ~~////~~ //// | 9 |
| white | /// | 3 |

4. Ms. April's class made a chart to show the color of shirts worn by the students. What color shirt would you predict to see most often in Mr. May's class? Probable answer: red

### Journal

6. Make a chart to show the color of shirts worn by the students in your class. What color shirt do you see most often?

**Notes for Home** Your child practiced adding tens, using mental math, estimating sums, and solving problems. *Home Activity:* Have your child look at Exercise 2 and tell you which of the problems has the greater sum and why.



Name ______________________

## Cumulative Review

Add or subtract.

1. $\begin{array}{r} 5 \\ +5 \\ \hline 10 \end{array}$ $\begin{array}{r} 10 \\ -5 \\ \hline 5 \end{array}$

2. $\begin{array}{r} 4 \\ +4 \\ \hline 8 \end{array}$ $\begin{array}{r} 8 \\ -4 \\ \hline 4 \end{array}$

3. $\begin{array}{r} 6 \\ +6 \\ \hline 12 \end{array}$ $\begin{array}{r} 12 \\ -6 \\ \hline 6 \end{array}$

4. $\begin{array}{r} 7 \\ +7 \\ \hline 14 \end{array}$ $\begin{array}{r} 14 \\ -7 \\ \hline 7 \end{array}$

Write how many. Then write **even** or **odd**.

5. 

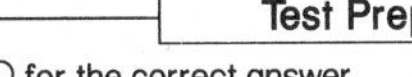

12 even

6. 13 odd

### Test Prep

Fill in the ○ for the correct answer.

Use the picture to answer the questions.

7. Which is clown C?
   - ○ first
   - ○ second
   - ● third
   - ○ fourth

8. Which is clown E?
   - ○ second
   - ○ third
   - ● fifth
   - ○ sixth

**Notes for Home** Your child reviewed concepts from earlier chapters. *Home Activity:* Ask your child which clown in the picture is first and which is last. (Clown A is first and clown F is last.)



Name ______________________

## Add Two-Digit Numbers With or Without Regrouping

Use tens ones, ▭▭▭▭, and ▫. Regroup if you need to.

1. $\begin{array}{r} 25 \\ +17 \\ \hline 42 \end{array}$ $\begin{array}{r} 46 \\ +23 \\ \hline 69 \end{array}$ $\begin{array}{r} 71 \\ +15 \\ \hline 86 \end{array}$ $\begin{array}{r} 35 \\ +47 \\ \hline 82 \end{array}$

2. $\begin{array}{r} 59 \\ +36 \\ \hline 95 \end{array}$ $\begin{array}{r} 86 \\ +12 \\ \hline 98 \end{array}$ $\begin{array}{r} 17 \\ +48 \\ \hline 65 \end{array}$ $\begin{array}{r} 64 \\ +26 \\ \hline 90 \end{array}$

3. $\begin{array}{r} 39 \\ +26 \\ \hline 65 \end{array}$ $\begin{array}{r} 58 \\ +41 \\ \hline 99 \end{array}$ $\begin{array}{r} 74 \\ +19 \\ \hline 93 \end{array}$ $\begin{array}{r} 41 \\ +39 \\ \hline 80 \end{array}$

### Problem Solving Visual Thinking

4. We started with this. | Now we have this. | Draw what was added.

**Notes for Home** Your child added two-digit numbers with and without regrouping. *Home Activity:* Have your child use dried beans or macaroni to explain why it sometimes is necessary to regroup.



Name ______________________

## Add Two-Digit Numbers

Add. Regroup if you need to.

1. $\begin{array}{r} 27 \\ +24 \\ \hline 51 \end{array}$ $\begin{array}{r} 52 \\ +9 \\ \hline 61 \end{array}$ $\begin{array}{r} 34 \\ +57 \\ \hline 91 \end{array}$ $\begin{array}{r} 19 \\ +43 \\ \hline 62 \end{array}$ $\begin{array}{r} 44 \\ +55 \\ \hline 99 \end{array}$

2. $\begin{array}{r} 51 \\ +29 \\ \hline 80 \end{array}$ $\begin{array}{r} 73 \\ +16 \\ \hline 89 \end{array}$ $\begin{array}{r} 18 \\ +36 \\ \hline 54 \end{array}$ $\begin{array}{r} 35 \\ +55 \\ \hline 90 \end{array}$ $\begin{array}{r} 67 \\ +11 \\ \hline 78 \end{array}$ $\begin{array}{r} 33 \\ +38 \\ \hline 71 \end{array}$

3. $\begin{array}{r} 14 \\ +66 \\ \hline 80 \end{array}$ $\begin{array}{r} 68 \\ +27 \\ \hline 95 \end{array}$ $\begin{array}{r} 26 \\ +72 \\ \hline 98 \end{array}$ $\begin{array}{r} 57 \\ +15 \\ \hline 72 \end{array}$ $\begin{array}{r} 35 \\ +36 \\ \hline 71 \end{array}$ $\begin{array}{r} 40 \\ +49 \\ \hline 89 \end{array}$

### Problem Solving

4. Kevin's apples weigh 32 pounds. Which two baskets are his?

17 and 15 pounds

**Write your own** math story about the apple baskets. Ask a friend to solve it.

Answers will vary.

**Notes for Home** Your child added two-digit numbers with and without regrouping. *Home Activity:* Have your child tell you how to find the sum of 46 + 25. (Add the ones. 6 + 5 = 11. Regroup. Add the tens. 1 + 4 + 2 = 7. The sum is 71.)

Name ______________________

Practice 8-11

## Add Money

Add.

1.

| 14¢ | 43¢ | 27¢ | 48¢ | 35¢ | 57¢ |
|---|---|---|---|---|---|
| + 18¢ | + 25¢ | + 53¢ | + 24¢ | + 44¢ | + 24¢ |
| 32¢ | 68¢ | 80¢ | 72¢ | 79¢ | 81¢ |

2.

| 61¢ | 83¢ | 78¢ | 35¢ | 57¢ | 82¢ |
|---|---|---|---|---|---|
| + 29¢ | + 16¢ | + 16¢ | + 63¢ | + 31¢ | + 10¢ |
| 90¢ | 99¢ | 94¢ | 98¢ | 88¢ | 92¢ |

**Mixed Practice** Add.

3.

| 45¢ | 21¢ | 37 | 13 | 56¢ | 78 |
|---|---|---|---|---|---|
| + 38¢ | + 49¢ | + 26 | + 57 | + 19¢ | + 7 |
| 83¢ | 70¢ | 63 | 70 | 75¢ | 85 |

4.

| 62 | 34¢ | 18 | 25¢ | 70 | 18¢ |
|---|---|---|---|---|---|
| + 24 | + 7¢ | + 63 | + 39¢ | + 16 | + 13¢ |
| 86 | 41¢ | 81 | 64¢ | 86 | 31¢ |

**Problem Solving Critical Thinking**

5. Peg has 75¢. Which two items could she buy?

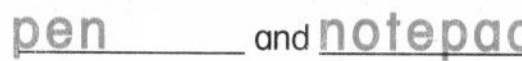

pen ______ and notepad

**Notes for Home** Your child added amounts of money up to 99¢. *Home Activity:* Ask your child: *How much money would you have in all if you had 25¢ and 38¢?* (63¢)



Name ______________________

Practice 8-12

## Add Three Numbers

Add.

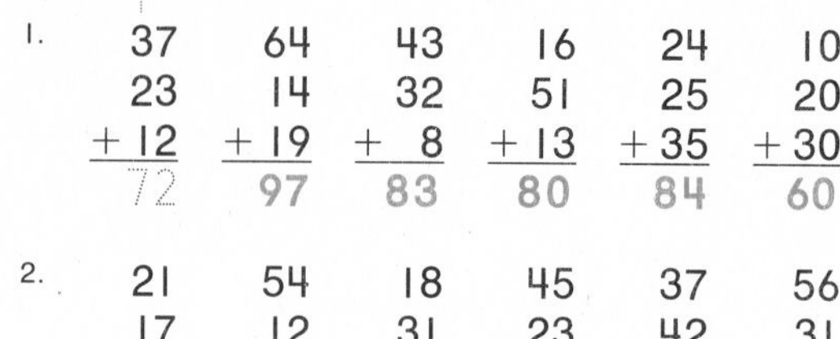

1.

| 37 | 64 | 43 | 16 | 24 | 10 |
|---|---|---|---|---|---|
| 23 | 14 | 32 | 51 | 25 | 20 |
| + 12 | + 19 | + 8 | + 13 | + 35 | + 30 |
| 72 | 97 | 83 | 80 | 84 | 60 |

2.

| 21 | 54 | 18 | 45 | 37 | 56 |
|---|---|---|---|---|---|
| 17 | 12 | 31 | 23 | 42 | 31 |
| + 31 | + 26 | + 8 | + 11 | + 1 | + 4 |
| 69 | 92 | 57 | 79 | 80 | 91 |

3.

| 14 | 68 | 26 | 52 | 35 | 16 |
|---|---|---|---|---|---|
| 31 | 10 | 32 | 11 | 34 | 17 |
| + 6 | + 7 | + 24 | + 15 | + 6 | + 10 |
| 51 | 85 | 82 | 78 | 75 | 43 |

**Problem Solving Critical Thinking**

The shelf cannot hold more than 90 pounds. How many pounds can be in the last box?

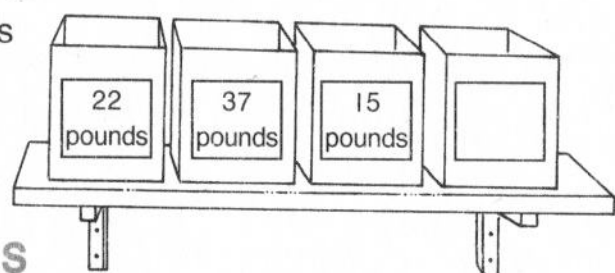


______ pounds

16 pounds or less

**Notes for Home** Your child has found the sum of 3 numbers. *Home Activity:* Ask your child to explain his or her reasoning for solving the Problem Solving exercise.



Name ______________________

Practice 8-13

## Problem Solving: Guess and Check

Solve. Show and check each guess.

1. Libis has 58¢. She wants to buy two toys. What can she buy?

Toys A & B, B & D, B & E, B & F, D & E, or D & F

Libis can buy the ____________ and the ____________.

2. Which other two toys can Libis buy with 58¢?

Libis can buy the ____________ and the ____________.

3. Armando has 50¢. He wants to buy two toys. What can he buy?

Toys B & D, B & E, B & F, or D & F

Armando can buy the ____________ and the ____________.

**Estimation**

4. Libis wants to buy 3 toys. Does she have enough money? How do you know?

No, because the sum of any 3 tens digits you chose is always 60¢ or more.

**Notes for Home** Your child solved problems by guessing and testing. *Home Activity:* Ask your child if it is possible to buy 3 toys with 70¢. (Yes, you can buy toys B, D, and F for less than 70¢.)



Name ______________________

Practice Chapter 8 B

## Mixed Practice: Lessons 9–13

Add. Regroup if you need to.

1.

| 26 | 58 | 32 | 16 | 45 | 27 |
|---|---|---|---|---|---|
| + 12 | + 29 | + 48 | + 33 | + 29 | + 18 |
| 38 | 87 | 80 | 49 | 74 | 45 |

2.

| 34¢ | 51¢ | 15¢ | 63¢ | 22¢ |
|---|---|---|---|---|
| + 49¢ | + 16¢ | + 28¢ | + 17¢ | + 51¢ |
| 83¢ | 67¢ | 43¢ | 80¢ | 73¢ |

3.

| 42 | 37 | 25 | 51 | 11 | 30 |
|---|---|---|---|---|---|
| 15 | 43 | 23 | 24 | 50 | 46 |
| + 15 | + 7 | + 22 | + 19 | + 6 | + 13 |
| 72 | 87 | 70 | 94 | 67 | 89 |

**Problem Solving**

Solve. Show and check each guess.

3. Sue has 56¢. She wants to buy two toys. What can she buy?

Toys A and C, or B and C.

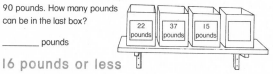

She can buy the ______ and the ______.

Toy A 31¢, Toy B 29¢, Toy C 24¢, Toy D 38¢

**Journal**

4. How does making a guess that is not the answer help you make the next guess?

**Notes for Home** Your child reviewed adding two-digit numbers with and without regrouping, adding three numbers, and using the strategy of guess and check to solve problems. *Home Activity:* Ask your child how much money he or she would need to buy the two most expensive toys shown in Exercise 3. (31¢ + 38¢ = 69¢.)

Name ______________________________

## Cumulative Review

Circle the numbers you would add first.
Look for doubles and numbers that make 10. Add.

1.

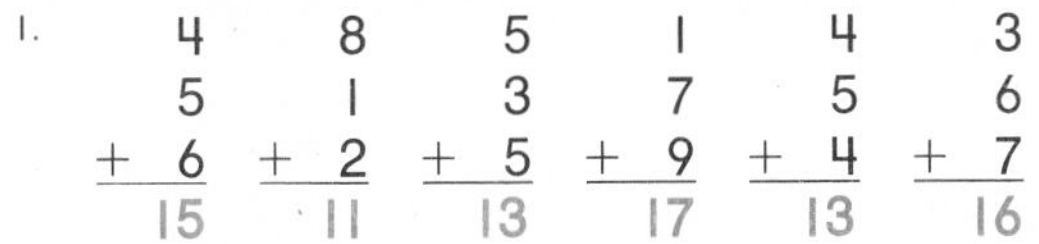

| 4 | 8 | 5 | 1 | 4 | 3 |
|---|---|---|---|---|---|
| 5 | 1 | 3 | 7 | 5 | 6 |
| + 6 | + 2 | + 5 | + 9 | + 4 | + 7 |
| 15 | 11 | 13 | 17 | 13 | 16 |

Draw coins. Show two different ways to make 75¢.

2. 
Sample answers: 3 quarters

3. 1 quarter and 5 dimes

Draw coins. Show two different ways to make 30¢.

4. 
Sample answers: 3 dimes

5. 6 nickels

### Test Prep

Fill in the ○ for the correct answer.
Which group of numbers is in order from the least to the greatest?

6. ○ 27, 36, 58, 45
○ 24, 22, 18, 9
● 48, 66, 75, 80
○ 53, 70, 68, 92

7. ○ 18, 28, 31, 16
○ 12, 22, 32, 23
○ 25, 37, 26, 38
● 39, 40, 78, 87

**Notes for Home** Your child reviewed skills from earlier chapters. *Home Activity:* Ask your child to think of 3 numbers that have a sum less than 10. (Possible answers: 1 + 2 + 3, 2 + 5 + 2, 4 + 4 + 1, and so on.)



Name ______________________________

## Explore Subtracting Tens

Use [tens blocks] to find how many are left.

1. 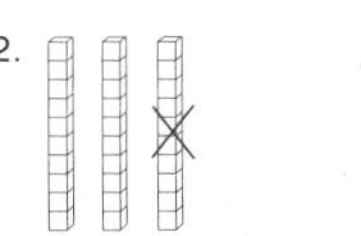

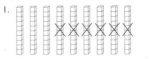

9 tens − 6 tens = 3 tens | 90 − 60 = 30

2. 3 tens − 1 tens = 2 tens | 30 − 10 = 20

3. 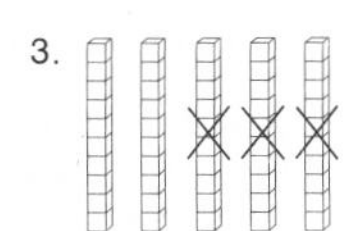

5 tens − 3 tens = 2 tens | 50 − 30 = 20

Subtract. You can use [tens blocks] to help.

4. 7 tens − 2 tens = 5 tens | 70 − 20 = 50

5. 6 tens − 4 tens = 2 tens | 60 − 40 = 20

**Talk About It** How does finding 9 − 6 help you find 90 − 60?

Answers will vary. Sample answer: Since 9 − 6 is 3 ones, I know that 90 − 60 is 3 tens.

**Notes for Home** Your child explored subtracting tens. *Home Activity:* Ask your child to find 5 tens minus 2 tens and then 50 minus 20. (3 tens, 30)



Name ______________________________

## Subtract Tens With a Hundred Chart

Subtract. You can use the hundred chart.

1. 56 − 20 = 36
2. 94 − 50 = 44
3. 35 − 10 = 25
4. 73 − 40 = 33

| 1 | 2 | 3 | 4 | 5 | 6 | 7 | 8 | 9 | 10 |
|---|---|---|---|---|---|---|---|---|---|
| 11 | 12 | 13 | 14 | 15 | 16 | 17 | 18 | 19 | 20 |
| 21 | 22 | 23 | 24 | 25 | 26 | 27 | 28 | 29 | 30 |
| 31 | 32 | 33 | 34 | 35 | 36 | 37 | 38 | 39 | 40 |
| 41 | 42 | 43 | 44 | 45 | 46 | 47 | 48 | 49 | 50 |
| 51 | 52 | 53 | 54 | 55 | 56 | 57 | 58 | 59 | 60 |
| 61 | 62 | 63 | 64 | 65 | 66 | 67 | 68 | 69 | 70 |
| 71 | 72 | 73 | 74 | 75 | 76 | 77 | 78 | 79 | 80 |
| 81 | 82 | 83 | 84 | 85 | 86 | 87 | 88 | 89 | 90 |
| 91 | 92 | 93 | 94 | 95 | 96 | 97 | 98 | 99 | 100 |

5.

| 64 | 27 | 88 | 49 | 61 | 78 | 54 |
|---|---|---|---|---|---|---|
| − 30 | − 10 | − 30 | − 20 | − 40 | − 50 | − 20 |
| 34 | 17 | 58 | 29 | 21 | 28 | 34 |

**Problem Solving** Patterns

6. Subtract.

70 − 20 = 50
70 − 30 = 40
70 − 40 = 30

Write your own number sentences to make a pattern.

Answers will vary.
____ − ____ = ____
____ − ____ = ____

**Notes for Home** Your child subtracted tens on a hundred chart. *Home Activity:* Ask your child to show you how he or she used the hundred chart to subtract tens.



Name ______________________________

Practice
9-3

## Estimate Two-Digit Differences

Find the nearest ten. Estimate the difference.

1. 67 − 43
Think: 70 − 40 = 30
67 − 43 is about 30.

2. 84 − 36
Think: 80 − 40 = 40
84 − 36 is about 40.

3. 43 − 27
Think: 40 − 30 = 10
43 − 27 is about 10.

4. 58 − 27
Think: 60 − 30 = 30
58 − 27 is about 30.

**Problem Solving** **Estimation**

Find the nearest ten. Estimate the difference.

5. The giant squid is about 17 meters long.
The whale shark is about 13 meters long.
About how much longer is the squid than the shark?

About 10 meters

**Notes for Home** Your child used nearest tens to estimate differences. *Home Activity:* Ask your child to tell you how to estimate 81–22. (81 is about 80 and 22 is about 20. 80 minus 20 is 60.)

Name ______________________

## Explore Subtraction With or Without Regrouping

Practice 9-4

Samantha counted 40 pennies in her piggy bank. She gave 9 pennies to her younger brother. How many pennies does she have now?

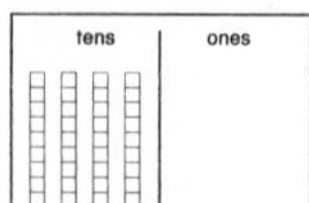


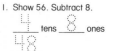

Start with 40.

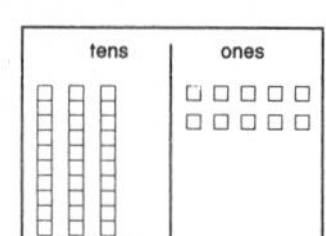


Regroup 1 ten as 10 ones.

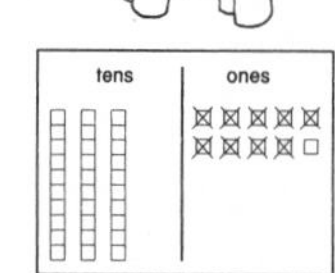


Subtract 9.

31 pennies

Use [tens/ones mat], [tens], and [ones].

Find how many are left.

1. Show 56. Subtract 8.
   4 tens 8 ones
   48
2. Show 37. Subtract 9.
   2 tens 8 ones
   28
3. Show 73. Subtract 6.
   6 tens 7 ones
   67
4. Show 26. Subtract 7.
   1 tens 9 ones
   19

**Talk About It** How does regrouping help you subtract?

**Notes for Home** Your child explored regrouping with subtraction. *Home Activity:* Have your child show how he or she regrouped to find the difference for Exercise 2.



Name ______________________

## Subtract With or Without Regrouping

Practice 9-5

Use [tens/ones mat], [tens], and [ones].

| | Show this many. | Subtract this many. | Do you need to regroup? | Solve. |
|---|---|---|---|---|
| 1. | 21 | 3 | yes | 21 − 3 = 18 |
| 2. | 56 | 5 | no | 56 − 5 = 51 |
| 3. | 27 | 9 | yes | 27 − 9 = 18 |
| 4. | 35 | 7 | yes | 35 − 7 = 28 |
| 5. | 44 | 3 | no | 44 − 3 = 41 |
| 6. | 18 | 7 | no | 18 − 7 = 11 |
| 7. | 42 | 4 | yes | 42 − 4 = 38 |
| 8. | 33 | 2 | no | 33 − 2 = 31 |
| 9. | 11 | 8 | yes | 11 − 8 = 3 |

### Problem Solving Critical Thinking

10. Which numbers in the first column above can you subtract from 75 without needing to regroup? For which numbers would you need to regroup? How do you know? Regrouping is needed for 56, 27, and 18 because the ones are greater than 5.

**Notes for Home** Your child decided when to regroup to subtract. *Home Activity:* Ask your child to show you two subtraction problems, one with regrouping and one without regrouping.



Name ______________________

## Record Subtraction

Subtract. You can use Use [tens/ones mat], [tens], and [ones] to help.

Then circle the difference if you regrouped.

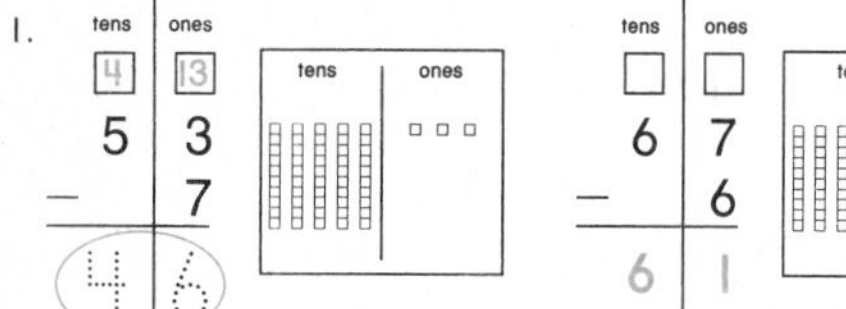




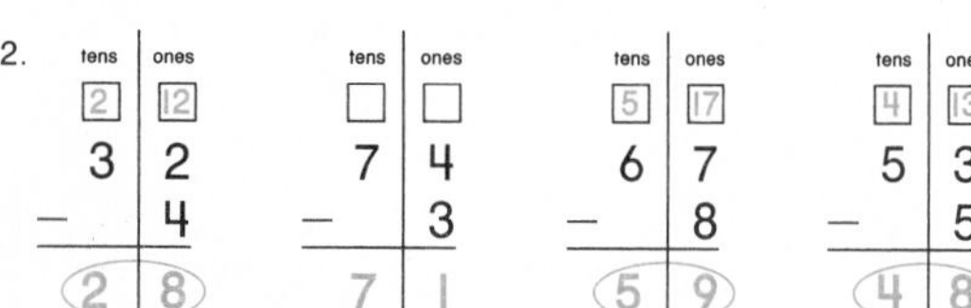


### Problem Solving Patterns

Subtract. What patterns do you see? Sample answer: Each difference is 10 less than the previous difference.

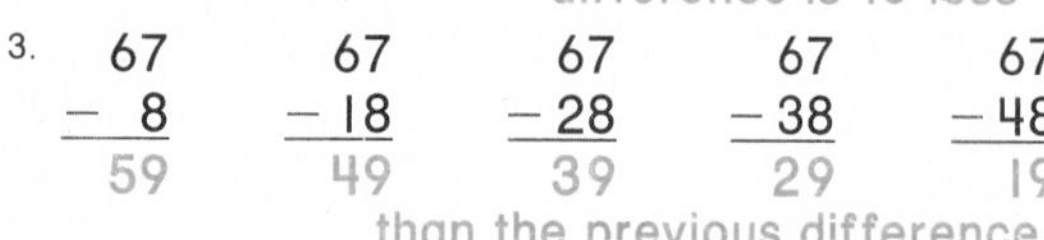

3.
67 − 8 = 59
67 − 18 = 49
67 − 28 = 39
67 − 38 = 29
67 − 48 = 19


**Notes for Home** Your child regrouped and wrote the differences for subtraction problems. *Home Activity:* Ask your child to explain his or her answer for one of the exercises on this page.



Name ______________________

## Problem Solving: Choose a Computation Method

Practice 9-7

Choose a strategy. Draw the blocks or write the number sentences.

1. 64 ants marched up the tree. 23 more joined them. Then 39 ants marched away carrying leaves. How many ants are left on the tree?
2. Monica counted 57 pennies in her bank. Her brother gave her 23 pennies. Her father gave her 15 more. How many pennies does Monica have now?

48 ants

95 pennies

### Visual Thinking

3. Write a story problem for the picture.

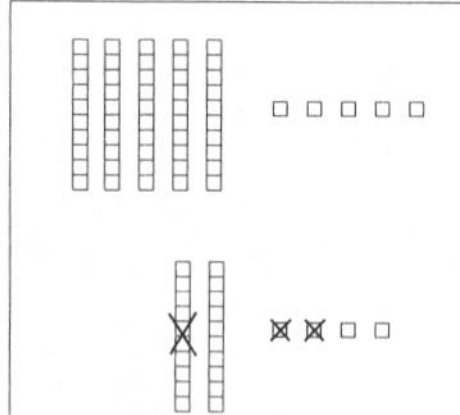

Story problems should begin with 55 + 24 = 79, and then conclude with 79 − 12 = 67.

**Notes for Home** Your child drew pictures, wrote number sentences, and made up a story to solve problems. *Home Activity:* Have your child write two number sentences for Exercise 3. (55 + 24 = 79 and 79 − 12 = 67)

Name ______________________

Practice Chapter 9 A

## Mixed Practice: Lessons 1–7

Subtract.

1. 6 tens − 4 tens = 2 tens; 60 − 40 = 20
2. 9 tens − 7 tens = 2 tens; 90 − 70 = 20

Use the chart to subtract.

3. 47 − 10 = 37
4. 36 − 30 = 6
5. 28 − 20 = 8

| 1 | 2 | 3 | 4 | 5 | 6 | 7 | 8 | 9 | 10 |
|---|---|---|---|---|---|---|---|---|---|
| 11 | 12 | 13 | 14 | 15 | 16 | 17 | 18 | 19 | 20 |
| 21 | 22 | 23 | 24 | 25 | 26 | 27 | 28 | 29 | 30 |
| 31 | 32 | 33 | 34 | 35 | 36 | 37 | 38 | 39 | 40 |
| 41 | 42 | 43 | 44 | 45 | 46 | 47 | 48 | 49 | 50 |

### Problem Solving

Choose a way to solve the problem. Draw the place-value blocks or write a number sentence.

6. 25 people get on the bus. At the next stop, 8 get off and 4 get on. How many people are on the bus now? 21 people

### Journal

7. Do you need to regroup to subtract? How do you know?

67 − 6 = 61 No

44 − 7 = 37 Yes

**Notes for Home** Your child practiced subtracting tens, using a hundred chart, and choosing a strategy to solve a problem. *Home Activity:* Have your child use a different strategy to solve Exercise 3.



Name ______________________

Practice Chapters 1–9 A

## Cumulative Review

Draw the clock hands. Write the ending time.

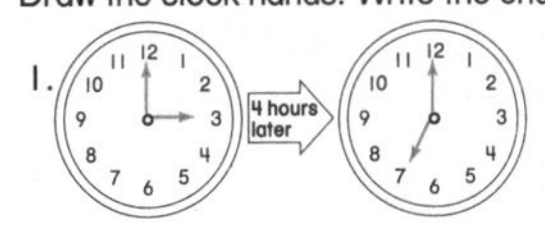

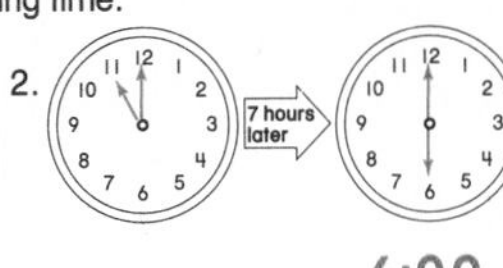

1. 3:00 — 4 hours later — 7:00
2. 11:00 — 7 hours later — 6:00

### Problem Solving

Circle **add** or **subtract**. Write a number sentence. Solve.

3. 5 children are at the park. 7 more join them. How many children are at the park now?
   (add) subtract
   5 + 7 = 12
   12 children

4. 8 horses are running in the field. 3 run away. How many are left?
   add (subtract)
   8 − 3 = 5
   5 horses

### Test Prep

Fill in ○ for the correct answer.
Add. Regroup if you need to.

5. 26 + 35: ○ 63 ● 61 ○ 51 ○ 53
6. 57 + 33: ○ 80 ● 90 ○ 89 ○ 70
7. 34 + 54: ○ 98 ○ 9 ● 88 ○ 78

**Notes for Home** Your child reviewed telling time, addition and subtraction facts, and writing number sentences. *Home Activity:* Ask your child to explain his or her answer for Exercise 4.



Name ______________________

Practice 9-8

## Explore Subtracting Two-Digit Numbers

Find 35 − 19.

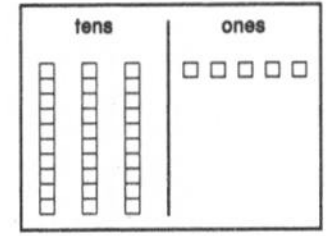

Take 35.

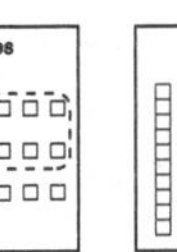

Regroup 1 ten as 10 ones.

Subtract 19. Write the difference.

35 − 19 = 16

Use and

| | Show this many. | Subtract this many. | Solve. |
|---|---|---|---|
| 1. | 33 | 27 | 33 − 27 = 6 |
| 2. | 72 | 35 | 72 − 35 = 37 |
| 3. | 48 | 19 | 48 − 19 = 29 |
| 4. | 55 | 38 | 55 − 38 = 17 |
| 5. | 17 | 9 | 17 − 9 = 8 |

### Talk About It

Choose a problem on this page. Tell a classmate how you solved it.

**Notes for Home** Your child subtracted two-digit numbers with regrouping. *Home Activity:* Have your child use dried beans or macaroni to model Exercise 2.



Name ______________________

Practice 9-9

## Subtract Two-Digit Numbers With or Without Regrouping

Subtract. Use , , and .

Regroup if you need to.

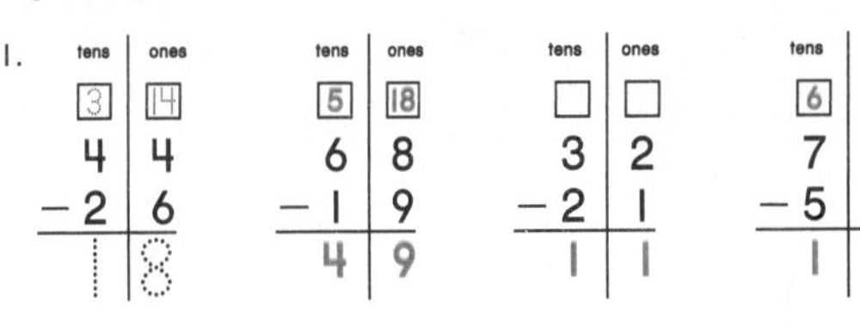

1. 44 − 26 = 18; 68 − 19 = 49; 32 − 21 = 11; 75 − 58 = 17

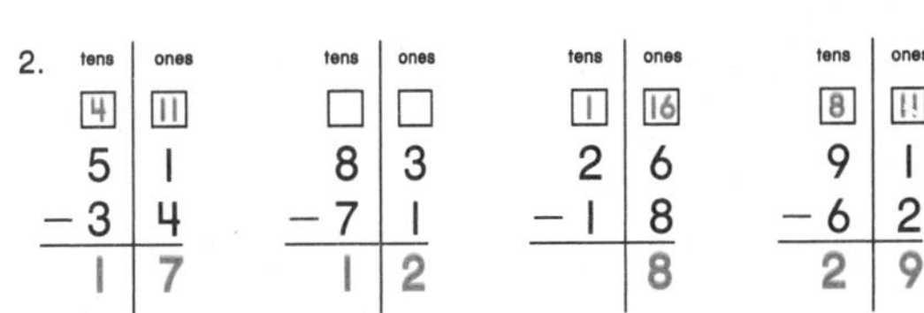

2. 51 − 34 = 17; 83 − 71 = 12; 26 − 18 = 8; 91 − 62 = 29

### Problem Solving Visual Thinking

3.

| We started with this: | Now we have this: | Draw what was subtracted. |
|---|---|---|
| | | |

**Notes for Home** Your child subtracted two-digit numbers with or without regrouping. *Home Activity:* Have your child tell you how to find the difference for 55 minus 37. (Regroup 1 ten for 10 ones. Subtract 7 ones from 15, and 3 tens from 4 tens; 18.)

Name ______________________

## Subtract Two-Digit Numbers

Practice 9-10

Subtract. Regroup if you need to.

1. 
| 5 17 | | 2 13 | 3 15 | | 1 17 |
|---|---|---|---|---|---|
| 67 | 58 | 33 | 45 | 16 | 27 |
| − 48 | − 26 | − 16 | − 37 | − 11 | − 19 |
| 19 | 32 | 17 | 8 | 5 | 8 |

2. 
| 4 10 | 3 18 | 2 13 | 7 15 | | 6 12 |
|---|---|---|---|---|---|
| 50 | 48 | 33 | 85 | 10 | 72 |
| − 16 | − 39 | − 14 | − 67 | − 7 | − 54 |
| 34 | 9 | 19 | 18 | 3 | 18 |

Follow the rule. Subtract. Find the rule. Write the missing number.

3. 
| Subtract 19. | |
|---|---|
| 70 | 51 |
| 69 | 50 |
| 50 | 31 |
| 39 | 20 |

4. 
| Subtract 14 | |
|---|---|
| 90 | 76 |
| 70 | 56 |
| 50 | 36 |
| 30 | 16 |

### Problem Solving Critical Thinking

5. Fill in the missing numbers.

4 16
5 6
− 3 8
1 8

(56 − 38 = 18)

**Notes for Home** Your child subtracted two-digit numbers. *Home Activity:* Have your child work through the problems in Exercise 3 with you.



Name ______________________

## Use Addition to Check Subtraction

Subtract. Write an addition problem to check.

1. 37 − 19 = 18; 18 + 19 = 37 | 53 − 25 = 28; 28 + 25 = 53 | 92 − 38 = 54; 54 + 38 = 92

2. 83 − 43 = 40; 40 + 43 = 83 | 37 − 8 = 29; 29 + 8 = 37 | 56 − 28 = 28; 28 + 28 = 56

3. 24 − 13 = 11; 11 + 13 = 24 | 45 − 29 = 16; 16 + 29 = 45 | 30 − 10 = 20; 20 + 10 = 30

### Problem Solving Critical Thinking

4. Lisa did these subtraction problems. Use addition to check her work. Did she do both problems correctly? Explain.

87 − 49 = 38 | 53 − 26 = 39

No; the second difference should be 27.

**Notes for Home** Your child used addition to check subtraction. *Home Activity:* Have your child explain how he or she solved Exercise 4



Name ______________________

## Subtract Money

Subtract.

1. 
| 4 14 | | | | |
|---|---|---|---|---|
| 54¢ | 81¢ | 27¢ | 95¢ | 43¢ |
| − 38¢ | − 63¢ | − 15¢ | − 75¢ | − 26¢ |
| 16¢ | 18¢ | 12¢ | 20¢ | 17¢ |

2. 
| 32¢ | 17¢ | 66¢ | 54¢ | 99¢ | 21¢ |
|---|---|---|---|---|---|
| − 4¢ | − 10¢ | − 57¢ | − 33¢ | − 65¢ | − 15¢ |
| 28¢ | 7¢ | 9¢ | 21¢ | 34¢ | 6¢ |

### Mixed Practice Add or subtract.

3. 
| 24 | 48 | 76¢ | 57 | 31¢ | 65 |
|---|---|---|---|---|---|
| + 34 | − 26 | + 15¢ | − 49 | − 13¢ | + 27 |
| 58 | 22 | 91¢ | 8 | 18¢ | 92 |

4. 
| 18¢ | 17 | 52¢ | 35 | 63 | 94¢ |
|---|---|---|---|---|---|
| − 4¢ | + 27 | − 33¢ | + 22 | + 9 | − 65¢ |
| 14¢ | 44 | 19¢ | 57 | 72 | 29¢ |

### Problem Solving

Solve.

5. 12 apples are in the basket.
8 children each take one.
How many apples are there now?

4 apples

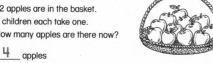

**Notes for Home** Your child solved addition and subtraction problems involving money. *Home Activity:* Ask your child to subtract 67¢ from 96¢. (29¢)



Name ______________________

## Problem Solving: Too Much Information

Practice 9-13

Solve. Cross out the information you do not need.

1. A swan can fly at about 55 miles in one hour. A crow can fly about 25 miles in one hour. ~~An ostrich can run at about 31 miles per hour.~~ How much faster can a swan fly than a crow?

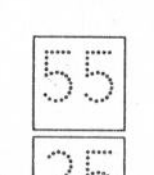

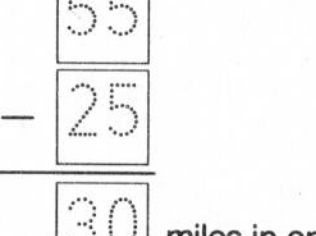

55 − 25 = 30 miles in one hour

2. The giant salamander is about 4 feet long. A python is the longest snake. It can grow to about 33 feet long. ~~The giant squid can grow to about 56 feet long.~~ How much longer is the python than the giant salamander?

33 − 4 = 29 feet longer

### Journal

3. Write a math problem about playing baseball or basketball with too much information. Have a friend solve it.

Problems will vary.

**Notes for Home** Your child crossed out the information not needed to solve problems. *Home Activity:* Ask your child to explain his or her reasoning.

Name

## Mixed Practice: Lessons 8–13

Subtract. Regroup if you need to.

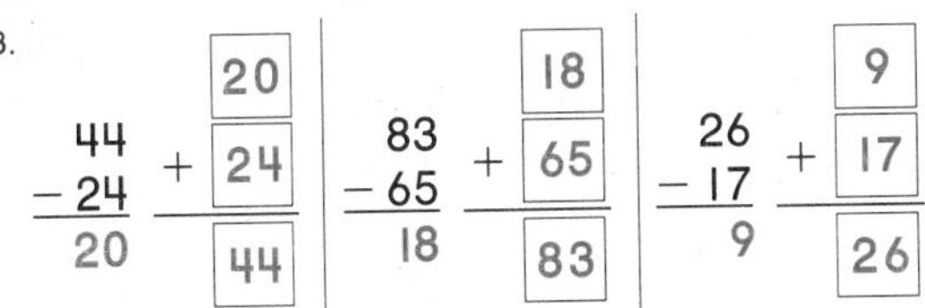

1.

| tens | ones |
|---|---|
| 6 | 6 |
| − 3 | 4 |
| 3 | 2 |

| tens | ones |
|---|---|
| 7 | 15 |
| 8 | 5 |
| − 6 | 7 |
| 1 | 8 |

2. 52¢ − 34¢ = 18¢  17¢ − 12¢ = 5¢

Subtract. Write an addition problem to check.

3. 44 − 24 = 20; 20 + 24 = 44  83 − 65 = 18; 18 + 65 = 83  26 − 17 = 9; 9 + 17 = 26

### Problem Solving

Solve. Cross out the information you do not need.

4. Maritza collected 57 stickers. ~~It took her 6 months.~~ Felipé collected 39 stickers. ~~It took him 4 months.~~ How many more stickers does Maritza have than Felipé?

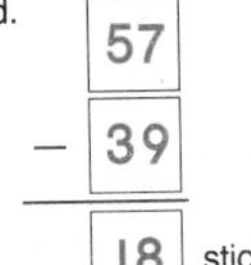

57 − 39 = 18 stickers

### Journal

5. Write an addition problem to check this problem: 44 − 26 = 18.
How do you know if it's correct? Explain. 18 + 26 = 44.
The sum equals the first number.

**Notes for Home** Your child practiced subtracting two-digit numbers with and without regrouping, checking subtraction with addition, and crossing out information not needed in problems. *Home Activity:* Ask your child to explain his or her answers for Exercise 1.



Name

## Cumulative Review

Write the time.

1. 
8 o'clock
8 : 00

2. 6 : 10

3. 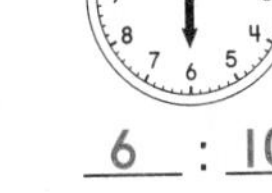
2 : 30

### Problem Solving

Use the chart.

| Marble colors | Tally | Totals |
|---|---|---|
| Green | ~~////~~ //// | 9 |
| Orange | ~~////~~ ~~////~~ | 10 |
| Blue | ~~////~~ / | 6 |

4. How many more green marbles are there than blue marbles?
3 more

5. What color marble is there fewest of in the jar? blue

### Test Prep

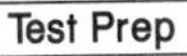

Fill in the ○ for the correct answer.
Use mental math to add.

6. 46 + 40 = ____
○ 56 ○ 67 ● 86 ○ 76

7. 23 + 60 = ____
○ 73 ● 83 ○ 63 ○ 93

**Notes for Home** Your child reviewed telling time, solving problems, and adding. *Home Activity:* Ask your child to use mental math to add 33 and 60. (93)



Name



## Explore Hundreds

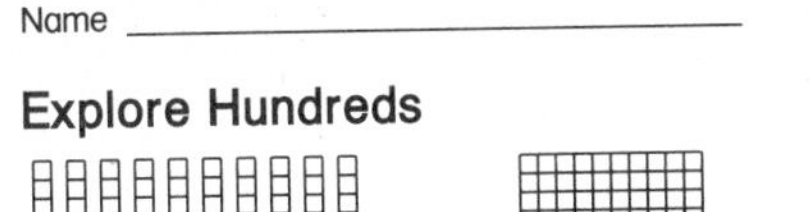

10 tens  100

10 tens = 1 hundred

Write how many hundreds.
Write the number.

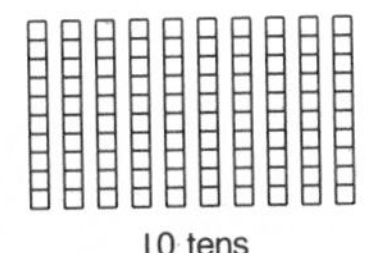
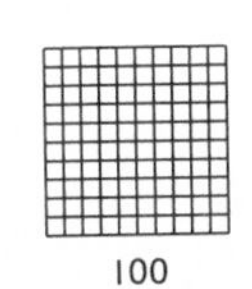

| | | How many hundreds? | Write the number. |
|---|---|---|---|
| 1. | | 1 hundred | 100 |
| 2. | | 2 hundreds | 200 |
| 3. | | 3 hundreds | 300 |
| 4. | | 4 hundreds | 400 |
| 5. | | 5 hundreds | 500 |
| 6. | | 6 hundreds | 600 |

### Journal

7. Write 2 things that you think might come packaged in hundreds.

**Notes for Home** Your child wrote how many hundreds and the number. *Home Activity:* Ask your child how many hundreds are in 700. (7 hundreds)



Name



## Identify Hundreds

Use [hundred flat] to complete the chart.

| | Show this many. Write the number. | Show 200 less. Write the number. | Show 200 more. Write the number. |
|---|---|---|---|
| 1. | 200 | 0 | 400 |
| 2. | 300 | 100 | 500 |
| 3. | 400 | 200 | 600 |

### Problem Solving Visual Thinking

4. Yani needs 800 cubes.
Circle bags to show 800.  Answers will vary.

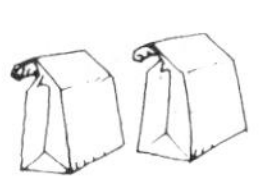
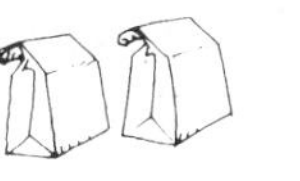
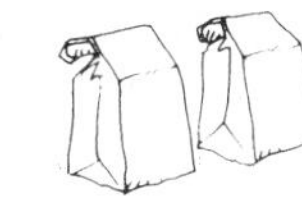
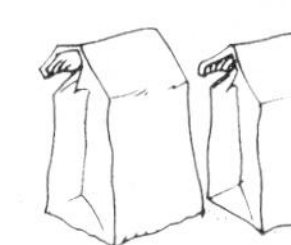

100 in each small bag  200 in each medium bag  400 in each large bag

**Notes for Home** Your child practiced writing numbers for groups of 100. *Home Activity:* Ask your child to write the number that is 200 less than 900 and the number that is 200 more than 100. (700 and 300)

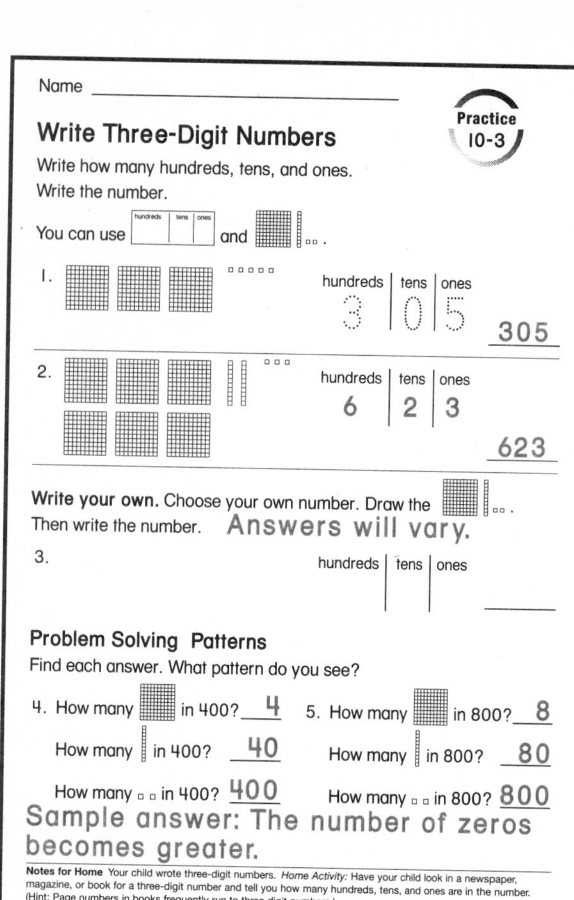

Name ______________________

Practice 10-3

## Write Three-Digit Numbers

Write how many hundreds, tens, and ones.
Write the number.

You can use [hundreds | tens | ones] and [blocks].

1. hundreds 3 | tens 0 | ones 5 — 305

2. hundreds 6 | tens 2 | ones 3 — 623

**Write your own.** Choose your own number. Draw the [blocks]. Then write the number. Answers will vary.

3. hundreds | tens | ones ______

### Problem Solving Patterns

Find each answer. What pattern do you see?

4. How many [hundreds] in 400? 4
How many [tens] in 400? 40
How many [ones] in 400? 400

5. How many [hundreds] in 800? 8
How many [tens] in 800? 80
How many [ones] in 800? 800

Sample answer: The number of zeros becomes greater.

**Notes for Home** Your child wrote three-digit numbers. *Home Activity:* Have your child look in a newspaper, magazine, or book for a three-digit number and tell you how many hundreds, tens, and ones are in the number. (Hint: Page numbers in books frequently run to three digit numbers.)

Use with pages 361–362. **133**

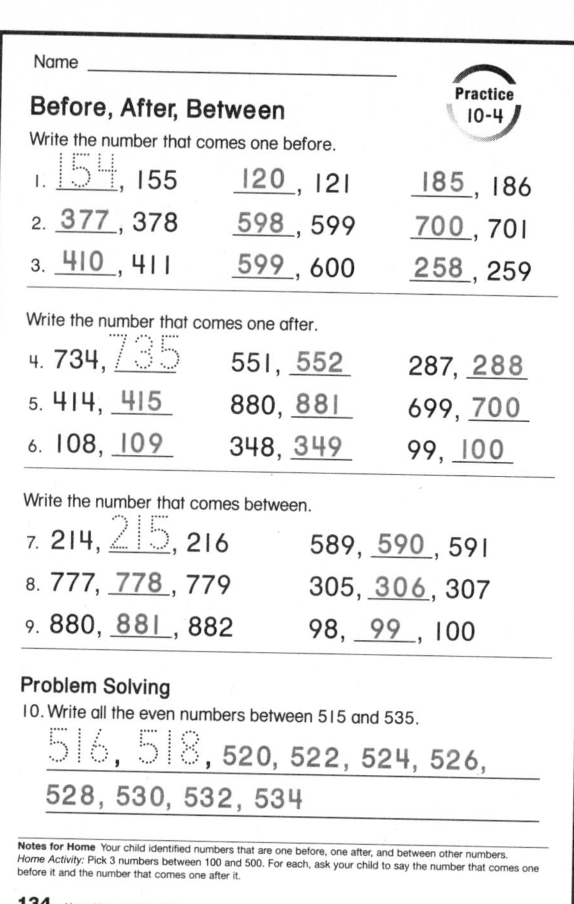

Name ______________________

Practice 10-4

## Before, After, Between

Write the number that comes one before.

1. 154, 155 120, 121 185, 186
2. 377, 378 598, 599 700, 701
3. 410, 411 599, 600 258, 259

Write the number that comes one after.

4. 734, 735 551, 552 287, 288
5. 414, 415 880, 881 699, 700
6. 108, 109 348, 349 99, 100

Write the number that comes between.

7. 214, 215, 216 589, 590, 591
8. 777, 778, 779 305, 306, 307
9. 880, 881, 882 98, 99, 100

### Problem Solving

10. Write all the even numbers between 515 and 535.

516, 518, 520, 522, 524, 526, 528, 530, 532, 534

**Notes for Home** Your child identified numbers that are one before, one after, and between other numbers. *Home Activity:* Pick 3 numbers between 100 and 500. For each, ask your child to say the number that comes one before it and the number that comes one after it.

**134** Use with pages 363–364.

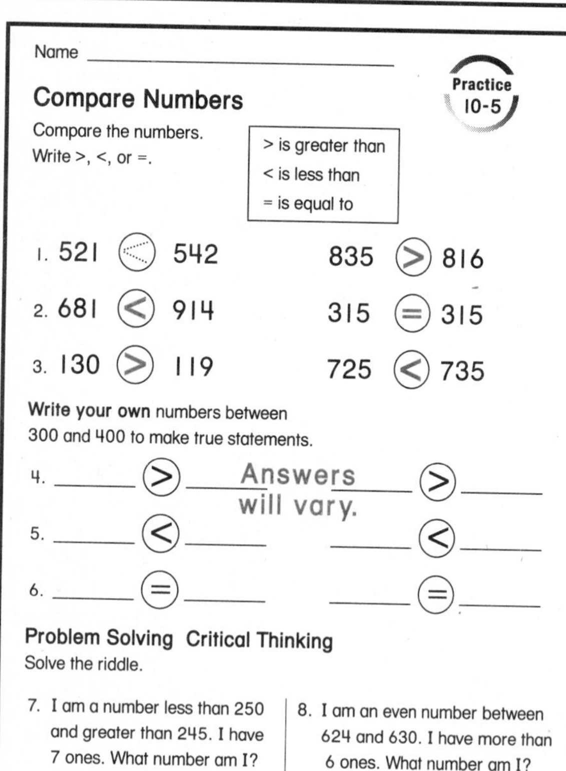

Name ______________________

Practice 10-5

## Compare Numbers

Compare the numbers.
Write >, <, or =.

> is greater than
< is less than
= is equal to

1. 521 < 542 835 > 816
2. 681 < 914 315 = 315
3. 130 > 119 725 < 735

**Write your own** numbers between 300 and 400 to make true statements.

4. ____ > ____ ____ > ____
5. ____ < ____ ____ < ____
6. ____ = ____ ____ = ____

Answers will vary.

### Problem Solving Critical Thinking

Solve the riddle.

7. I am a number less than 250 and greater than 245. I have 7 ones. What number am I? 247

8. I am an even number between 624 and 630. I have more than 6 ones. What number am I? 628

**Notes for Home** Your child compared numbers. *Home Activity:* Choose two numbers between 100 and 500. Ask your child to write the numbers and symbols to show "is greater than" and "is less than." (Possible choice and answers: 350 and 375; 350 < 375, 375 > 350.)

Use with pages 365–366. **135**

Name ______________________

Practice 10-6

## Order Numbers

Write the numbers in order from least to greatest.

1. 225, 98, 187, 309 98, 187, 225, 309
2. 470, 417, 428, 459 417, 428, 459, 470

Write the numbers in order from greatest to least.

3. 518, 377, 801, 495 801, 518, 495, 377
4. 350, 96, 606, 428 606, 428, 350, 96
5. 770, 765, 707, 777 777, 770, 765, 707

**Write your own.**

6. List four numbers in order from least to greatest. Choose numbers between 200 and 300. ____, ____, ____, ____

Answers will vary.

7. List four numbers in order from greatest to least. Choose numbers between 800 and 900. ____, ____, ____, ____

### Problem Solving Estimation

8. These stacks of crayons will be sent to different schools. Draw lines to match each number to a stack. Then write the numbers in order from least to greatest.

264 216 288 240

216, 240, 264, 288

**Notes for Home** Your child put numbers in order. *Home Activity:* Ask your child where he or she would place a stack of 228 crayons in Exercise 8. (Between 216 and 240.)

**136** Use with pages 367–368.

Name ______________________

Practice 10-7

## Problem Solving: Group Decision Making

Work with your group to solve the problem.

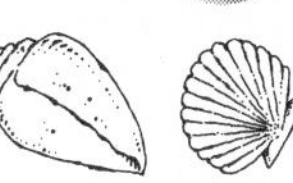
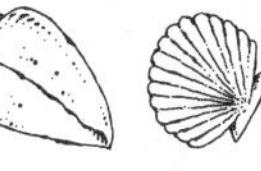

1. Roy and Reba are buying shells to make jewelry. They need 60 shells in all for their projects. Roy buys 12 shells. Reba buys 18 shells. How many more shells do they need to buy?

**Understand** What does the problem ask? How many more shells do Roy and Reba need to buy?

**Plan** How can you solve the problem? Possible answer: Use counters to add and subtract.

**Solve** Solve the problem. They buy 18 + 12, or 30 shells. They need 60 − 30, or 30 more.

**Look Back** Check your work. Possible answer: 18 + 12 + 30 = 60

**Write your own.**

2. Work as a group to write a problem for another group to solve.
Answers will vary.

**Notes for Home** Your child used the Problem Solving Guide. *Home Activity:* Ask your child what way his or her group used to find, and then check, the answer to the problem.



Name ______________________

Practice Chapter 10 A

## Mixed Practice: Lessons 1–7

Write 100 less and 100 more. You can use [hundreds block].

| | Show this many. Write the number. | Show 100 less. Write the number. | Show 100 more. Write the number. |
|---|---|---|---|
| 1. | 200 | 100 | 300 |

Write how many hundreds, tens, and ones. Then write the number.

2.

| hundreds | tens | ones |
|---|---|---|
| 2 | 4 | 7 |

247

Write the number one before, one after, or between.

3. 147, 148 589, 590 399, 400, 401

Compare. Write >, <, or =.

4. 380 > 320 540 = 540 793 < 801

### Problem Solving

Solve. Use the Problem Solving Guide to help.

5. Sabrina brought a box of 200 buttons for a project. Later she brought a box of 500 buttons. She used 190 buttons. How many buttons does she have now? 510 buttons

**Notes for Home** Your child practiced writing and comparing three-digit numbers. *Home Activity:* Ask your child what page in a book comes before and after page 381. (380 and 382)



Name ______________________

Practice Chapters 1–10 A

## Cumulative Review

Count the money.
Write the total amount.

1.

99¢

### Problem Solving

Use the graph to answer the questions.

| Coin Collections | |
|---|---|
| Tao | O O O |
| Jin | O O |
| Lee | O O O O |
| Each O means 10 coins. | |

2. How many more coins does Tao have than Jin?
10 coins

3. How many coins in all do Tao, Jin, and Lee have?
90 coins

**Test Prep**

Fill in the O for the correct answer.
Subtract.

4. 80 − 45
45 O, 35 ●, 65 O, 25 O

5. 92 − 60
30 O, 32 ●, 20 O, 22 O

**Notes for Home** Your child reviewed counting money, using a graph to solve problems, and subtracting. *Home Activity:* Ask your child to look at the graph and tell how many fewer coins Jin has than Lee. (20 fewer coins)



Name ______________________

Practice 10-8

## Add and Subtract Mentally

Add or subtract. Use mental math.

1. 60 + 30 = 90 400 + 200 = 600 300 + 100 = 400 50 + 20 = 70 300 + 500 = 800

2. 70 − 10 = 60 800 − 300 = 500 600 − 200 = 400 80 − 30 = 50 40 − 30 = 10

Follow the rule.

3.

| Add 100 | |
|---|---|
| 200 | 300 |
| 500 | 600 |
| 100 | 200 |
| 600 | 700 |

4.

| Subtract 10 | |
|---|---|
| 340 | 330 |
| 410 | 400 |
| 790 | 780 |
| 950 | 940 |

5.

| Add 30 | |
|---|---|
| 800 | 830 |
| 620 | 650 |
| 270 | 300 |
| 440 | 470 |

### Problem Solving Patterns

Add or subtract. What patterns do you see?

6. 3 + 6 = 9 33 + 66 = 99 333 + 666 = 999

7. 8 − 2 = 6 88 − 22 = 66 888 − 222 = 666

Sample answer: Answers have the same numeral.

**Notes for Home** Your child added and subtracted using mental math. *Home Activity:* Ask your child to explain how to use mental math to subtract 500 − 200. (5 − 2 = 3; 500 − 200 = 300)

Name ______________________________

## Add Three-Digit Numbers

Show each number. Add.

You can use 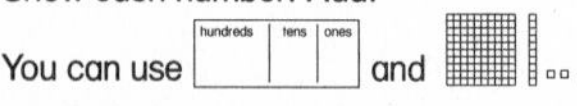 and

1.

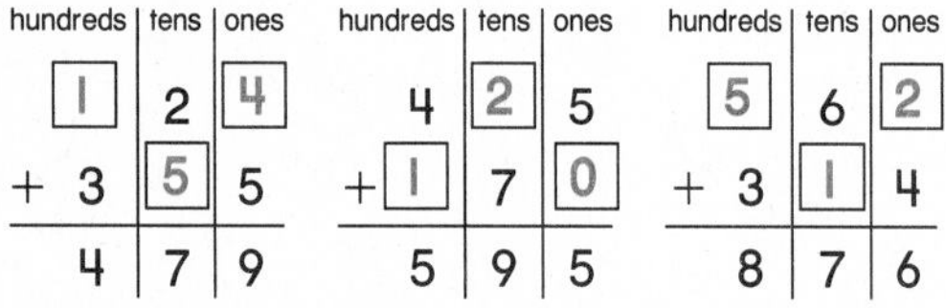

| hundreds | tens | ones | | hundreds | tens | ones | | hundreds | tens | ones |
|---|---|---|---|---|---|---|---|---|---|---|
| 2 | 4 | 6 | | 3 | 5 | 1 | | 6 | 0 | 4 |
| + 2 | 1 | 3 | | + 1 | 0 | 7 | | + 2 | 6 | 3 |
| 4 | 5 | 9 | | 4 | 5 | 8 | | 8 | 6 | 7 |

2. 231 + 137 = 368  125 + 64 = 189  726 + 203 = 929  205 + 381 = 586  523 + 263 = 786

3. 146 + 132 = 278  219 + 260 = 479  307 + 92 = 399  115 + 151 = 266  430 + 305 = 735

### Problem Solving

4. Fill in the missing numbers.

| hundreds | tens | ones | | hundreds | tens | ones | | hundreds | tens | ones |
|---|---|---|---|---|---|---|---|---|---|---|
| [1] | 2 | [4] | | 4 | [2] | 5 | | [5] | 6 | [2] |
| + 3 | [5] | 5 | | + [1] | 7 | [0] | | + 3 | [1] | 4 |
| 4 | 7 | 9 | | 5 | 9 | 5 | | 8 | 7 | 6 |

**Notes for Home** Your child added three-digit numbers. *Home Activity:* Ask your child to tell you what the missing three-digit number is in 352 + ___ = 586. (234)



Name ______________________________

## Add Three-Digit Numbers With or Without Regrouping

Add. Regroup if you need to.

You can use and

1.

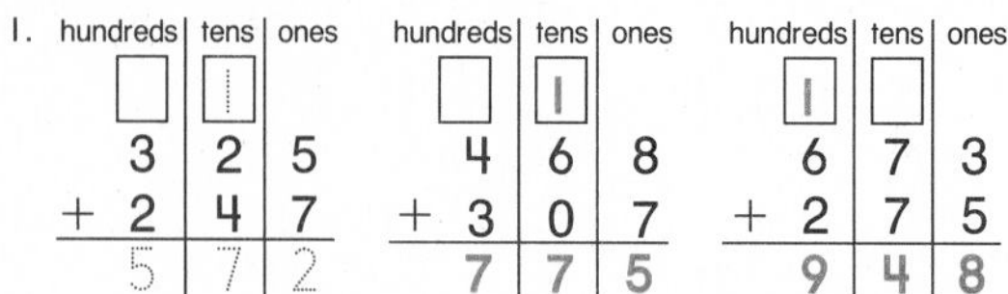

| hundreds | tens | ones | | hundreds | tens | ones | | hundreds | tens | ones |
|---|---|---|---|---|---|---|---|---|---|---|
| [ ] | [1] | | | [ ] | [1] | | | [1] | [ ] | |
| 3 | 2 | 5 | | 4 | 6 | 8 | | 6 | 7 | 3 |
| + 2 | 4 | 7 | | + 3 | 0 | 7 | | + 2 | 7 | 5 |
| 5 | 7 | 2 | | 7 | 7 | 5 | | 9 | 4 | 8 |

2. 335 + 48 = 383  619 + 124 = 743  380 + 65 = 445  155 + 793 = 948  518 + 291 = 809

3. 258 + 327 = 585  775 + 19 = 794  406 + 285 = 691  670 + 86 = 756  189 + 150 = 339

### Problem Solving

Solve.

4. Jose made 125 cat pins for the craft fair. Martina made 148 dog pins. How many pet pins did they make in all?

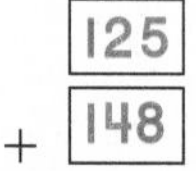

125 + 148 = 273 pet pins

**Notes for Home** Your child added with and without regrouping. *Home Activity:* Pick a number between 100 and 500. Have your child pick another number between 100 and 500. Ask your child to tell you whether he or she must regroup to add the two numbers. (Examples: 326, 142, no; 326, 184, yes.)



Name ______________________________

Practice 10-11

## Subtract Three-Digit Numbers

Show each number. Subtract.

You can use and

1.

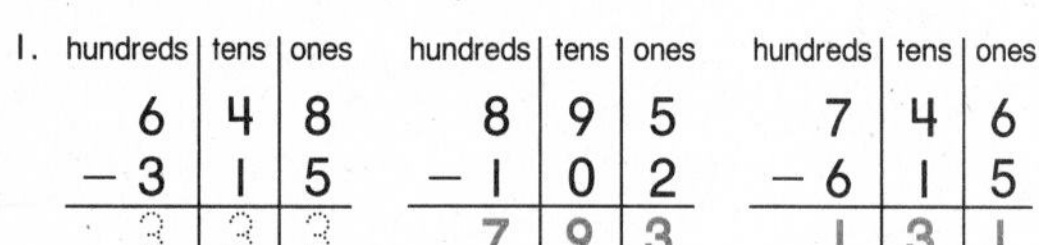

| hundreds | tens | ones | | hundreds | tens | ones | | hundreds | tens | ones |
|---|---|---|---|---|---|---|---|---|---|---|
| 6 | 4 | 8 | | 8 | 9 | 5 | | 7 | 4 | 6 |
| − 3 | 1 | 5 | | − 1 | 0 | 2 | | − 6 | 1 | 5 |
| 3 | 3 | 3 | | 7 | 9 | 3 | | 1 | 3 | 1 |

2. 745 − 234 = 511  386 − 62 = 324  942 − 301 = 641  555 − 43 = 512  489 − 115 = 374

3. 678 − 26 = 652  896 − 143 = 753  357 − 245 = 112  779 − 320 = 459  935 − 20 = 915

### Write a math story.

4. Use these numbers to write a math story. Then solve.

745 − 234 = 511

Children's stories will vary.

**Notes for Home** Your child subtracted three-digit numbers. *Home Activity:* Ask your child to estimate the answer then check the estimate on paper for the problem 678 − 214. (Estimates will vary. Sample estimate is 700 − 200, or 500. Answer is 464.)



Name ______________________________

Practice 10-12

## Subtract Three-Digit Numbers With or Without Regrouping

Subtract. Regroup if you need to.

You can use and

1.

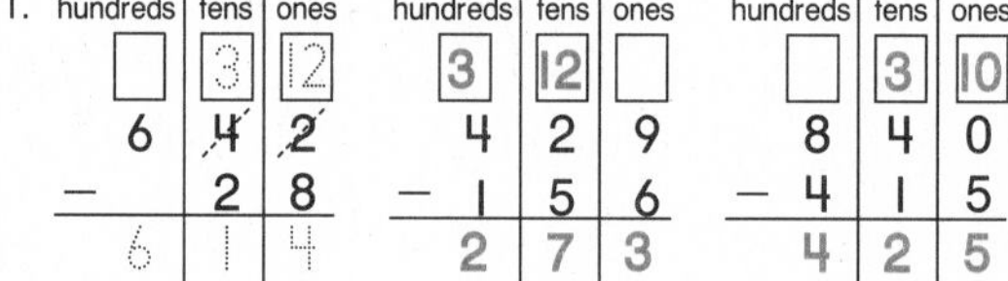

| hundreds | tens | ones | | hundreds | tens | ones | | hundreds | tens | ones |
|---|---|---|---|---|---|---|---|---|---|---|
| [ ] | [3] | [12] | | [3] | [12] | [ ] | | [ ] | [3] | [10] |
| 6 | 4 | 2 | | 4 | 2 | 9 | | 8 | 4 | 0 |
| − | 2 | 8 | | − 1 | 5 | 6 | | − 4 | 1 | 5 |
| 6 | 1 | 4 | | 2 | 7 | 3 | | 4 | 2 | 5 |

2. 562 − 147 = 415  864 − 329 = 535  318 − 42 = 276  624 − 273 = 351  295 − 76 = 219

3. 480 − 126 = 354  709 − 225 = 484  593 − 328 = 265  854 − 309 = 545  666 − 107 = 559

### Problem Solving Critical Thinking

4. You need to regroup twice. What could the missing numbers be?

| hundreds | tens | ones |
|---|---|---|
| 6 | [ ] | 8 |
| − 4 | 5 | [ ] |

The number in the ones column must be a 9. The numbers in the tens column could be 0–5.

**Notes for Home** Your child subtracted three-digit numbers with regrouping. *Home Activity:* Ask your child to write a subtraction problem that needs regrouping and a problem that does not need regrouping. Then have him or her show you how to solve the problems.

Name ______________________

Practice 10-13

## Problem Solving: Use Data from a Picture

1. Kris puts the tub of stones in the box. What else can he put in?
   shells

2. Sarah puts 570 items in the box. What did she put in?
   buttons and beads

3. Leon put the buttons in the box. What else can he put in?
   shells or beads

4. Lana put 500 items in the box. What did she put in?
   shells and beads

5. Dana puts 540 items in the box. What did she put in?
   shells and craft sticks

### Critical Thinking

6. Are there any 3 tubs that could be put in the box together? Explain your answer.
   No, because the sum of any 3 numbers is greater than 600.

**Notes for Home** Your child used the numbers in the picture to solve problems. *Home Activity:* Ask your child which two tubs together hold the least number of items. (Shells and beads)



Name ______________________

Practice Chapter 10 B

## Mixed Practice: Lessons 8–13

Add or subtract. Use mental math.

1. $\begin{array}{r}400\\+300\\\hline 700\end{array}$ $\begin{array}{r}700\\+200\\\hline 900\end{array}$ $\begin{array}{r}60\\-40\\\hline 20\end{array}$ $\begin{array}{r}800\\-200\\\hline 600\end{array}$ $\begin{array}{r}55\\+33\\\hline 88\end{array}$

Add or subtract. Regroup if you need to.

2. $\begin{array}{r}463\\+26\\\hline 489\end{array}$ $\begin{array}{r}748\\-153\\\hline 595\end{array}$ $\begin{array}{r}537\\+281\\\hline 818\end{array}$ $\begin{array}{r}638\\-18\\\hline 620\end{array}$ $\begin{array}{r}370\\+426\\\hline 796\end{array}$

### Problem Solving

Use the picture to answer the questions.

3. Doreen needs 125 beads to make a Navaho necklace. How many bags of beads does she need?
   5 bags of beads

4. Donny has 2 bags of beads. How many more bags of beads does he need to make a Navaho necklace?
   3 bags of beads

### Journal

5. How did the pictures help you answer the problems?

**Notes for Home** Your child practiced the skills and concepts from this section. *Home Activity:* Ask your child how many bags of beads would be needed if it takes 150 beads to make a different necklace. (6 bags of beads)



Name ______________________

Practice Chapters 1–10 B

## Cumulative Review

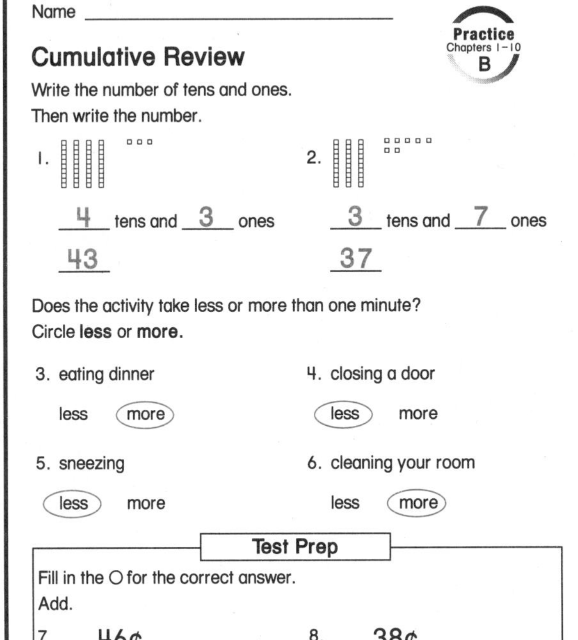

Write the number of tens and ones. Then write the number.

1. 4 tens and 3 ones
   43

2. 3 tens and 7 ones
   37

Does the activity take less or more than one minute? Circle **less** or **more.**

3. eating dinner — less (more)
4. closing a door — (less) more
5. sneezing — (less) more
6. cleaning your room — less (more)

**Test Prep**

Fill in the ○ for the correct answer. Add.

7. $46¢ + 23¢$
   ● 69¢ ○ 79¢ ○ 13¢ ○ 23¢

8. $38¢ + 15¢$
   ○ 43¢ ● 53¢ ○ 23¢ ○ 48¢

**Notes for Home** Your child reviewed identifying and writing tens and ones, estimating if activities take more or less than one minute, and adding amounts of money. *Home Activity:* Ask your child to tell you the fewest number of coins that make 43¢. (1 quarter, 1 dime, 1 nickel, 3 pennies)



Name ______________________

Practice 11-1

## Explore Nonstandard Units

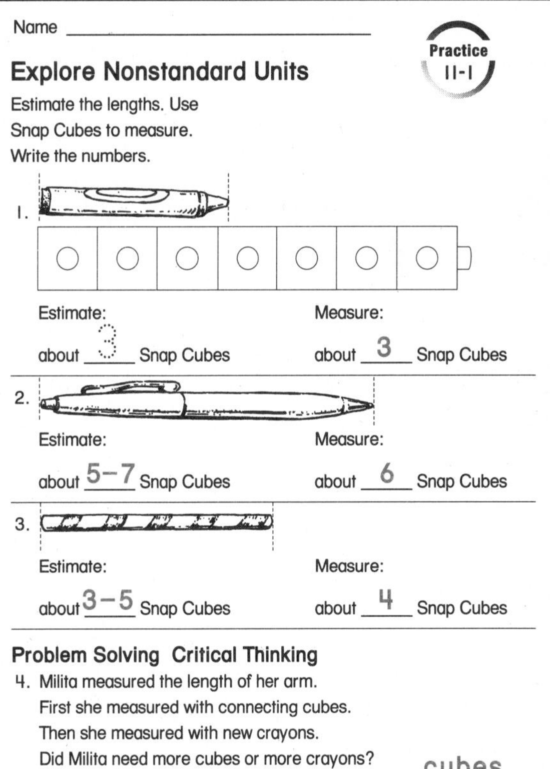

Estimate the lengths. Use Snap Cubes to measure. Write the numbers.

1. Estimate: about 3 Snap Cubes — Measure: about 3 Snap Cubes
2. Estimate: about 5–7 Snap Cubes — Measure: about 6 Snap Cubes
3. Estimate: about 3–5 Snap Cubes — Measure: about 4 Snap Cubes

### Problem Solving Critical Thinking

4. Milita measured the length of her arm. First she measured with connecting cubes. Then she measured with new crayons. Did Milita need more cubes or more crayons?
   cubes

**Notes for Home** Your child estimated and measured the lengths of objects using cubes. *Home Activity:* Ask your child to use a spoon to measure the length of a table in your home.

Name ______________________

## Inches and Feet

Estimate about how many inches.
Measure with your inch ruler.

| 1. What to Measure | Estimate | Measurement |
|---|---|---|
| width of your hand | about ____ inches | about ____ inches |

Estimate about how many feet. **Estimates and**
Measure with your yardstick. **measurements will vary.**

| 2. What to Measure | Estimate | Measurement |
|---|---|---|
| width of a door | about ____ inches | about ____ inches |

### Write your own.

Draw or write what you will measure.
Use inches or feet to measure.

| 3. What to Measure | Estimate | Measurement |
|---|---|---|
| | about ____ | about ____ |

### Problem Solving Visual Thinking

4. Look at the two ant paths.
   Circle the path you think is longer.
   Explain. You can use string to check.

**Notes for Home** Your child practiced estimating and measuring lengths in inches and feet. *Home Activity:* Ask your child to estimate and measure the width of a window in your home and tell you the measurement.



Name ______________________

Practice 11-3

## Inches, Feet, and Yards

**Objects and measurements will vary.**

Complete the chart.

| | Estimate. Find an object about this long. | Write or draw the object. | Measure length to check. |
|---|---|---|---|
| 1. | about 2 inches | | about ____ |
| 2. | about 2 feet | | about ____ |
| 3. | about 2 yards | | about ____ |

### Problem Solving Estimation

Circle the best estimate of length.

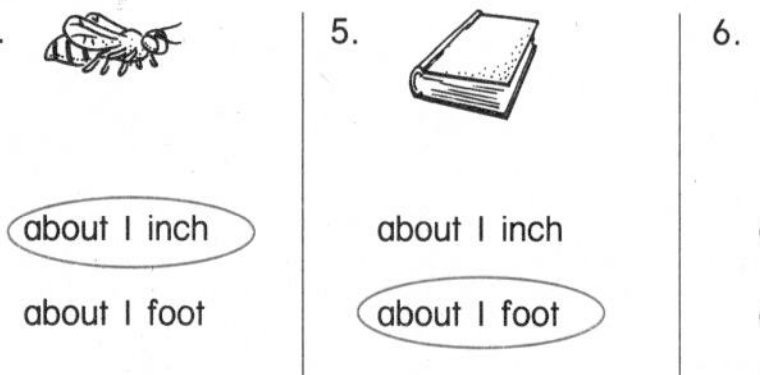

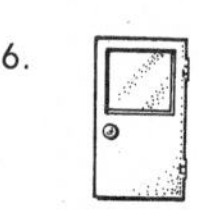

| 4. | 5. | 6. |
|---|---|---|
| (about 1 inch) | about 1 inch | about 1 inch |
| about 1 foot | (about 1 foot) | about 1 foot |
| about 1 yard | about 1 yard | (about 1 yard) |

**Notes for Home** Your child found and measured objects that were about 1 inch, 1 foot, and 1 yard long. *Home Activity:* Give your child a measurement, such as 3 inches, and have him or her find an object around home that is about that long.



Name ______________________

Practice 11-4

## Centimeters and Meters

Estimate about how many meters.
Measure with a meter stick.

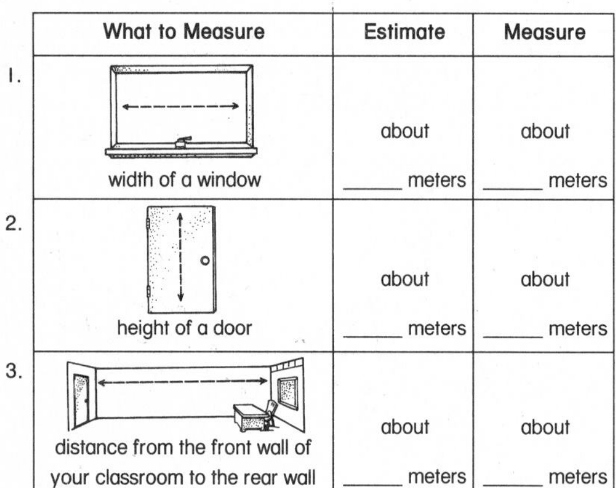

| | What to Measure | Estimate | Measure |
|---|---|---|---|
| 1. | width of a window | about ____ meters | about ____ meters |
| 2. | height of a door | about ____ meters | about ____ meters |
| 3. | distance from the front wall of your classroom to the rear wall | about ____ meters | about ____ meters |

### Mental Math

4. Solve.
   Jon is 132 centimeters tall. Jennie is 128 centimeters tall.
   How much taller is Jon?

   __4__ centimeters taller

**Notes for Home** Your child estimated and measured length and height in meters. *Home Activity:* Ask your child to estimate the width of a room in your home in meters.



Name ______________________

Practice 11-5

## Perimeter

1. Mark an X on the shape that you estimate has the greatest perimeter. Measure the lengths of the sides. Add to find the perimeter. Circle the shape with the greatest perimeter.

   __12__ inches around

   __10__ inches around

   __4__ inches around

### Problem Solving Visual Thinking

2. Do not measure. Which has the greater perimeter, the square or the rectangle. How do you know?

   **the rectangle Sample answer: The square fits inside of the rectangle.**

**Notes for Home** Your child practiced finding the perimeter of different shapes and objects. *Home Activity:* Give your child a book or magazine and ask him or her to find the perimeter.

Name ____________________

Practice 11-6

## Explore Area

Estimate how many [cube] will cover the shape.
Draw square units to show what you did.

For Exercises 1 and 2, estimates will vary.

1. Estimate: ______ Snap Cubes

   Measure: 6 square units

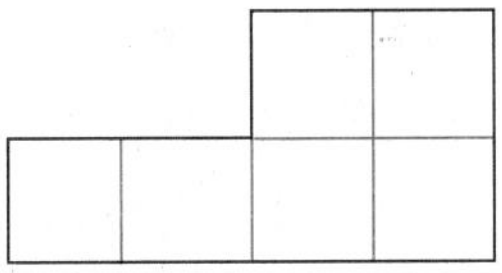

2. Estimate: ______ Snap Cubes

   Measure: 4 square units

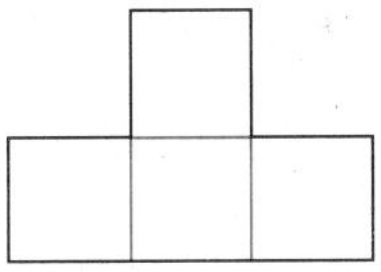

Estimate how many [cube] will cover each of these objects.
Use [cube] to check your estimate.

3. top of a chalkboard eraser

   Estimate: ______ Snap Cubes

   Measure: ______ Snap Cubes

4. this piece of paper

   Estimate: ______ Snap Cubes

   Measure: ______ Snap Cubes

Estimates and measurements will vary.

### Problem Solving Critical Thinking

5. Each side of the large square is twice as long as a side of the small square. Which would you need fewer of to cover the top of your desk? Why? Circle your answer. The large square is 4 times the area of the small square.

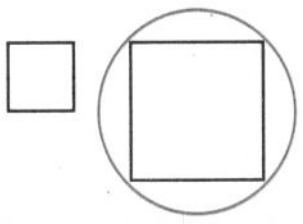

**Notes for Home** Your child practiced using Snap Cubes to cover the area of different shapes. *Home Activity:* Ask your child to tell you how he or she would use a Snap Cube to find the area of a table top.



Name ____________________

Practice 11-7

## Problem Solving: Use Objects

Use centimeter cubes to make each shape. Color the grid to show the shape.

Position of rectangles may vary.

1. Make a rectangle that covers 8 square units inside and has a perimeter of 12 units around the outside.

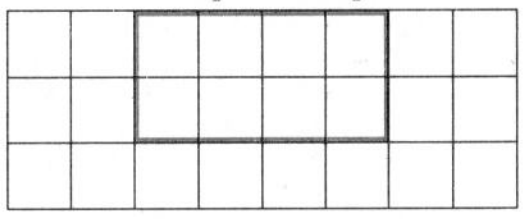

2. Make a rectangle that covers 14 square units inside and has a perimeter of 18 units around the outside.

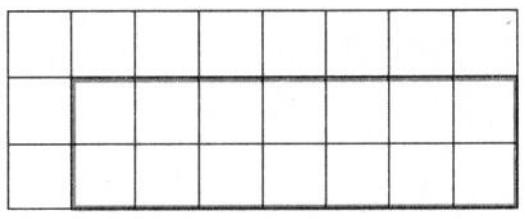

### Write your own.

3. Draw your own shape. Tell about your shape.

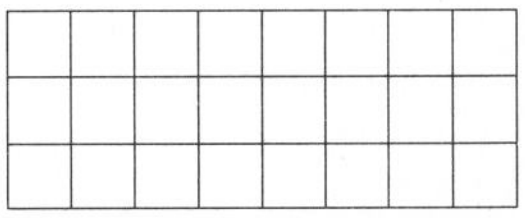

   My shape:
   is ______________.
   has a perimeter of ______ units.
   has ______ square units inside.

   Answers will vary.

### Journal

4. Make some shapes that have the same number of square units inside, but different perimeters. Draw the shapes. Tell about them.

**Notes for Home** Your child solved problems involving area and perimeter. *Home Activity:* Work with your child to make a chart that shows the perimeters of different rectangles that have an area of 16 square units. You may find something interesting about the one with the smallest perimeter.



Name ____________________

Practice Chapter 11 A

## Mixed Practice: Lessons 1–7

Estimate the length. Measure with a centimeter ruler.

Estimates will vary.

1. 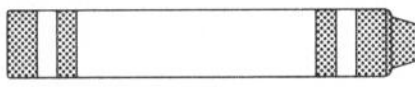 Estimate: about ______ centimeters long

   Measure: about 7 centimeters long

Estimate the perimeter and area.
Measure with an inch ruler and use [tile] to cover the shape.

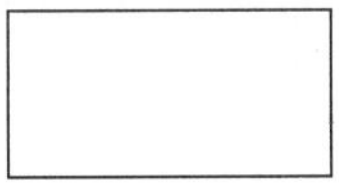

2. Perimeter

   Estimate: ______ inches around

   Measure: 6 inches around

3. Area

   Estimate: ______ square units

   Measure: 2 square units

### Problem Solving

Draw a different shape with the same area.

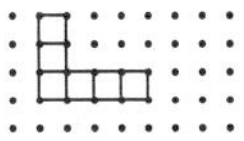

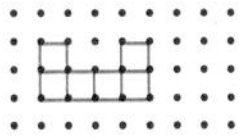

4. Area: 6 square units

   Perimeter: 14 units

5. Area: 6 square units

   Perimeter: 14 units

Answers will vary.

### Journal

6. Draw a shape. Label it A. Draw another shape with the same area as A but a different perimeter. Draw another shape with the same perimeter as A but a different area.

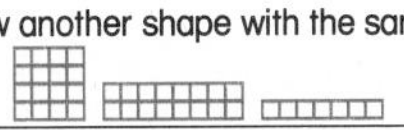

**Notes for Home** Your child practiced estimating and measuring length, perimeter, and area. *Home Activity:* Have your child find the perimeter of an object such as a book or magazine. Then have him or her find another object in your home with a greater perimeter.



Name ____________________

Practice Chapters 1–11 A

## Cumulative Review

Add

1.

| 47 | 60 | 72 | 14 | 28 | 53 |
|---|---|---|---|---|---|
| + 24 | + 38 | + 8 | + 13 | + 35 | + 24 |
| 71 | 98 | 80 | 27 | 63 | 77 |

Write how many hundreds, tens, and ones.
Then write the number.

2.

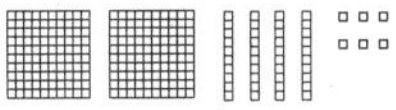

| hundreds | tens | ones | |
|---|---|---|---|
| 2 | 4 | 6 | 246 |

### Problem Solving

Solve.

4. Penny packs 16 cartons with soda crackers. Then she packs 14 cartons with cheese crackers. How many cartons did Penny pack?

   30 cartons

5. Pete packs 28 bags of peppers in the morning. He packs 32 bags in the afternoon. How many bags did Pete pack?

   60 bags

### Test Prep

Fill in the ○ for the correct answer.

6. Choose the number that comes just before 749.

   ○ 750 ● 748 ○ 794

7. Choose the number that comes just after 519.

   ○ 518 ○ 529 ● 520

**Notes for Home** Your child reviewed 2-digit addition, writing large numbers, and using addition to solve problems. *Home Activity:* Ask your child to make up an addition problem. Then have him or her tell you how to solve it and give the sum.

Name ____________________

## Explore One Pound

Practice 11-8

Is each object **heavier than**, **lighter than**, or **about** 1 pound? Estimate. Then use a pound weight to check. Complete the chart.

| | Object | Estimate | Measure |
|---|---|---|---|
| 1. | | lighter than 1 pound | ____ 1 pound |
| 2. |  | heavier than 1 pound | ____ 1 pound |
| 3. | | about 1 pound | ____ 1 pound |
| 4. | | heavier than 1 pound | ____ 1 pound |
| 5. | | about 1 pound | ____ 1 pound |

### Tell a Math Story

6. Write a math story about something that is heavier than a pound and something that is lighter than a pound.

**Notes for Home** Your child estimated whether objects weigh more or less than 1 pound. *Home Activity:* Visit a food store with your child and check the labels on different foods. Explain that 16 oz (ounces) is a pound, anything over 16 oz is heavier than a pound and anything under 16 oz is lighter than a pound. Have him or her make lists of the foods over, about, or under a pound.



Name ____________________

## Kilograms

Practice 11-9

1. Circle in red the objects that are lighter than 1 kilogram
2. Circle in blue the objects that are heavier than 1 kilogram.

**Write your own.** Choose an object. Is your object lighter or heavier than 1 kilogram?

My object: Answers will vary. ________ ________ than a kilogram

### Problem Solving Critical Thinking

3. Which weighs more, a football or a bowling ball? Explain. A bowling ball weighs more. A football is thrown and kicked by players.

**Notes for Home** Your child identified objects that are lighter or heavier than 1 kilogram. *Home Activity:* Ask your child to make a list of 5 objects that are heavier than a kilogram and 5 objects that are lighter than a kilogram. (A kilogram is about 2 1/5 pounds.)



Name ____________________

## Cups, Pints, and Quarts

Practice 11-10

Solve.

1. Larry has 3 pints of milk. Color the number of cups he could fill.

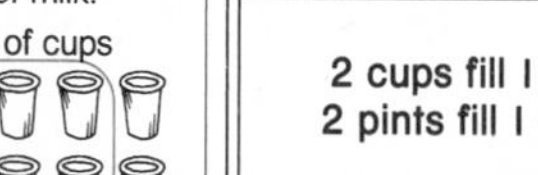

2 cups fill 1 pint;
2 pints fill 1 quart

2. Shelly buys 2 pints of milk. Color the number of cups she could fill.

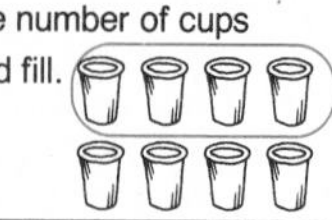

3. Ms. Ito has 1 quart of milk. Color the number of cups she could fill.

4. Indra wants 6 pints of juice. Color the number of quarts that hold the same amount.

5. Sani wants 3 quarts of juice. Color the number of pints that hold the same amount.

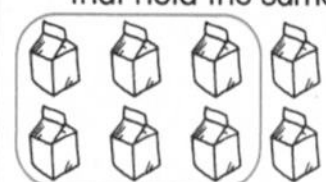

### Problem Solving Visual Thinking

6. Draw cups to solve.
   Raul has 3 quarts of juice.
   Rita has 10 cups of juice. Who has more?

   Raul has more.

**Notes for Home** Your child solved problems about cups, pints, and quarts. *Home Activity:* Give your child a measuring cup and some empty containers. Have him or her find the number of cups that each container can hold.



Name ____________________

## Liters

Practice 11-11

1. Which things hold less than one liter? Circle them.
2. Which things hold more than one liter? Mark an X on them.

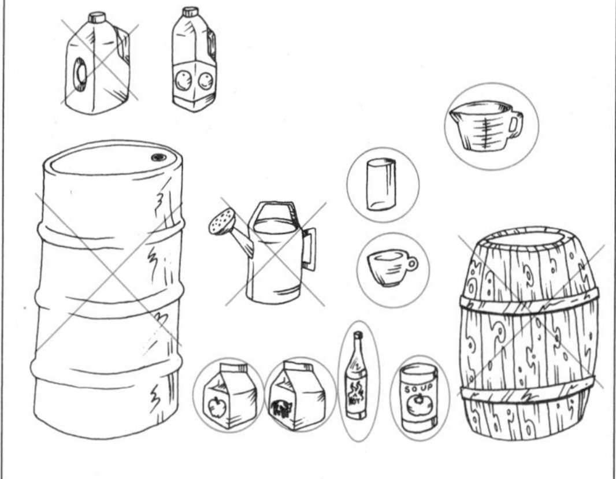

### Mental Math

3. A keg holds eight liters of cider. How many liters will ten kegs hold?

   80 liters

**Notes for Home** Your child identified containers that hold more or less than one liter. *Home Activity:* When you visit a grocery store, ask your child to identify containers that hold more than, less than, and about one liter.

Name ____________________

Practice 11-12

## Problem Solving: Group Decision Making

Make your own recipe for punch.
You need to make 40 cups.

1. Write your recipe on this card.
   Write a name for your punch.

| Our Recipe: ____________________ | |
|---|---|
| How much? | What kind of juice? |
| | |
| | |
| | |
| | |

Answer these questions about your punch recipe.

2. How many cups of punch does your recipe make? 40
3. How many pints of punch does your recipe make? 20
4. How many quarts of punch does your recipe make? 10

**Journal**

5. Write a punch recipe for your family.
   Make enough for each person to have 2 cups.

**Notes for Home** Your child explored making decisions with a group to create recipes. *Home Activity:* Ask your child to tell you how many cups of each kind of juice would be needed in his or her family recipe if each member wanted 4 cups. (Double each ingredient.)



Name ____________________

Practice 11-13

## Temperature

Color to show the temperature.

1. 10° F
2. 30° C

**Write your own.**
Choose and write a temperature. Color in the thermometer.
Draw a picture to show an activity you might do at that temperature.

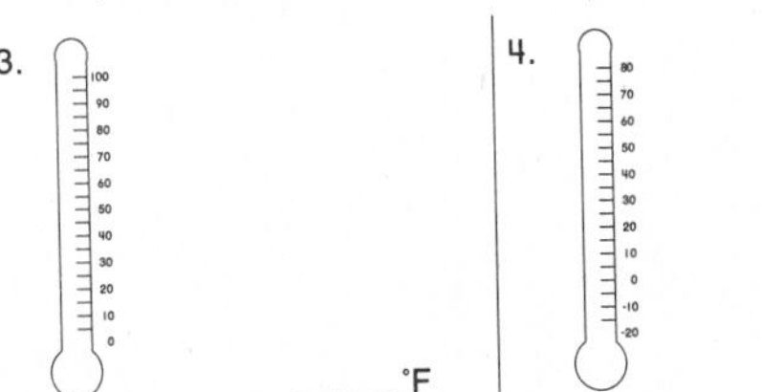

3. ____ °F
4. ____ °C

**Problem Solving Critical Thinking**

5. It is 20° Celsius outside today. You must walk to school. Should you wear a heavy coat or just a light sweater? Why?
   A lightweight sweater because 20°C is about 70° Fahrenheit.

**Notes for Home** Your child practiced showing different temperatures on thermometers. *Home Activity:* Ask your child when the temperature in Celsius and Fahrenheit will be cool enough outside for you to want to wear a coat. (At about 50° Fahrenheit and 10° Celsius, you might want to wear a coat, or at least a sweater, outside.)



Name ____________________

Practice Chapter 11 B

## Mixed Practice: Lessons 8–13

1. Color to show the temperature.

86° F

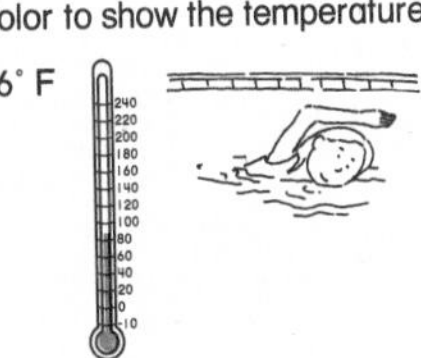

2° F

2. Is the pencil heavier or lighter than 1 pound? Write **heavier** or **lighter.**
   A pencil is lighter

3. Is the TV heavier or lighter than 1 kilogram? Write **heavier** or **lighter.**
   A TV is heavier

**Problem Solving**
Solve.

PUNCH
4 pints of grape juice
2 quarts of apple juice
8 cups of lemonade

4. You need to make 2 cups of punch for each of 10 party guests. Do you have enough? Circle **yes** or **no.**
   yes (no)

5. Which juice do you need more of in this recipe?
   You need the same amount for each juice.

**Journal**

6. Keep track of the **temperature** at the same time each evening. Write about what you find.

**Notes for Home** Your child practiced finding temperatures, the weights of objects using kilograms and pounds, and amounts of liquids. *Home Activity:* Ask your child to estimate how much different objects around the home weigh. Weigh each object and compare the result with the estimate.



Name ____________________

Practice Chapters 1–11 B

## Cumulative Review

Use the hundred chart to subtract.

1. 58 − 30 = 28
2. 34 − 10 = 24
3. 85 − 40 = 45
4. 62 − 50 = 12
5. 42 − 40 = 2
6. 98 − 60 = 38

| 1 | 2 | 3 | 4 | 5 | 6 | 7 | 8 | 9 | 10 |
|---|---|---|---|---|---|---|---|---|---|
| 11 | 12 | 13 | 14 | 15 | 16 | 17 | 18 | 19 | 20 |
| 21 | 22 | 23 | 24 | 25 | 26 | 27 | 28 | 29 | 30 |
| 31 | 32 | 33 | 34 | 35 | 36 | 37 | 38 | 39 | 40 |
| 41 | 42 | 43 | 44 | 45 | 46 | 47 | 48 | 49 | 50 |
| 51 | 52 | 53 | 54 | 55 | 56 | 57 | 58 | 59 | 60 |
| 61 | 62 | 63 | 64 | 65 | 66 | 67 | 68 | 69 | 70 |
| 71 | 72 | 73 | 74 | 75 | 76 | 77 | 78 | 79 | 80 |
| 81 | 82 | 83 | 84 | 85 | 86 | 87 | 88 | 89 | 90 |
| 91 | 92 | 93 | 94 | 95 | 96 | 97 | 98 | 99 | 100 |

**Problem Solving**
Write each number sentence. Solve.

7. 26 pumpkins are on the wagon. 8 more pumpkins are loaded on. 26 + 8 = 34 pumpkins

   At the first store, 10 pumpkins are unloaded. How many pumpkins are on the wagon now? 34 − 10 = 24 pumpkins

**Test Prep**

Fill in the ○ for the correct answer.

8. 418 + 152
   - ○ 266
   - ○ 562
   - ○ 560
   - ● 570

9. 256 + 183
   - ● 439
   - ○ 336
   - ○ 339
   - ○ 133

**Notes for Home** Your child reviewed subtracting tens, multiple-step problems, and adding and subtracting large numbers. *Home Activity:* Ask your child to choose a number between 30 and 70, add 10 to the number, subtract 20 from the result and tell you the new number. (The new number will be 10 less than the number your child chose.)

Name ______________________

Practice 12-1

## Explore Solid Figures

Use solid figures. Find how many faces, corners, and edges.

| | Solid | Name | Faces | Corners | Edges |
|---|---|---|---|---|---|
| 1. | | pyramid | 5 | 5 | 8 |
| 2. | | cylinder | 2 | 0 | 0 |
| 3. | | rectangular prism | 6 | 8 | 12 |
| 4. | | sphere | 0 | 0 | 0 |
| 5. | | cube | 6 | 8 | 12 |

### Problem Solving Critical Thinking

What is the same about these solids?

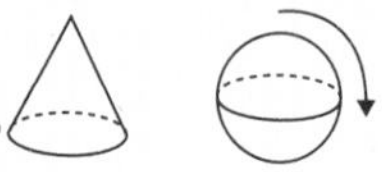

What can they do? They can roll.

Draw another shape that belongs.

**Notes for Home** Your child explored the properties of solid figures. *Home Activity:* Ask your child to look through your kitchen cabinets to find containers that roll and containers that stack.

Use with pages 445–446. 165

Name ______________________

Practice 12-2

## Explore Solid and Plane Figures

Circle a shape you would make if you traced the face the object is sitting on.

1. 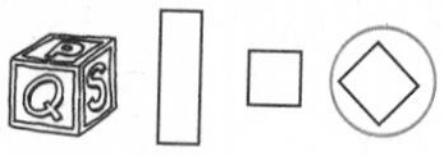

2. 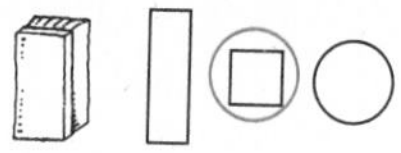

3. 

4. 

### Problem Solving Visual Thinking

5. Write the name of the solid shape you could make with the pieces.

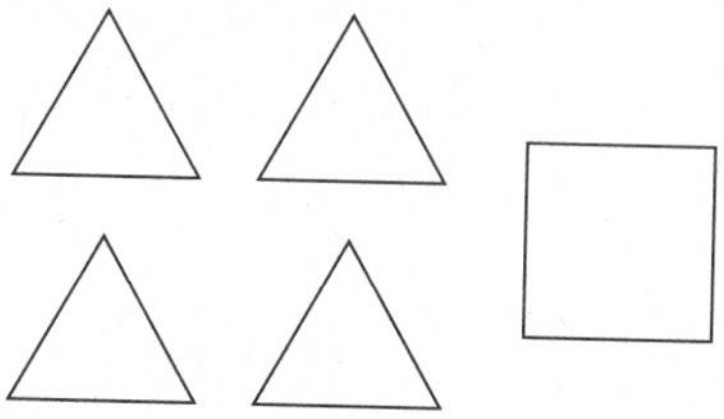

pyramid

**Notes for Home** Your child explored tracing the faces of solid shapes to make plane figures. *Home Activity:* Ask your child to trace some different shapes from a cereal or cracker box.

166 Use with pages 447–448.

Name ______________________

Practice 12-3

## Make Shapes

Write your own. Use pattern blocks.
Make new shapes.
Complete the chart.

| | Blocks I Used | New Shape I Made | How many sides? | How many corners? |
|---|---|---|---|---|
| 1. | Drawings and answers will vary. | | | |
| 2. | | | | |

### Problem Solving Patterns

3. Draw what comes next.

**Notes for Home** Your child used pattern blocks to make new shapes and found the number of sides and corners for the new shape. *Home Activity:* Using objects such as napkins or paper, ask your child to match the edges to make a new shape and to count the number of sides and corners.

Use with pages 449–450. 167

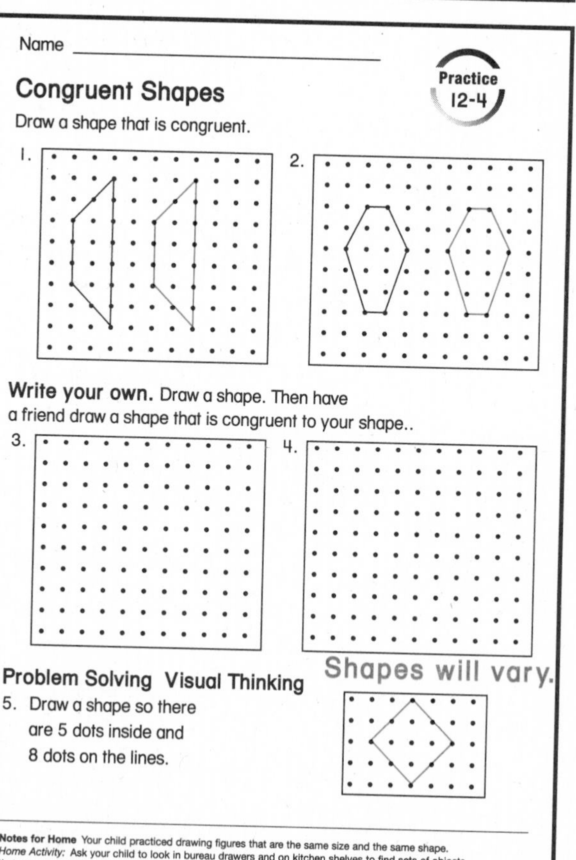

Name ______________________

Practice 12-4

## Congruent Shapes

Draw a shape that is congruent.

1. 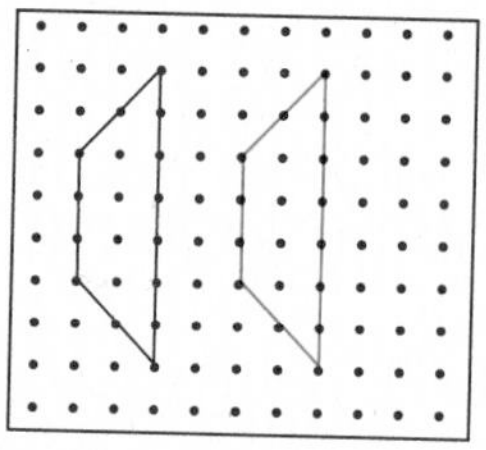

2. 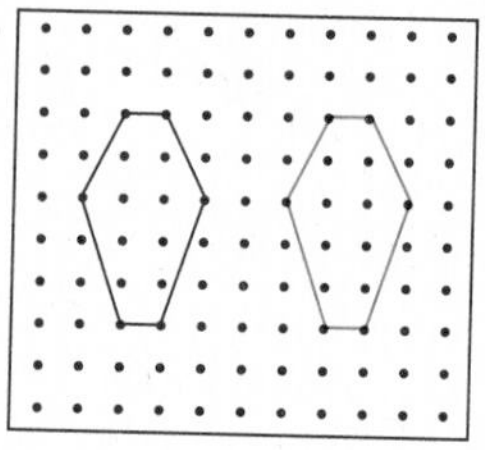

**Write your own.** Draw a shape. Then have a friend draw a shape that is congruent to your shape..

3. 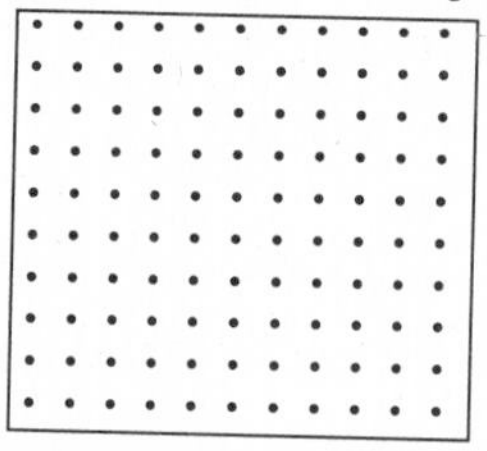

4. 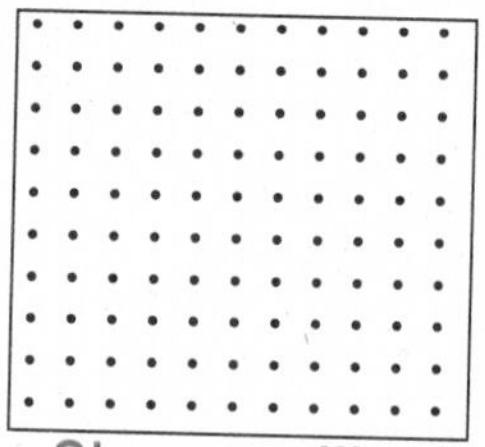

Shapes will vary.

### Problem Solving Visual Thinking

5. Draw a shape so there are 5 dots inside and 8 dots on the lines.

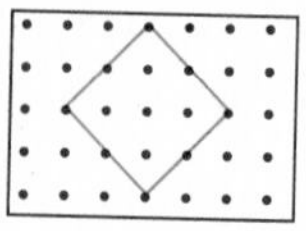

**Notes for Home** Your child practiced drawing figures that are the same size and the same shape. *Home Activity:* Ask your child to look in bureau drawers and on kitchen shelves to find sets of objects that are congruent.

168 Use with pages 451–452.

Name ______________________

Practice 12-5

## Slides, Flips, and Turns

Write **slide, flip** or **turn.** Use pattern blocks to check.

1. 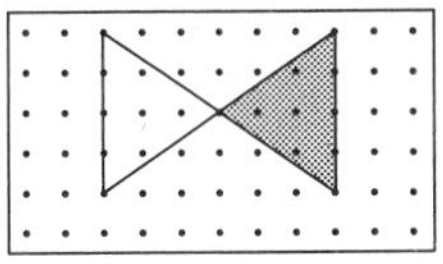 flip or turn
2. 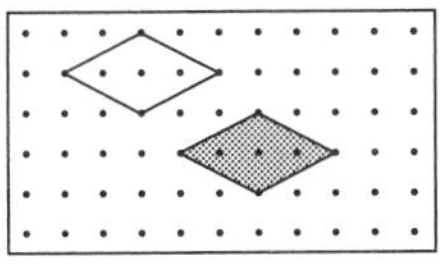 slide
3. 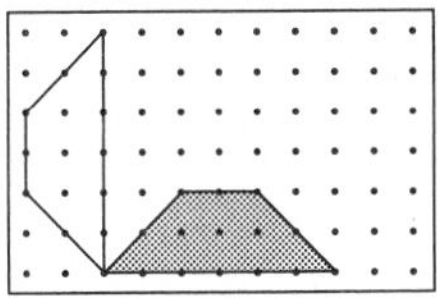 turn
4. 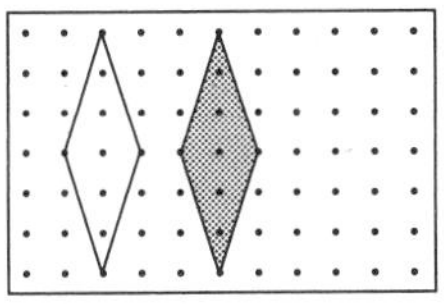 slide

### Problem Solving

5. How many of each shape do you need to make a hexagon?
Use pattern blocks to help you.

2 (trapezoid)
6 (triangle)

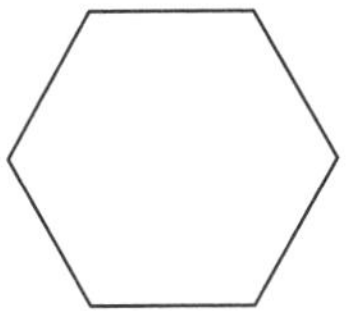

Hexagon

**Notes for Home** Your child used pattern blocks to tell whether a shape changed by sliding, flipping, or turning. *Home Activity:* Ask your child to use an irregular shape, such as a puzzle piece or spoon, and demonstrate three ways of moving it.



Name ______________________

Practice 12-6

## Symmetry

Make the shapes show symmetry.
Draw to show the matching part.

1. 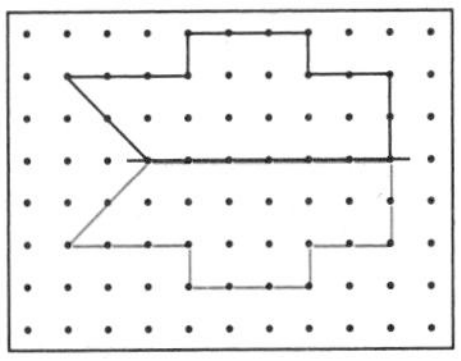
2.

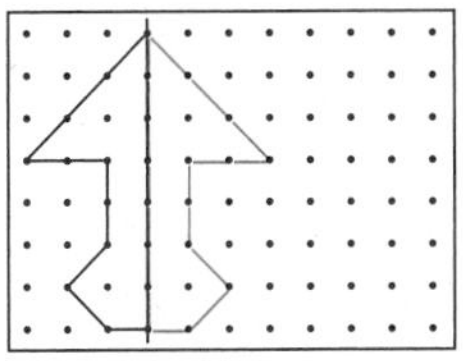

### Mixed Practice

Trace each shape. Flip the pattern block. Trace again.
Draw one line of symmetry for the new shape.

3. Use □. 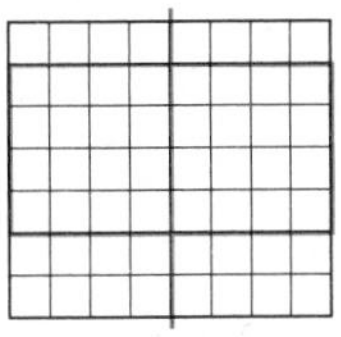
4. Use ◇.

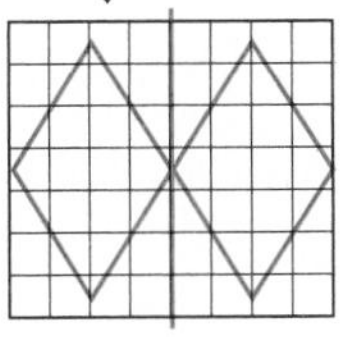

### Problem Solving Visual Thinking

5. Draw a different line of symmetry on each shape.

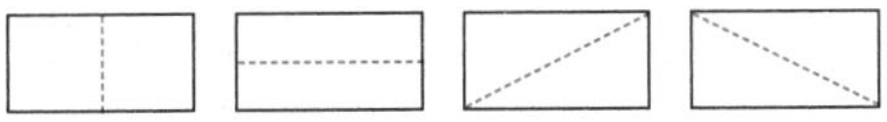

**Notes for Home** Your child completed shapes to show matching parts and drew lines of symmetry. *Home Activity:* Ask your child to draw one picture that has symmetry and another picture that has no line of symmetry.



Name ______________________

Practice 12-7

## Problem Solving: Use Logical Reasoning

Solve the riddles. Cross out pictures that don't match the clues.
Circle the answers.

1. Which plate am I?
I have a congruent partner.
I have no stripes.

2. Which sticker am I?
If you traced around a cube, you would draw my shape.
I am greater than 3.

5 4 1 2 8

3. Which paper hat am I?
My shape shows symmetry.
I have more than 3 corners.

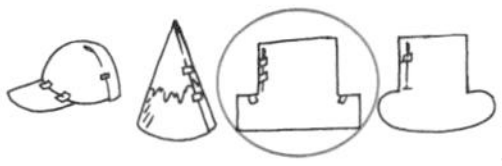

### Write About It

4. Write your own riddle.

Draw your shapes.

Drawings and riddles will vary.

**Notes for Home** Your child practiced using logical reasoning to solve and make riddles. *Home Activity:* Ask your child to solve this riddle: "I have sides. I have 4 corners. What shape am I—a circle, a triangle, or a square?" (a square)



Name ______________________

Practice Chapter 12 A

## Mixed Practice: Lessons 1–7

Write how many faces, corners, and edges for this solid.

1. 5 faces 2. 5 corners 3. 8 edges

4. Draw a shape that is congruent.

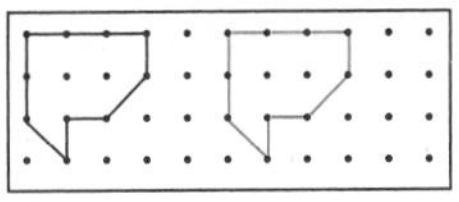

5. Write **slide**, **flip**, or **turn**.

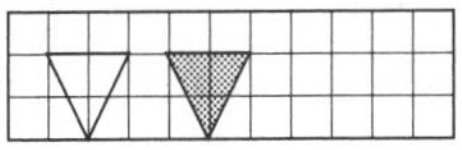

slide

Make the shapes show symmetry. Draw matching parts.

6. 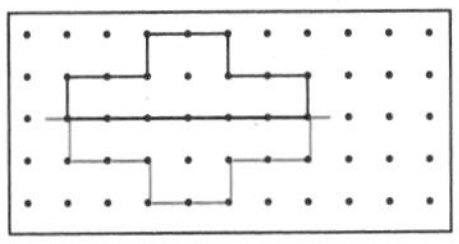
7.

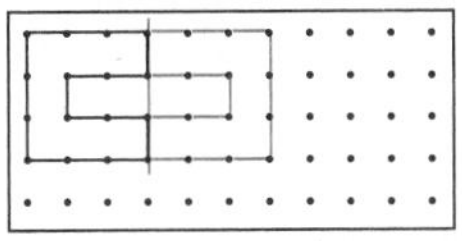

### Problem Solving

Solve the riddle. As you read the riddle, cross out the pictures that don't match the clues. Circle the answer.

8. I am a rectangle.
I have more than 1 line of symmetry.
I have 4 equal sides.

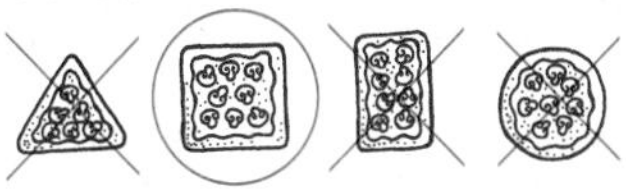

### Journal

9. Draw 2 squares. Draw a different line of symmetry on each square.

**Notes for Home** Your child practiced identifying and drawing shapes. *Home Activity:* Play "I Spy" with your child. Look for examples of circles, squares, rectangles, and triangles, and include clues about the number of sides and corners each shape has.

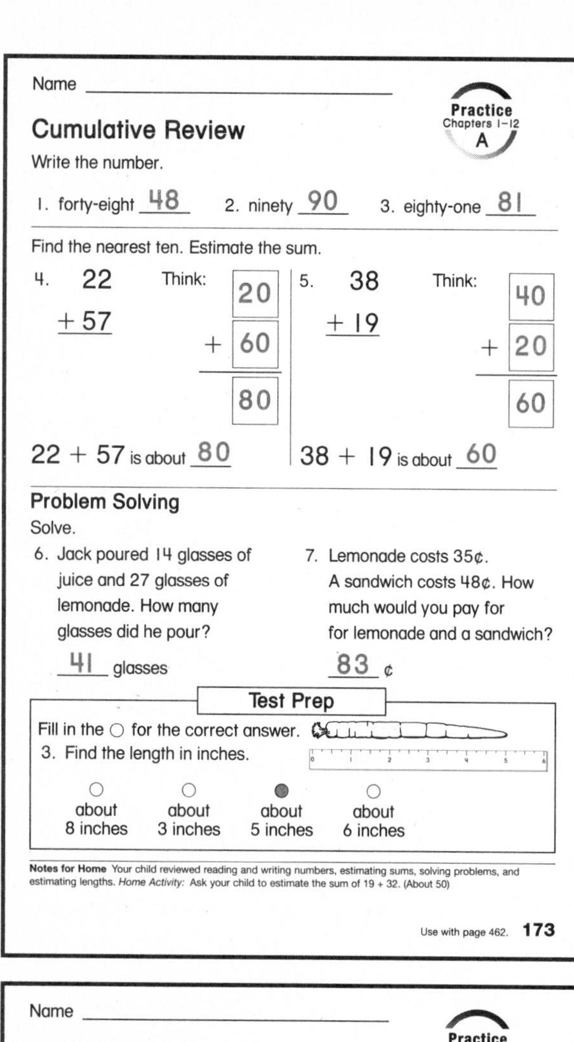

Name ______________________

Practice Chapters 1–12 A

## Cumulative Review

Write the number.

1. forty-eight 48   2. ninety 90   3. eighty-one 81

Find the nearest ten. Estimate the sum.

4. 22 + 57   Think: 20 + 60 = 80
22 + 57 is about 80

5. 38 + 19   Think: 40 + 20 = 60
38 + 19 is about 60

### Problem Solving

Solve.

6. Jack poured 14 glasses of juice and 27 glasses of lemonade. How many glasses did he pour?
41 glasses

7. Lemonade costs 35¢. A sandwich costs 48¢. How much would you pay for for lemonade and a sandwich?
83 ¢

### Test Prep

Fill in the ○ for the correct answer.

3. Find the length in inches.

○ about 8 inches   ○ about 3 inches   ● about 5 inches   ○ about 6 inches

**Notes for Home** Your child reviewed reading and writing numbers, estimating sums, solving problems, and estimating lengths. *Home Activity:* Ask your child to estimate the sum of 19 + 32. (About 50)

Use with page 462. **173**

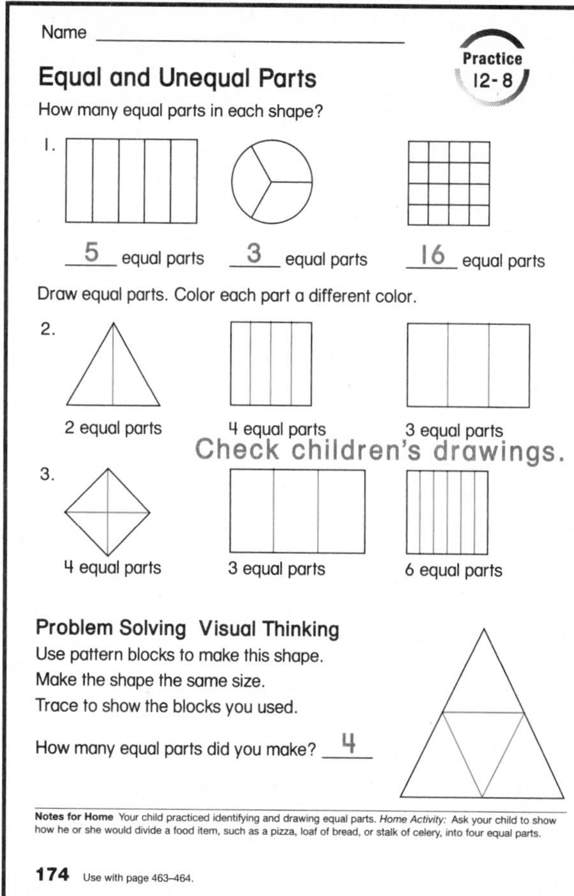

Name ______________________

Practice 12-8

## Equal and Unequal Parts

How many equal parts in each shape?

1. 5 equal parts   3 equal parts   16 equal parts

Draw equal parts. Color each part a different color.

2. 2 equal parts   4 equal parts   3 equal parts

Check children's drawings.

3. 4 equal parts   3 equal parts   6 equal parts

### Problem Solving Visual Thinking

Use pattern blocks to make this shape.
Make the shape the same size.
Trace to show the blocks you used.

How many equal parts did you make? 4

**Notes for Home** Your child practiced identifying and drawing equal parts. *Home Activity:* Ask your child to show how he or she would divide a food item, such as a pizza, loaf of bread, or stalk of celery, into four equal parts.

**174** Use with page 463–464.

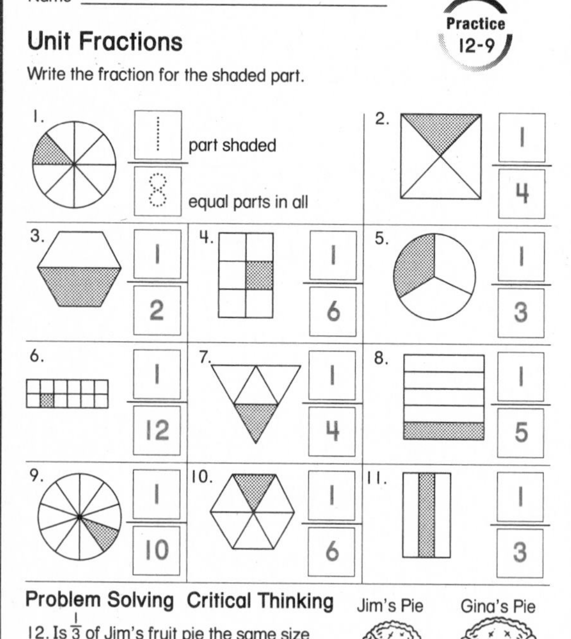

Name ______________________

Practice 12-9

## Unit Fractions

Write the fraction for the shaded part.

1. 1 part shaded / 8 equal parts in all
2. 1/4
3. 1/2
4. 1/6
5. 1/3
6. 1/12
7. 1/4
8. 1/5
9. 1/10
10. 1/6
11. 1/3

### Problem Solving Critical Thinking

12. Is $\frac{1}{3}$ of Jim's fruit pie the same size as $\frac{1}{3}$ of Gina's pie? Why or why not?

Jim's Pie   Gina's Pie

No. Gina's whole pie is bigger, so 1/3 of her pie is bigger.

**Notes for Home** Your child practiced writing different fractions. *Home Activity:* Draw a circle and ask your child how he or she would draw a line to cut the "pie" into fair shares for 4 people. (Draw two lines to divide the pie into fourths.)

Use with pages 465–466. **175**

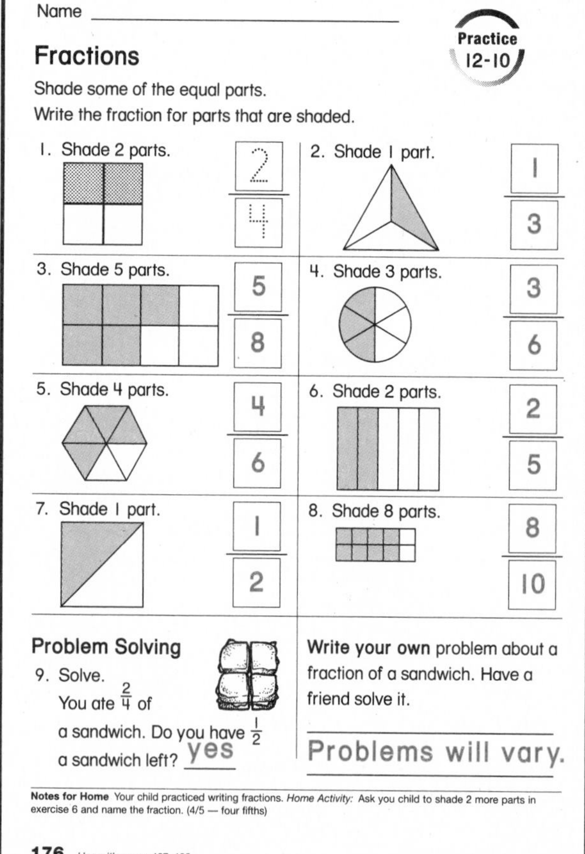

Name ______________________

Practice 12-10

## Fractions

Shade some of the equal parts.
Write the fraction for parts that are shaded.

1. Shade 2 parts. 2/4
2. Shade 1 part. 1/3
3. Shade 5 parts. 5/8
4. Shade 3 parts. 3/6
5. Shade 4 parts. 4/6
6. Shade 2 parts. 2/5
7. Shade 1 part. 1/2
8. Shade 8 parts. 8/10

### Problem Solving

9. Solve.
You ate $\frac{2}{4}$ of a sandwich. Do you have $\frac{1}{2}$ a sandwich left? yes

Write your own problem about a fraction of a sandwich. Have a friend solve it.

Problems will vary.

**Notes for Home** Your child practiced writing fractions. *Home Activity:* Ask you child to shade 2 more parts in exercise 6 and name the fraction. (4/5 — four fifths)

**176** Use with pages 467–468.

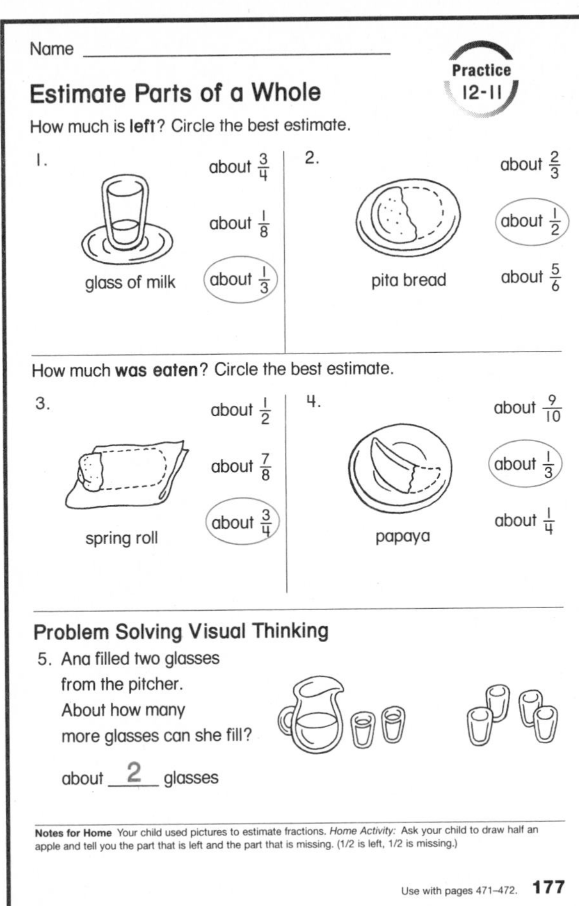
Name ____________________

Practice 12-11

## Estimate Parts of a Whole

How much is **left**? Circle the best estimate.

1. glass of milk — about $\frac{3}{4}$ / about $\frac{1}{8}$ / (about $\frac{1}{3}$)

2. pita bread — about $\frac{2}{3}$ / (about $\frac{1}{2}$) / about $\frac{5}{6}$

How much **was eaten**? Circle the best estimate.

3. spring roll — about $\frac{1}{2}$ / about $\frac{7}{8}$ / (about $\frac{3}{4}$)

4. papaya — about $\frac{9}{10}$ / (about $\frac{1}{3}$) / about $\frac{1}{4}$

### Problem Solving Visual Thinking

5. Ana filled two glasses from the pitcher. About how many more glasses can she fill?

about __2__ glasses

**Notes for Home** Your child used pictures to estimate fractions. *Home Activity:* Ask your child to draw half an apple and tell you the part that is left and the part that is missing. (1/2 is left, 1/2 is missing.)

Use with pages 471–472. **177**

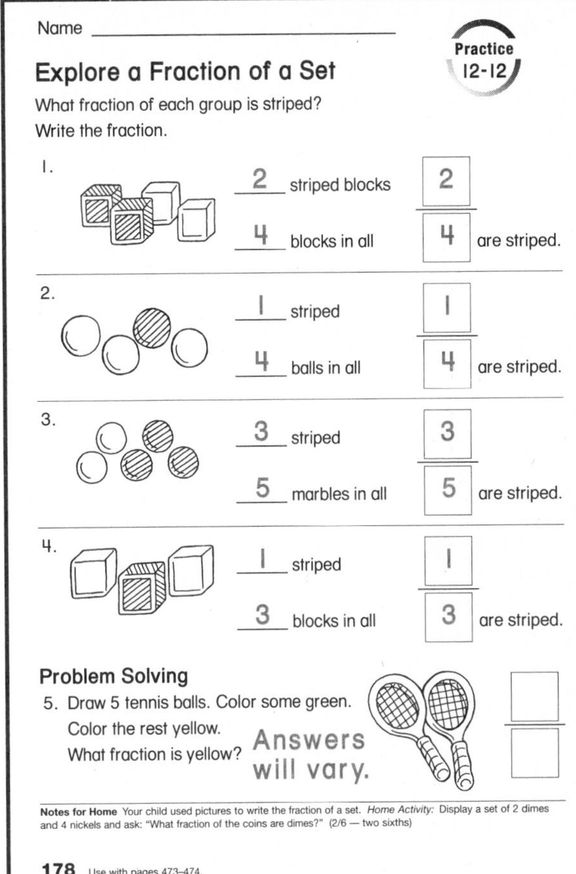
Name ____________________

Practice 12-12

## Explore a Fraction of a Set

What fraction of each group is striped?
Write the fraction.

1. __2__ striped blocks; __4__ blocks in all; $\frac{2}{4}$ are striped.

2. __1__ striped; __4__ balls in all; $\frac{1}{4}$ are striped.

3. __3__ striped; __5__ marbles in all; $\frac{3}{5}$ are striped.

4. __1__ striped; __3__ blocks in all; $\frac{1}{3}$ are striped.

### Problem Solving

5. Draw 5 tennis balls. Color some green. Color the rest yellow. What fraction is yellow?

Answers will vary.

**Notes for Home** Your child used pictures to write the fraction of a set. *Home Activity:* Display a set of 2 dimes and 4 nickels and ask: "What fraction of the coins are dimes?" (2/6 — two sixths)

**178** Use with pages 473–474.

Name ____________________

Practice 12-13

## Fraction of a Set

1. Draw a group of buttons.
   Color $\frac{2}{5}$ blue. Color $\frac{3}{5}$ orange.

Check children's drawings.

2. Draw a group of beads.
   Color $\frac{1}{4}$ red. Color $\frac{3}{4}$ black.

3. Draw a group of rings.
   Color $\frac{5}{6}$ green. Color $\frac{1}{6}$ yellow.

### Mental Math

Solve.

4. $\frac{1}{4}$ of my bracelets are cotton.
   The rest of my bracelets are plastic.
   What fraction of my bracelets are plastic? $\frac{3}{4}$ are plastic
   How many bracelets are plastic? __3__

**Notes for Home** Your child practiced drawing and coloring a group to show a fraction. *Home Activity:* Ask your child to draw and color to show this group: 1/3 of the apples are green. 2/3 of the apples are red. (Draw 1 green and 2 red apples.)

Use with pages 475–476. **179**

Name ____________________

Practice 12-14

## Explore Probability

Reach in the bag and pick 1 cube at a time.
Write what color you pick on a piece of paper.
Put the cube back in the bag. Pick 10 times in all.

1. Put red, blue, and yellow cubes in a bag. Make the red cubes more likely to be picked. Use 30 cubes in all.

   Do the activity.

| Number of cubes in my bag. | My results. |
|---|---|
| R _____ | R _____ |
| B _____ | B _____ |
| Y _____ | Y _____ |

2. Put red, blue, and yellow cubes in a bag. Make the yellow cubes more likely to be picked. Use 30 cubes in all.

   Do the activity.

| Number of cubes in my bag. | My results. |
|---|---|
| R _____ | R _____ |
| B _____ | B _____ |
| Y _____ | Y _____ |

### Journal

3. Why are you more likely to pick blue if you have 10 blue cubes, 5 red cubes, and 5 yellow cubes in a bag? Explain.

**Notes for Home** Your child made up and completed a probability activity. *Home Activity:* Ask your child to collect a group of 2 different kinds of objects so that one kind of object is more likely to be picked, and then show you how to complete a probability experiment like the one above.

**180** Use with pages 477–478.

Name ______________________

Practice 12-15

## Problem Solving: Make a Prediction

1. Predict. If you were to spin once, would this spinner be more likely to land on plain, dots, or stripes?

   What makes you think so?

   Plain. Answers will vary.

2. Predict. If you were to spin 12 times, how many times would the spinner land on plain? _____ On dots? _____ On stripes? _____

3. Spin 12 times. Color a square for each spin. Write the results.

   Graphs and results will vary.

   _____ red
   _____ blue
   _____ yellow

**Write About It**

Write whether the outcome is certain, cannot happen or is likely to happen.

4. land on stripes — cannot
5. land on plain — likely
6. land on dots — certain

**Notes for Home** Your child practiced making predictions. *Home Activity:* Ask your child to predict what time the sun will go down tonight.



Name ______________________

Practice Chapter 12 B

## Mixed Practice: Lessons 8–15

How many equal parts in each shape?

1.

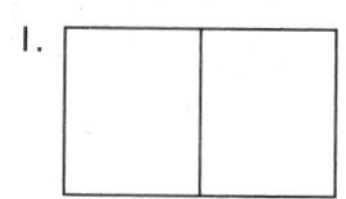

2 equal parts

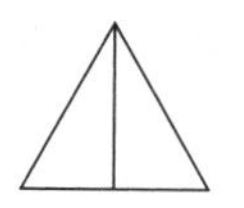

2 equal parts

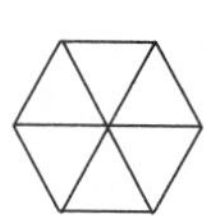

6 equal parts

Write the fraction for the shaded part.

2.

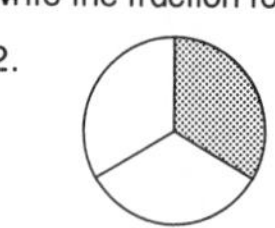

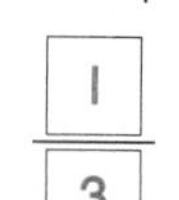

$\frac{1}{3}$

3.

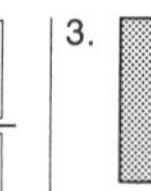

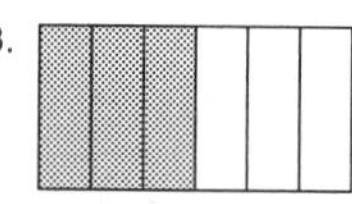

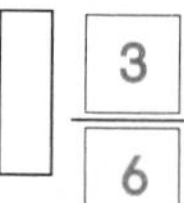

$\frac{3}{6}$

How much is left? Circle the best estimate.

4.

about $\frac{1}{3}$

(about $\frac{1}{2}$)

Draw a group of marbles. Color $\frac{3}{5}$ yellow. Color $\frac{2}{5}$ blue.

5.

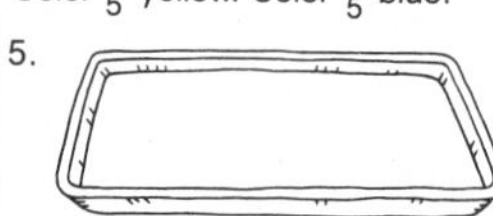

**Problem Solving**

6. Predict. If you were to spin this spinner once, would it be more likely to land on plain, dots, or stripes? stripes

**Journal**

7. How does knowing about equal parts help you if you want to share a pizza with friends? Explain.

**Notes for Home** Your child practiced identifying fractions. *Home Activity:* Ask your child to show you a way to cut a sandwich or piece of toast into 4 equal parts.



Name ______________________

Practice Chapters 1–12 B

## Cumulative Review

Add or subtract.

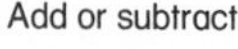

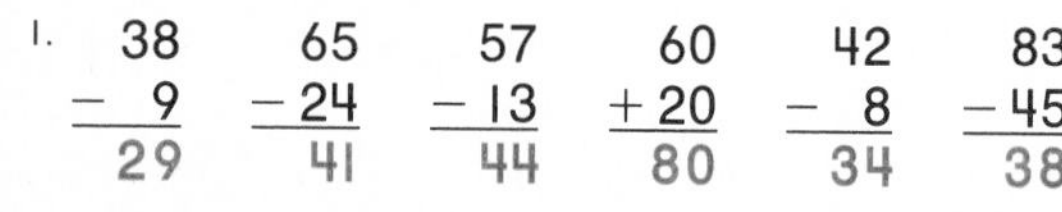

1. 38 − 9 = 29; 65 − 24 = 41; 57 − 13 = 44; 60 + 20 = 80; 42 − 8 = 34; 83 − 45 = 38

2. 29 + 46 = 75; 74 − 20 = 54; 31 − 18 = 13; 50 + 17 = 67; 76 − 26 = 50; 47 − 19 = 28

**Problem Solving**

3. Jason made 15 jelly sandwiches. He made 23 tuna sandwiches. How many sandwiches did he make in all?

   38 sandwiches

4. Mee has 45 oranges to sell. She sells 26 oranges to Jason's class. How many does she have left to sell?

   19 oranges

**Test Prep**

Fill in the ○ for the correct answer.

3. Choose the correct symbol to compare the numbers.

   45 ◯ 36

   ○ <  ○ =  ● >

4. Which numbers are in order from greatest to least?

   ○ 7, 42, 103, 324, 15
   ● 324, 103, 42, 15, 7
   ○ 7, 15, 42, 103, 324

**Notes for Home** Your child reviewed adding and subtracting two-digit numbers, comparing numbers, and ordering numbers. *Home Activity:* Ask your child to subtract 37–18. (19)



Name ______________________

Practice 13-1

## Explore Joining Equal Groups

You can add to find how many oranges in all.

4 + 4 + 4 + 4 = 16

Use counters to show the oranges. Find how many oranges in all.

| | | Draw the oranges. | How many oranges in all? |
|---|---|---|---|
| 1. | 1 bag | | 4 |
| 2. | 2 bags | | 4 + 4 = 8 |
| 3. | 3 bags | | 4 + 4 + 4 = 12 |
| 4. | 4 bags | | 4 + 4 + 4 + 4 = 16 |

**Talk About It** How could you find out how many oranges would be in 5 bags?

Answers will vary.

**Notes for Home** Your child made equal groups and added to find how many in all. *Home Activity:* Ask your child to use objects such as spoons to make 4 groups of 3 objects each. Ask your child to add to find how many objects in all. (12)

Name ______________________

## Addition and Multiplication

Practice 13-2

Find how many in all. You can use cubes.

1. How many wheels?
   3 groups of 3

3 + 3 + 3 = 9

3 × 3 = 9

2. How many sails?
   3 groups of 2

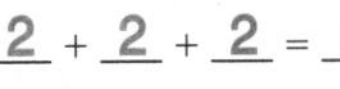

2 + 2 + 2 = 6

3 × 2 = 6

3. How many tennis balls?
   4 groups of 3

3 + 3 + 3 + 3 = 12

3 × 4 = 12

4. How many marbles?
   3 groups of 6

6 + 6 + 6 = 18

6 × 3 = 18

### Problem Solving Visual Thinking

Can you multiply to tell how many in all?
Tell why or why not.

5. 

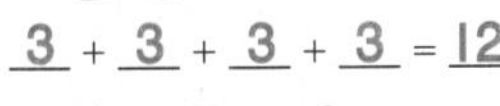

(yes) no

6. 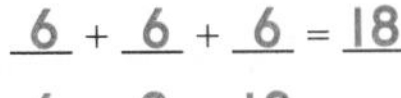

yes (no)

7. (yes) no

**Notes for Home** Your child added and multiplied to find the total number in several groups. *Home Activity:* Ask your child to find the total number of wheels for 5 bicycles with 2 wheels each. (5 x 2 = 10)



Name ______________________

## Explore Building Arrays

Practice 13-3

2 rows of 6 bowling pins

2 × 6 = 12

There are 12 bowling pins in all.

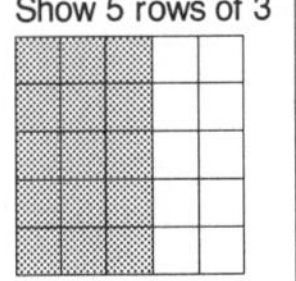

Color equal rows. Write how many. Find the product.

1. Show 5 rows of 3

5 rows

3 in each row

5 × 3 = 15

2. Show 4 rows of 4

4 rows

4 in each row

4 × 4 = 16

3. Show 2 rows of 5

2 rows

5 in each row

2 × 5 = 10

### Problem Solving

4. Draw groups to show 3 x 4.

How many in all? 12

5. Draw groups to show 4 x 6.

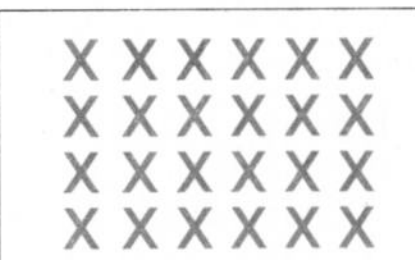

How many in all? 24

Drawings will vary. Sample drawings shown

**Notes for Home** Your child colored equal rows on a grid and completed a multiplication number sentence. *Home Activity:* Draw a picture which shows 3 groups of 7 objects and ask your child to write the multiplication sentence. (3 x 7 = 21)



Name ______________________

## Multiplication in Any Order

Practice 13-4

Find the product. You can use cubes.

1. 

3 × 4 = 12    4 × 3 = 12

2. 

5 × 2 = 10    2 × 5 = 10

**Write your own.** Use the same numbers. Color different rows.
Write different multiplication sentences.

3. Answers will vary.

4.

____ × ____ = ____    ____ × ____ = ____

5. 7 × 2 = 14
   2 × 7 = 14

6. 6 × 3 = 18
   3 × 6 = 18

7. 3 × 5 = 15
   5 × 3 = 15

### Problem Solving Patterns

8. Find the products. What pattern do you see?

2 × 1 = 2    2 × 2 = 4    2 × 3 = 6    2 × 4 = 8

**Notes for Home** Your child found answers to related multiplication facts. *Home Activity:* Ask your child to arrange rows of pennies to show related multiplication facts such as 3 x 2 and 2 x 3.



Name ______________________

## Multiplication in Vertical Form

Practice 13-5

Write the multiplication fact in two ways.

1. 3 rows of 6

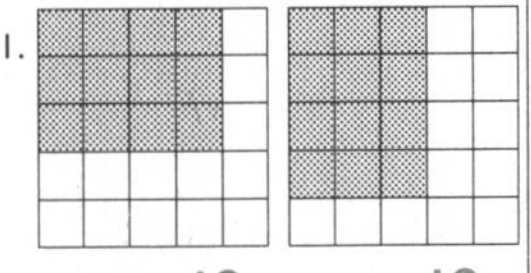

3 × 6 = 18

$$\begin{array}{r} 6 \\ \times\ 3 \\ \hline 18 \end{array}$$

2. 2 groups of 7

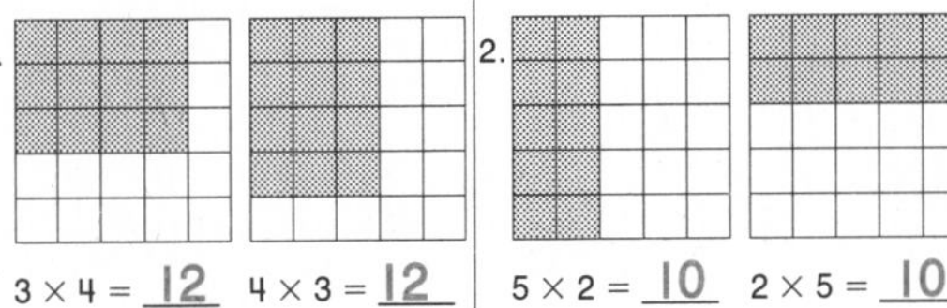

2 × 7 = 14

$$\begin{array}{r} 7 \\ \times\ 2 \\ \hline 14 \end{array}$$

3. 4 rows of 3

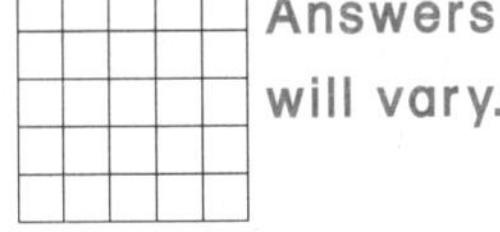

4 × 3 = 12

$$\begin{array}{r} 3 \\ \times\ 4 \\ \hline 12 \end{array}$$

4. 5 rows of 4

5 × 4 = 20

$$\begin{array}{r} 4 \\ \times\ 5 \\ \hline 20 \end{array}$$

### Problem Solving Patterns

5. Find the number pattern. Write the missing numbers.

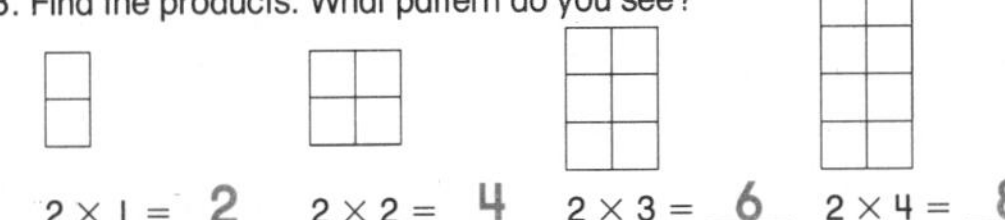

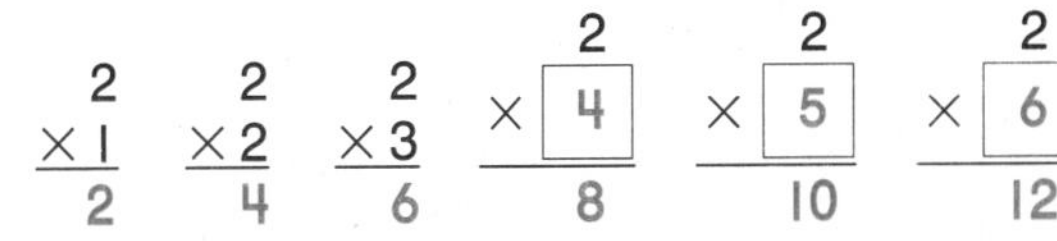

$$\begin{array}{r} 2 \\ \times 1 \\ \hline 2 \end{array}\quad \begin{array}{r} 2 \\ \times 2 \\ \hline 4 \end{array}\quad \begin{array}{r} 2 \\ \times 3 \\ \hline 6 \end{array}\quad \begin{array}{r} 2 \\ \times 4 \\ \hline 8 \end{array}\quad \begin{array}{r} 2 \\ \times 5 \\ \hline 10 \end{array}\quad \begin{array}{r} 2 \\ \times 6 \\ \hline 12 \end{array}$$

**Notes for Home** Your child wrote multiplication facts in two different ways. *Home Activity:* Have your child write the multiplication fact for 3 groups of 4 two different ways.

Name ______________________________

## Problem Solving: Choose a Strategy

Choose a way to solve each problem.
Show what you did. Drawings will vary.

1. Jamal packed 5 bananas in each of 4 bags. How many bananas did he pack?

   Answer shows 20 bananas.

2. Kendra and Miguel each packed 8 baskets with fruit. How many baskets did they pack in all?

   Answer shows 16 baskets.

3. Erin made 6 gift baskets. Julie made 6 gift baskets. Andy made 6 gift baskets. How many gift baskets did the children make in all?

   Answer shows 18 baskets.

### Problem Solving Estimation

4. About how many mangos are ready to be packed?

   Circle the best estimate.

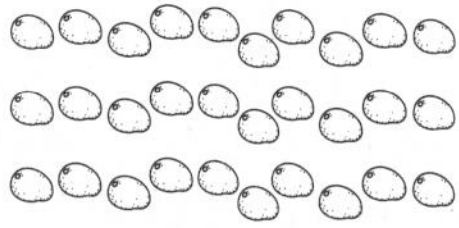

about 20 (about 40) about 60

**Notes for Home** Your child chose strategies to solve problems involving multiplication. *Home Activity:* Ask your child to solve this problem: *6 children packed 2 gift baskets each. How many baskets did they pack?* (6 x 2 = 12)

Use with pages 505–506. **189**

---

Name ______________________________

Practice
Chapter 13
A

## Mixed Practice: Lessons 1–6

Find how many in all. You can use snap cubes.

1. How many grapes?
   4 groups of 4 grapes

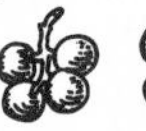

$4 + 4 + 4 + 4 = 16$ grapes

$4 \times 4 = 16$ grapes

Color equal rows. Find the product.

2. 4 rows of 3    3 rows of 4

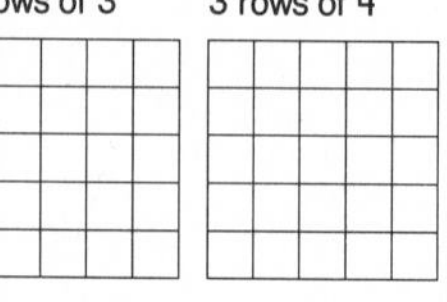

3. 5 rows of 2    2 rows of 5

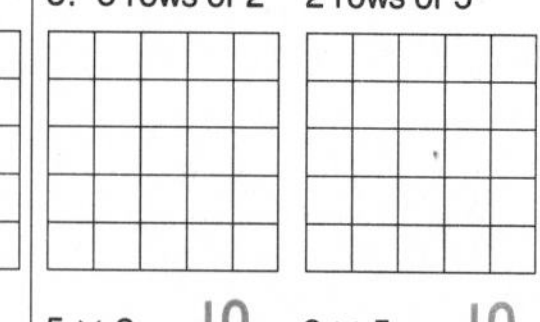

$4 \times 3 = 12$   $3 \times 4 = 12$   $5 \times 2 = 10$   $2 \times 5 = 10$

### Problem Solving

Draw a picture to solve the problem. Sample drawing shown.

4. There are 3 plants on a shelf. Each plant has 5 flowers. How many flowers are there in all?

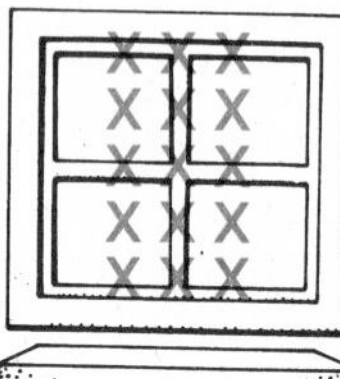

$5 \times 3 = 15$ flowers

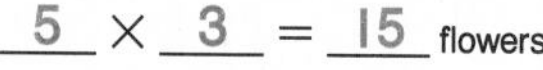

### Journal

5. Tell two ways you can find the total number of 3 + 3 + 3 + 3.

**Notes for Home** Your child practiced using pictures and drawing pictures to solve multiplication problems. *Home Activity:* Ask your child to explain how he or she responded to the Journal question.

**190** Use with page 507.

---

Name ______________________________

## Cumulative Review

Shade some of the equal parts.
Write the fraction for the parts that are shaded.
Parts shaded may vary for Exercises 1-2.

1. Shade 5 equal parts.    2. Shade 3 equal parts.

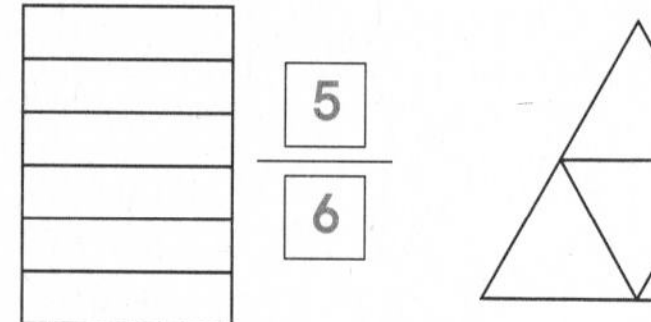

$\frac{5}{6}$    $\frac{3}{4}$

### Getting Ready for Next Year

Copy each problem on a separate piece of paper. Add or subtract.

3.

| 346 | 493 | 851 | 172 | 685 | 574 |
|---|---|---|---|---|---|
| + 125 | − 268 | − 419 | + 634 | − 372 | + 185 |
| 471 | 225 | 432 | 806 | 313 | 759 |

### Test Prep

Fill in the ○ for the correct answer.
Which shape would you make if you traced each object?

4.   5.   6.

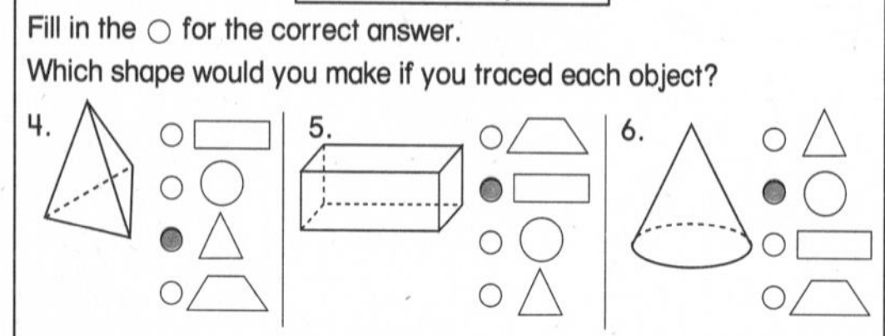

**Notes for Home** Your child reviewed fractions, solids, and addition and subtraction. *Home Activity:* Provide your child with an unopened can and ask him or her to show you one of the faces that is a circle.

Use with page 508. **191**

---

Name ______________________________

Practice
13-7

## Explore Making Equal Groups

At camp, 4 children share 12 plums equally. How many plums does each child get?

Each child gets 3 plums.

Use counters to make equal groups.
Draw a picture to show your work.

1. 5 children share 10 flippers. How many flippers for each child?

   2 flippers

2. 6 children share 2 canoes. How many children in each canoe?

   3 children

3. 3 children share 15 beads. How many beads for each child?

   5 beads

4. 12 children share 2 tents. How many children in each tent?

   6 children

**Talk About It** Could 3 children share 7 ears of corn equally? How do you know? No. 1 ear would be left over.

**Notes for Home** Your child drew pictures to share amounts equally. *Home Activity:* Give your child 8 pennies or other small objects and ask him or her to show you how to share them equally with you.

**192** Use with pages 509–510.

Name ____________________

## Share and Divide

You can use counters. Draw a picture to show equal groups. Write the number sentence.

1. 12 balls in 3 boxes.

12 ÷ 3 = 4 balls

2. 16 pencils in 2 boxes.

16 ÷ 2 = 8 pencils

3. 18 beads in 3 bags.

18 ÷ 3 = 6 beads

4. 8 oranges in 4 bags.

8 ÷ 4 = 2 oranges

5. 20 peanuts in 5 bags.

20 ÷ 5 = 4 peanuts

6. 6 apples shared by 2 children.

6 ÷ 2 = 3 apples

### Problem Solving

Solve. You can use counters.

7. Suli has 12 hula hoops to pass out in the playground. If she gives 2 hula hoops to each child, how many children will get hula hoops?

6 children

**Notes for Home** Your child drew pictures and completed number sentences. *Home Activity:* Ask your child to draw a picture and write a division sentence to show 14 hula hoops shared by 7 children. (14 ÷ 7 = 2)



Name ____________________

Practice 13-9

## Problem Solving: Choose an Operation

Circle the number sentence that helps you solve the problem.

1. 7 children were hiking. Each child found 3 acorns. How many acorns did the children find?

7 − 3 = 4 21 ÷ 7 = 3 (7 × 3 = 21)

2. 15 children take swim class. The coaches separate them into 3 equal groups. How many children are in each group?

5 × 3 = 15 (15 ÷ 3 = 5) 15 + 3 = 18

3. 9 children enter a running race. 6 children finish the race. How many children didn't finish?

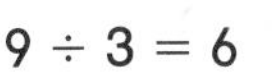

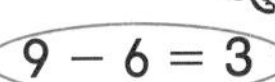

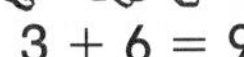

9 ÷ 3 = 6 (9 − 6 = 3) 3 + 6 = 9

### Tell a Math Story

Tell a story for each number sentence.

4. 15 − 5 = 10 5. 10 ÷ 2 = 5 6. 8 × 2 = 16

**Notes for Home** Your child identified a number sentence that could be used to solve a word problem. *Home Activity:* Ask your child to tell you a word problem for Exercise 5. (Possible answer: 10 children play a game. They play in 2 equal teams. How many children are on each team? 5)



Name ____________________

Practice Chapter 13 B

## Mixed Practice: Lessons 7–9

You can use counters to make equal groups. Draw a picture to show your work. Write the number sentence.

1. 9 children share 3 benches equally. How many children at each bench?

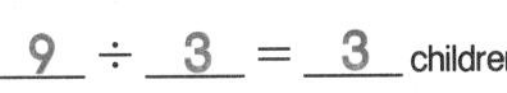

9 ÷ 3 = 3 children

2. 14 balls go in 2 boxes equally. How many balls in each box?

14 ÷ 2 = 7 balls

### Problem Solving

Circle the number sentence that solves the problem.

3. At a picnic, 4 people share 12 ears of corn equally. How many ears of corn did each person get?

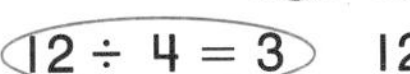

4 × 3 = 12 (12 ÷ 4 = 3) 12 − 4 = 8

4. There are 5 children playing with hula hoops. Each child has 2 hula hoops. How many hula hoops are there?

(5 × 2 = 10) 5 + 2 = 7 10 ÷ 5 = 2

### Journal

5. Write a story for this number sentence. 8 ÷ 4 = 2 Stories will vary.

**Notes for Home** Your child practiced multiplying and dividing. *Home Activity:* Ask your child to draw to find how many balls there are if 5 children each have 3 balls. (5 x 3 = 15)



Name ____________________

Practice Chapters 1–13 B

## Cumulative Review

Draw a shape that is congruent to each shape.

1.

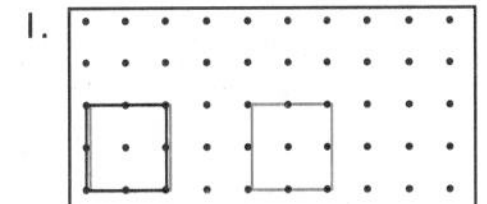

2.

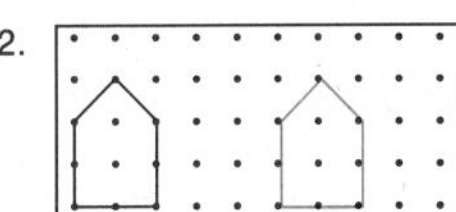

### Problem Solving

3. Tasha cooked 30 hot dogs and 18 hamburgers at the picnic. How many lunches did she cook in all?

48 lunches

4. At the picnic, there were 45 adults and 29 children. How many more adults were there than children?

16 adults

### Getting Ready for Next Year

Copy each problem on a seperate piece of paper. Add.

5.

| 11 | 25 | 33 | 24 | 46 | 18 |
|---|---|---|---|---|---|
| 12 | 14 | 10 | 15 | 21 | 19 |
| + 13 | + 3 | + 29 | + 17 | + 16 | + 20 |
| 36 | 42 | 72 | 56 | 83 | 57 |

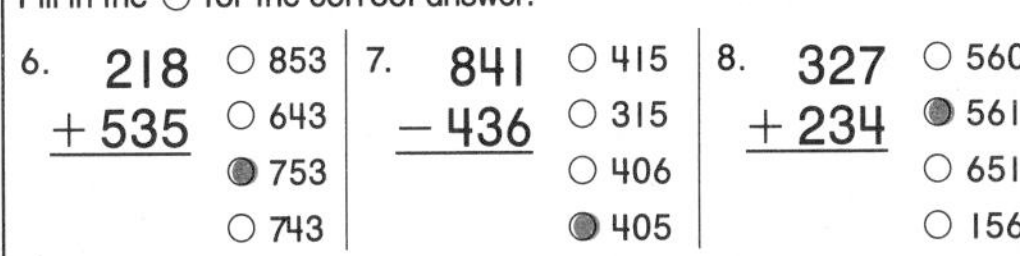

**Test Prep**

Fill in the ○ for the correct answer.

6. 218 + 535 — ○ 853 ○ 643 ● 753 ○ 743

7. 841 − 436 — ○ 415 ○ 315 ○ 406 ● 405

8. 327 + 234 — ○ 560 ● 561 ○ 651 ○ 156

**Notes for Home** Your child reviewed congruence, addition, subtraction, and word problems. *Home Activity:* Draw a shape. Ask your child to draw a shape that is congruent, or has the same shape and size.